VIZ

THE BROON WINDSORS

ONE MORNING...

BRRRRRRR! HELL'S BELLS. IT'S BLUIDY CHANKIN' IN 'ERE...

...WHIT A DAY FUR TH' BOILER TAE BREAK DOON.

OCH, HAUD YER WHEESHT, PA.

OCH, IT'S A'RICHT FUR YE, HEN, YE'V GIT YER ERMINE ROBES O' STATE TAE KEEP YE TOASTY.

AYE!...I'M CHANKIN' MAH BAWBAGS AFF 'ERE, MA.

AH'VE PHONED MR MCCREEDY TH' PLUMBER, AN' HE'S COMIN' OWER THIS AFTAE TAE FIX IT.

THIS AFTAE? WHY CAN HE NAE COME NOO?...

...WUR TH' RYLE BLUIDY FAMILY, FUR FUD'S SAKE.

HE'S UNBLOCKING TH' BOGS AT TH' PUB IN THE VILLAGE THIS MORNIN'.

WHIT?!? SAE SOME PLEBS' JOBBIES UR MAIR IMPORTANT THAN TH' MONARCH'S COMFORT, IS IT?

OCH! WHIT'S TH' WORLD COMIN' TAE?

IT WAS LIKELIE YE WHIT BLOCKED TH' FUCKERS, PA.

WAS IT FUD, AH WASNAE DOON TH' BOOZER LEST NICHT.

AYE. WEEL, DON'T FRET. HE'LL BE 'ERE SOON TAE FIX IT, WON'T HE MA?

IF HE KIN FIX IT... THAT BOILER'S NINETY YEAR AULD...

...GOD KENS HOWFUR MUCH IT'LL COST IF WE NEED A FREISH YIN.

TH' BEST PAIRT O' FUFTY THOOSAND POONDS FUR A BOILER TAE HEAT THIS STEID, AH RECKON...

MAH PAL TH' DUKE O' CUMBERLAND PAID THIRTY THOOSAND... AN' HIS WEE HOOSE HAS AINLIE GIT FORTY BEDROOMS.

HELP MA BOAB! AH DON'T KEN WHERE WE'D FIN' THAT KIND O' DOSH, PA.

YOU'LL HAE TAE SELL YER YER CROON JEWELS, MA...

...I'M CHANKIN' MAH TIT ENDS AFF 'ERE.

WHIT!?! AWA' AN' SHITE, WOMAN. AH'M NAE SELLIN' MA' JEWELS. YE KIN SELL SOME O' YER HORSES.

WULL AH SHITE! CHARLES KIN SELL A WEE BIT O' CORNWALL OR SOMETHING.

GANG BILE YER HEID, WOMAN

DING! DONG!

OCH! THAT'LL BE MCCREEDY NOO.

OCH! AWRIGHT, MR MCCREEDY.

HULLO, YIR MAJESTY. WHIT SEEMS TAE BE TH' FASH?

WEEL, TH' BALMORAL BOILER IS OAN TH' BLINK AN' WE'VE HUD NAE HEATIN' A' DAY.

IS THAT SAE!?...

...LET ME HAE A KEEK AT IT.

CRIVVENS! IT'S A HADES MARK 1000...

AH HAVENAE SEEN YIN O' THEY FUR YEARS...

IT'S AN ANTIQUE THIS...

I'M FEART THAY STOPPED MAKING BITS FUR THIS AFORE TH' WAR.

BUGGER!

TH' PUMP'S OKAY... TH' SEALS OAN TH' OUTLET PIPES SEEM FINE...

...TH' PRESSURE GAUGE IS WORKING...

I DINNAE UNDERSTAND IT...

OCH! THERE'S YER PROBLEM, MA'AM...

YIR STOKER'S HAD IT!

STOKER!? WHIT'S THAT?

IT'S TH' WEE MAN WHIT SHOVEL'S TH' COAL INTAE TH' FURNACE... HE'S DEED AS A DOORNAIL. NAE WONDER YIR BOILER WENT OOT.

MYND YE, YE GIT A GUID RUN OOT O' HIM. HE LOOKS ABOOT 90...

...YE USUALLY OANLY GIT ABOOT 60 YEARS OOT A STOKER AFORE THAY BREAK DOON...

...IT'S USUALLY A VALVE IN THAIR HEART GIVES OOT.

GUID NEWS, PA... TH' BOILER'S BRAW, ...IT'S JIST TH' STOKER THIT'S HUD IT.

KIN YE GIT A REPLACEMENT?

OCH, AYE! NAE FASH. I'LL PICK YE ANITHER YIN UP FRAE TH' JOB CENTRE THIS AFTIE.

OCH, BONNIE!

I'LL GIT RID O' YIR AULD STOKER AN' BE BACK WI' TH' FRESH YIN.

OCH! THANK YE, MR MCCREEDY.

A' PAIRT O' TH' SERVICE, MA'AM.

LATER...

MR. MCCREEDY SAYS WE COULD GIT ANITHER 90 YEARS OOT O' THAT BOILER.

AYE! IT'S A GUID JOB IT WASNAE ANYTHIN' SERIOUS.

You'll like it! Not a lot. It's

VIZ

THE
WIZARD'S
SLEEVE

A Badly Spelled Hermione's Handbag of Hocus Pocus from Issues 272~281

Stage Illusionists
Graham Dury and Simon Thorp

Glamorous Assistants

Mark Bates, Alex Collier, Terry Corrigan, Simon Ecob, Tom Ellen, Barney Farmer, David Glasper, Mat Greaves, Lee Healey, Jacob Hutchinson, Davey Jones, Marc Jones, Shaun Madrid, Steve McGarry, Alex Morris, Paul Palmer, Tom Paterson, Aaron Rice, Kent Tayler, Nick Tolson and Stevie White.

Rabbits Inside Top Hats

Dharmesh Mistry, Kerin O'Connor and Stephen Catherall

Published by Dennis Publishing Ltd
31-32 Alfred Place, London WC1E 7DP

ISBN 9 781781 067277
First Printing Autumn 2020

Subscribe online at www.viz.co.uk
Find us at facebook.com/vizcomic and twitter.com/vizcomic

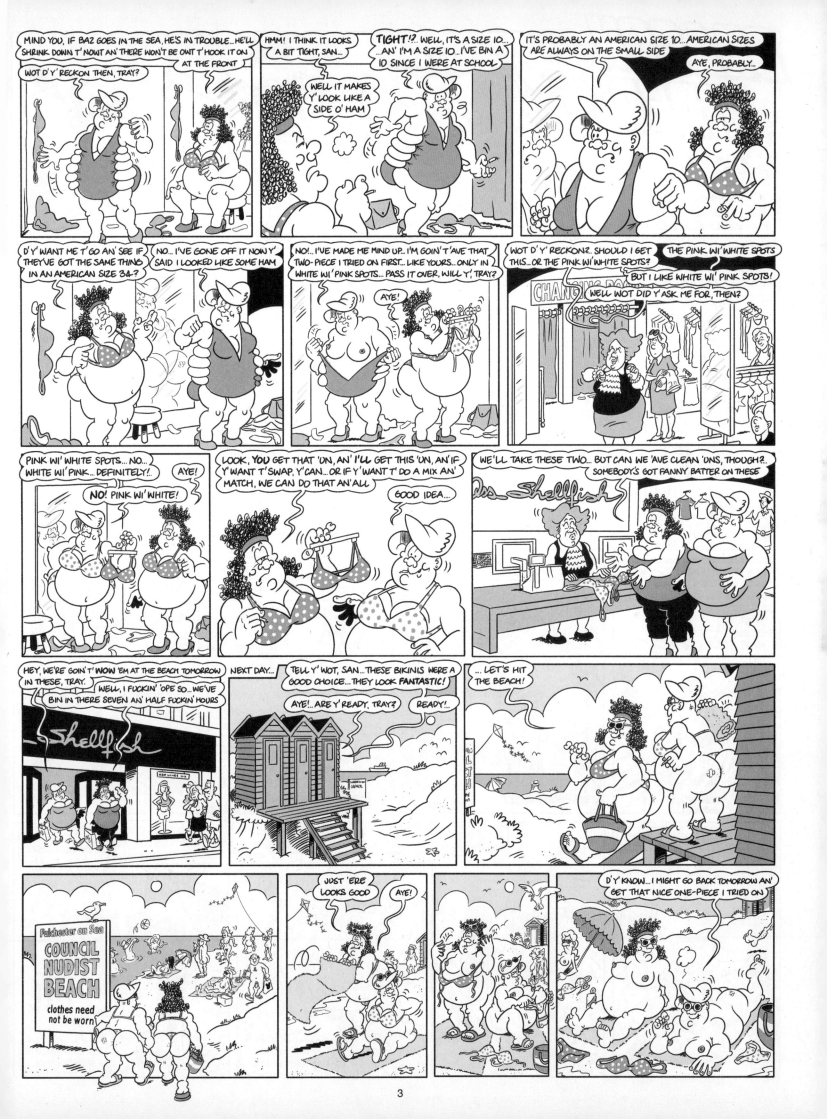

3

DRAGON RIDER

IN the mystical land beyond the mountains of Thjor, Princess Xandrar is being crowned Mistress of Dragons following the death of her mother Queen Pyrophor...

Do you pledge to hold dominion over the fire-breathing beasts of the mountains with dignity... with mercy... and with steadfastness?

Upon the seven Gods of Mythordia, so do I swear.

Arise Xandrar, Mistress of the Dragons!

Hoorah!

Behold, your majesty- the Dragon Vulton. You must mount him and fly to the Castle of Golgor to complete your initiation.

Erm...Where do you have to sit?

Well, just there, I suppose... in that curvy bent bit on its neck.

Are you sure? It looks a bit spiky.

And it looks a bit high. How do I get up?

I think you just stand on the wing and it sort of lifts you up.

That's what your mam used to do.

Which bit of the wing?

That bit there, his elbow.

It's not an elbow. That's the wrist, that.

Wrist... elbow...it doesn't matter. It's that bit there, look. Put your foot on that bit, grab hold here, and it'll just lift you up.

Get a good hold of that boney spur, Highness.

That's it... get your leg over.

Lift it up, that's it... champion

Argh! Bugger! Ow! Ow! Jesus!

Bloody Nora! Them spiky bits go right up your arse crack. It's like sitting on a big conker.

Well your mum used to do it.

She had big, thick deer-skin trousers. I've only got this flimsy loincloth thing.

What if you sat a bit further back, behind its shoulders?

Yes, that looks a bit smoother there.

4

5

THE END

ROGER MELLIE
THE MAN ON THE TELLY

GOOD MORNING, TOM

NO IT ISN'T, ROGER... HAVE YOU SEEN THE PAPERS?

Sun SHAME OF TV SEA PEST MELLIE!

I HAVE! THEY'RE COMING OUT THE FUCKING WOODWORK, AREN'T THEY?

HONESTLY, EVERY BIRD WHOSE ARSE I'VE EVER SLAPPED ALL GETTING ON THEIR HIGH HORSES TCHOH!

WELL, IT IS SEXUAL ASSAULT AT THE END OF THE DAY, ROGER

BUT IT WAS ALRIGHT IN THOSE DAYS

IT WAS LAST WEEK, ROGER

THAT'S WHAT I MEAN, TOM...

... THEY WERE DIFFERENT TIMES.

THAT HERVEY WINESTAIN'S GOT A LOT TO ANSWER FOR... HE'S SPOILT IT FOR EVERYONE

WHAT!?. LOOK, YOU'VE GOT TO GET AN APOLOGY OUT, ROGER... AND QUICK!

... SAY YOU'RE SORRY TO ALL YOUR VICTIMS

WELL, IT'LL HAVE TO BE VERY CAREFULLY WORDED, TOM

YES, OF COURSE IT WILL

I MEAN, IT'S GOT TO SAY I'M SORRY WITHOUT ACTUALLY **SAYING** I'M SORRY...

... AND IT'S GOT TO MAKE IT CLEAR THAT THE BIRDS LED ME ON AND THAT ACTUALLY I'M THE REAL VICTIM

WHAT!?!.. **YOU'RE** THE VICTIM!?..

YES!. I'LL SAY IT'S AN ADDICTION AND I'VE BEEN WRESTLING WITH MY DEMONS FOR YEARS AND I'M FINALLY GOING TO GET SOME TREATMENT, THAT SORT OF BOLLOCKS...

... THERE WON'T BE A DRY EYE IN THE HOUSE, TOM

ACTUALLY, COULD YOU KNOCK IT UP FOR ME?. JUST CUT AND PASTE THAT LOUIS CK ONE... OR THE KEVIN SPACEY ONE... THEY WERE SPOT ON.

ANYWAY... WHAT YOU GOT FOR ME, TOM? ANY GOOD SHOWS IN THE PIPELINE?

WELL, YES, AS IT HAPPENS. THEY WANT YOU TO GO ON *SATURDAY KITCHEN* TOMORROW MORNING.

GREAT! AND DOUBLE TIME FOR WORKING ON A SATURDAY, EH!?.. KER-*CHING!*

LOOK, JUST BEHAVE YOURSELF, ROGER... THIS COULD BE YOUR LAST ROLL OF THE DICE

DON'T WORRY, TOM... I'M A PRO.

... WHAT TIME'S KICK OFF AGAIN?

ON AIR AT 10:00, SO BE THERE FOR 9.00 AM

9:58 NEXT MORNING...

I DON'T KNOW WHAT'S HAPPENED TO ROGER, BUT THANK YOU FOR STEPPING IN AT SUCH SHORT NOTICE, MR. ROSS.

NO PROBLEM, TOM...

IT'S £15 AN HOUR, ISN'T IT?

Saturday Kitchen BBC

Saturday Kitchen BBC

MORNING, TOM!

ROGER!

COULD YOU GET A TAXI FOR PAUL ROSS, PLEASE, EMMA... AND GIVE HIM A TENNER OUT OF PETTY CASH

SURE, TOM

WHERE THE **HELL** HAVE YOU BEEN, ROGER?.. THE SHOW STARTS IN THIRTY SECONDS

THAT'S ALL I NEED, TOM... THEY DON'T CALL ME "HALF MINUTE MELLIE" FOR NOTHING

WHERE'S JAMES MARTIN?. I'LL GO AND SAY HELLO.

IT'S NOT JAMES MARTIN ANYMORE, ROGER. ...IT'S MATT TEBBUTT...

THERE HE IS...

JAMES! JAMES! HOW ARE YOU, OLD MATE?

IT'S **MATT**, ACTUALLY, ROGER.

LISTEN, JAMES... I'M JUST GOING TO STAND MY NEW AUTOBIOGRAPHY AT THE FRONT, OKAY?

ER...

SORRY I'M LATE TOM ROGER MELLIE

...AND I'LL JUST PUT A BOTTLE OF MY SIGNATURE SCENT 'PRIAPIC' HERE...

...DON'T FORGET TO ASK ME ABOUT IT A COUPLE OF TIMES, WILL YOU, JAMES?

IT'S MATT...

SORRY I'M LATE TOM

OH, I NEARLY FORGOT MY NEW C.D... MELLIE SINGS THE GREAT AMERICAN SONGBOOK...

...GOT LOADS LEFT OVER FROM CHRISTMAS... GOT TO SHIFT THE FUCKERS SOMEHOW, JAMES

SORRY I'M LATE TOM

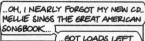

LOOK, ROGER...NO SWEARING...THIS IS A FAMILY SHOW...JUST LIGHT CHAT ABOUT YOUR FAVOURITE AND LEAST FAVOURITE FOOD, OKAY?

GOTCHA, TOM. I'LL BE AS GOOD AS GOLD

OKAY, EVERYBODY... TITLES RUNNING... GOING **LIVE** IN 5... 4... 3... 2... 1...

ACTION!

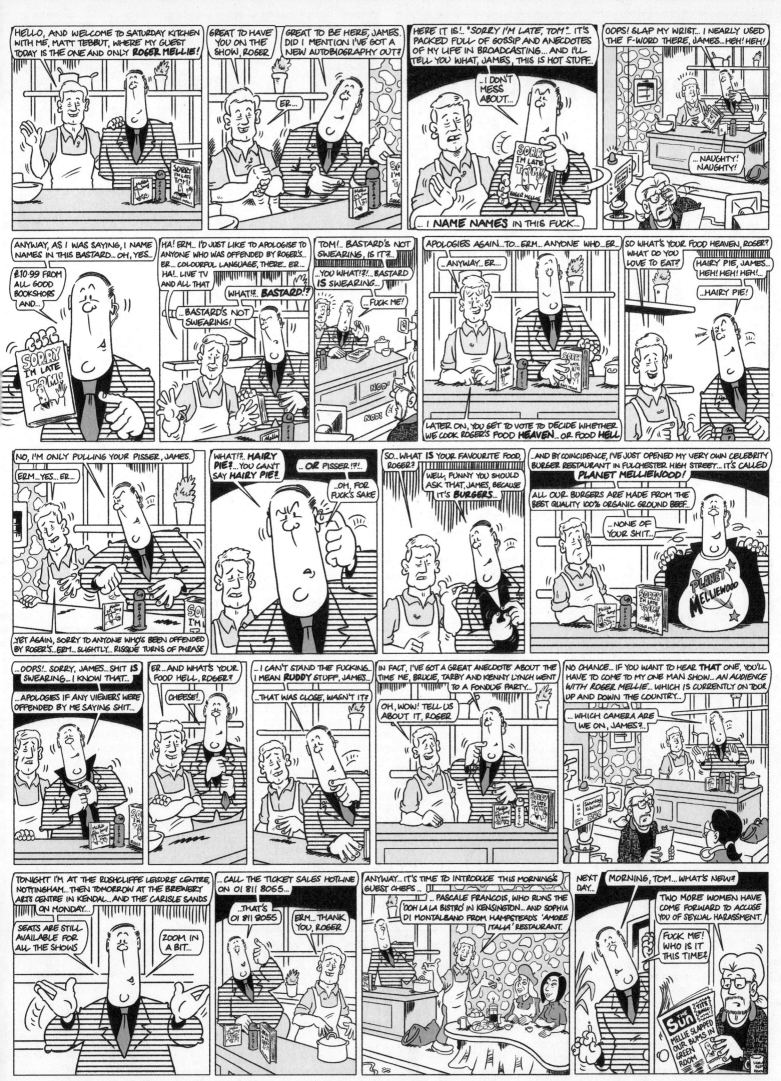

What to Do and How to Cope...

So You're Having a
Vegan for Christmas

VEGANS ARE EVERYWHERE these days. It's a scientific certainty that you're never more than 20 feet from one of these animal-product-eschewing kale-nibblers. In fact, they're getting so common that there's a very good chance that one of them could be coming round to your house for Christmas dinner this year; perhaps your daughter has started going out with one at university, or maybe your son's recently taken up with some animal rights types who spend their days sat on their arses in the town centre. But how will you cope with having a gastronomic fundamentalist sat at YOUR festive table? Here's a few preparations to make and precautions to take in order to make sure your Christmas with a vegan goes off smoothly.

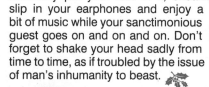

4 **ASK** Santa Claus to bring you a pair of flesh-coloured bluetooth earphones. At some point during the festivities, you will almost certainly make an innocent remark - for example "Who fancies a nice glass of Merlot?" - that will be leapt upon as an excuse for the vegan to launch into a guilt-inducing diatribe about how red wine is clarified using isinglass, a product made from the swim bladders of fish. As soon as you invariably put your foot in it, sneakily slip in your earphones and enjoy a bit of music while your sanctimonious guest goes on and on and on. Don't forget to shake your head sadly from time to time, as if troubled by the issue of man's inhumanity to beast.

5 **IT MAY** seem a stran thing to do, but invite vegetarian. If there's one thing gets a vegan's dander up m than a carnivore, it's someo who doesn't eat meat but still li cheese, wears a wool tank and has milk in their tea. Veg view these people as weak-wil spineless hypocrites who lack courage of their convictions. C Christmas, your vegetarian gu will serve as a decoy to d the vegan's sanctimonious while you take the opportu to nip out to the shed enjoy a pork pie, a Pepera and some of your Ter Chocolate Orange.

3 **FIRST** thing on Christmas morning, unplug your internet router and hide it under the stairs or down the back of the couch. At some point during their visit, your vegan will undoubtedly try to make you watch distressing Youtube videos of pigs being slaughtered, day-old chicks going along a conveyor belt into a big mincing machine, or battery hens being de-beaked with pliers, and they won't be able to do that if they can't get on the internet. Ask your neighbours to turn their routers off or password-protect their signal in case your vegan attempts to piggy-back onto their wi-fi.

8

2 **NEXT**, go through the house and collect anything made of leather, such as shoes, jackets, belts, National Trust bookmarks, Chesterfield chairs etc., and put them in the garage, well away from your eagle-eyed vegan's judgemental gaze. Then comb the house again for anything made from wool, including carpets, jumpers, blankets and bobble hats, and put them in the garage too. Finally, gather up and hide away any silk items you may own, such as ties, handkerchiefs and jockeys' shirts. There is nothing more guaranteed to set your vegan off on a two-hour, holier-than-thou sermon about caterpillar abuse in the silk industry than spotting some French knickers, stockings and suspender belts when they're suspiciously rooting through your wife's underwear drawer looking for hidden cheese.

1 **BEFORE** your vegan arrives, go through all the groceries in your house and carefully check the ingredients for animal products, such as milk, eggs, gelatine, rennet etc. Gather these foodstuffs together and hide them in your shed. The vegan will almost certainly go through your fridge and larder as soon as they get in the house, looking for things to take offence at. A bottle of mayonnaise, a Babybel or even a Quorn pie can set the average vegan off on an arse-numbing, tub-thumping lecture about the evils of the dairy industry that can easily last as long as a James Bond film.

6 **FEEDING** your vegan isn't as difficult as you might think. Most of them are happy with a plate of sprouts and a spoonful of cranberry sauce (check there's no gelatine in it, unless you fancy spending Christmas afternoon on the receiving end of a humourless, gruelling tirade about the rendering down of cows' hooves). Under no circumstances attempt to serve your guest something that says it's suitable for vegans, as the explanation for why it isn't could go on well into the evening. If you do cook them something that claims to be vegan, remember to burn the packaging to stop them retrieving it from the bin in order to check the ingredients. Other titbits to avoid putting in front of them include honey which, as your vegan will explain at tedious length, is the product of bee slave labour in sweatshop hives, and figs, which incarcerate fig wasps during their pollination process, even though - as you will at length learn - wasps have just as much right to live as you do, actually.

7 **AS YOU** settle down with your vegan to watch the Queen's Speech after lunch, you might think your troubles are over, but you'd be wrong. The feathers in your settee's cushions could easily trigger a meandering and repetitive monologue, which begins with a graphic description of the inhumane conditions in Canadian goose and eider duck farms, before moving on to the clubbing and live-skinning of seal cubs in Novia Scotia, the annual Faroe Islands whaling festival, and finishes up with commercial fish-farming, trout lice, caviar and shark fin soup. Head off this risk in plenty of time by removing all the feathers from your cushions on Christmas Eve, and storing them in your attic. Replace them with some form of vegan-friendly alternative stuffing such as rice, dried peas, or lentils. But do not use dried pasta, unless it's the durum wheat egg-free variety.

NEXT WEEK: *So you're having a Yorkshireman for New Year.*

LETTERBOCKS

P.O. Box 841 Whitley Bay, NE26 9EQ : letters@viz.co.uk

MY missus only wants to have sex with me after I've freshly showered. But I always have a wank in the shower, so I am physically incapable of sex for a few hours afterwards, by which time she is no longer interested. Do any of your readers have a simple solution to break this pitiful cycle that doesn't involve me not having a wank in the shower?
Sammy S, email

IMAGINE if dogs had hands, what sort of mischief would they get up to? Honestly, it doesn't bear thinking about.
Neil Mainey, Ross on Wye

LAST night I dreamt I had a car called a Sausage Cooper. This morning I had a sausage sandwich for breakfast, then had a fridge delivered by a bloke called Barry Cooper. How spooky is that?
Fat Al White, Wrenthorpe

MY girlfriend complains every time I leave the toilet seat up at her place because, she says, she doesn't like to touch it. But she lives on her own, so it's only ever her arse that's been on it. I've seen it and it's a very nice arse, so I really don't know why she gets so annoyed.
Eton Trifles, Accrington-by-the-Sea

WHILST shopping in Norway recently, I discovered that in the towns they charge you 10Kr to use the loo. That's about a quid. *A quid!* Surely that has to be the most expensive shit in Europe? If any readers know of more expensive places than Norway to leave a stool I would love to know.
Andrew Ward, Blyth

I WAS telling a joke to some friends recently, the punchline of which mentions Prince Charles's foreskin. One of them asked me if the next in line to reign over our Commonwealth of nations does indeed possess a foreskin, and I have to admit that I didn't know. The answer probably won't alter my opinion of our future monarch, but if he doesn't have one I should probably stop telling the joke.
Granty T Wandi, Australia

* Well, readers. Do you know whether or not Prince Charles has a foreskin? Perhaps you've stood next to him at the urinals in Buckingham Palace. Maybe you've sat near to Camilla Parker Bowles in the hairdressers whilst she gossips with her friends. Or perhaps you are one of the physicians to the House of Windsor who has scant regard for the bit about doctor/patient confidentiality in the medical code of ethics. Write in and let us know.

STAR LETTER

I UNDERSTAND that fish are having terrible trouble digesting plastics that have been thrown into the sea. When my granny has trouble eating her potatoes, I simply cut them up into small pieces for her. Surely if we all did the same thing, chopping up all those plastic bags and other bits of rubbish before we chucked them in the sea, the fish would have no trouble eating them.
D Attenborough, London

HOW come everyone in the old days built their houses underground? Archeologists have to dig for ages to find their stuff. No wonder they all died out. If they'd built their houses above ground they would still be here.
Mick Laffey, Hebburn

I'VE just paid six quid for some passport photos, but I only need one. If anyone needs a passport photo of me for anything, just give me a shout.
Mal Alcock, email

SO Frankie Valli lost his cherry at party in late December back in '63. Well there's no need to keep making a song and dance about it for the last 50 odd years. I lost my cherry behind the public lavvies in the park during the Easter holidays in 1977, but I don't keep banging on about it.
Reg Corvette, St Albans

IN *Star Trek*, it's always struck me that, when beaming down to some planet, no one ends up in some dog shit or a large pile of puke. If he boldly went where I live, the chances are more than likely that Captain Kirk would start his trip wiping his shoe on some grass.
Richard Devereux, Hereford

EVERY time I call Paypal's Help Centre, an automated voice tells me they are experiencing unforeseen high caller numbers and I'm put on lengthy hold. I have to say, it's not fucking unforeseen by me, Paypal.
Alwyne Kennedy, London

I SAW an ant in my kitchen the other day and so I placed a sugar cube in front of him. He had some of it and then went to tell his mates, so I quickly hid it because I wanted them to think he was a liar.
Martin Dunn, Jesmond

LIKE many of your readers, I too have noticed the disgusting words that can be sung to BBC programme themes. I am particularly offended by the theme tune to *Strictly Come Dancing* which can be accompanied by:

Take a stick of celery,
Stick it up your bum,
Take a stick of celery,
Stick it up your bum,
Shaaaaake it,
Da-da-daaa-da-da!
Take a stick of celery,
Stick it up your bum.

Not only is this disgusting to be on at prime time while children are watching, I often find that the celery slips out during the 'shake it' part.
Kev Crocombe, N'pton

I MET a girl today who wouldn't say boo to a goose. Fortunately, even though I do have a goose, I have no particular desire for anybody to startle it, so that isn't really a problem.
Mike Hatchard, St Leonards-on-Sea

I WOULD imagine that somewhere there are people who count all the tea bags in a box, just to make sure the supermarkets aren't ripping them off. Have these people got nothing better to do with their time? On the other hand, I imagine that there are also some people who never bother to check their teabag quantity, thus enabling big business and supermarkets to keep ripping us off to their hearts' content. Who are these people? Either way, the world has gone mad.
Dandino, York

I'LL never understand why that bloke whose car has broken down on the QuickQuid loans advert doesn't simply go through everyone's wallets and handbags when the world around him freezes and time stands still.
Tristram Bellend, Luton

I NOTE that no female actors, politicians or talkshow hosts have been accused of sexual harassment or abuse. This situation is overtly sexist and should be rectified immediately.
Boyce Van Rensburg, Tzaneen

THERE'S just no pleasing my missus. She's always going on about saving the planet, recycling and going paperless. However, when I went paperless and used her towel to wipe my arse, she started kicking off. Women eh?
Brian Trousers, Tring

I DON'T know why some of these homeless people don't take a leaf out of Charlie Chaplin's book and start twiddling a walking stick, twitching their noses and kicking a copper up the arse now and again. It would easily elicit fifty pence from me, and I'm not widely known for my generosity.
Tarquin Balls, Hull

DRY JANUARY
GO ON! HAVE A HALF!! / YEAH! A SMALL ONE WON'T KILL YOU!! / YOU'RE NOT MAKING THIS ANY EASIER, LADS! / SULK! / SIGH! / JUST A MINERAL WATER, PLEASE! / DECEMBER 9 / AUGUST 21 / HIC! / JANUARY 1

TOP

CELEBRITIES. Carry a swanee whistle with you at all times to disguise serious sexual transgressions as necessary research for a *Carry-On* film role.
Nick, Abbeyfeale, Limerick

MAKE your neighbour think that they have an apple tree by scattering some apples under a random tree or shrub in their garden.
Pooley, Thornbury

WHEN out walking alone, always carry a spare mobile in your pocket. If anyone then tries to mug you for your phone, you can make their day by giving them both.
James Pockett, Painswick

CHECK that there are exactly 50 metres of Sellotape on the roll by carefully unwinding it alongside an Olympic-sized swimming pool. If it has been correctly dispensed at the factory the tape will sit flush against either end.
Matt Ward, Leeds

SEW rubber swimming caps into your trouser pockets for an effective hot liquid transportation system.
Fat Al White, Wrenthorpe

CONTACT lens wearers. Don't waste money on expensive binoculars, simply stack your lenses on top of each other until you have achieved the desired magnification.
Nick Lyon, Truro

FOOTBALL referees. Get all of the chants accusing you of being a wanker out of the way early doors by knocking one out in the centre circle just before kick-off.
Steve Crouch, P'borough

toptips@viz.co.uk

IF we know so much more about the surface of Mars than the bottom of our oceans, then why don't the BBC do a documentary on it? They could call it *The Red Planet*. I'm sure the licence payer would much prefer to see that than a few ugly fish. If Sir David Attenborough isn't interested, I'm sure you could get Matt Damon on board. Anybody as long as it isn't that fucking Brian Cox.
Steve Grigg, Cardiff

I COOKED Christmas dinner this year and somehow managed to give my wife and all her family severe food poisoning while avoiding it myself. As a result, none of them spoke to me for the whole of the festive period. Did any of your readers have a better Christmas break than that? I doubt it.
Steve Crouch, P'borough

"BUMS on seats, please, shoes on floor" read a quirky sign in the carriage of the the train from Sheffield to Leeds. But I'm sure if the management of Northern Rail saw the state of my arse sometimes, particularly the morning after a really good night out, they'd much rather I put my feet on the seats.
H Plynth, email

THESE yellow safety vests are all very well, but they won't help you in a custard factory.
Pete Busby, Australia

I'M currently in northern Sweden and took the liberty of walking out onto a frozen lake to tread this rendering of a comedy cock with giant gonads and all spunk coming out its bell-end. Do I win a fiver? Actually, make that a tenner, only the beer over here is extortionate.
Brian "Timberlands" Melican, Sweden

PERSONALLY, I'd scrap any funding for these so-called archaeological digs. Every time I watch one on telly, they're all using tablespoons or tiny little trowels. I know we all like to drag a cushy job out a bit, but that is just taking the piss.
Cromerty Forth, Tyneside

I RECENTLY purchased a roll of Sellotape and noticed a 'helpline' telephone number on the packaging. How much trouble has anyone ever got into using a roll of Sellotape?
Martin Langley, Surrey

CAN anything else but something unsafe be "deemed"?
Mez, Canada

HOW come people from the future, can make faster-than-light drives, androids that are indistinguishable from humans and can cure open wounds with the wave of a wand, yet they can't make a reliable hologram that doesn't crackle, splutter and break down? Come on, future folk, get your shit together.
Scotty Trotter, Norwich

I DON'T know why Egyptologists reckon that if they find a mummy with all its belongings buried with it, then it was a pharaoh, or whatever. They could have just as easily had been some bloke who'd recently split up with his missus and had to live in a bachelor flat (or pyramid). He had all his shit with him because he couldn't afford storage and then died. After all, they reckon that divorce, death and moving house are the most stressful things we have to endure.
Sir Robert Eversley, email

I WAS considering becoming a vegan, but I'm not sure that I have the time to constantly tell people that I'm a vegan. Can you just let all your readers know that I'm going vegan and they should be ashamed to eat meat, so I can just get it over with in one go?
Mark Jorgensen, M'chester

"NEW Zealand is closer than you think" said the New Zealand tourist board advert on my Facebook page. Well actually, no. I thought it was only about 750 miles away until I looked it up.
Gareth Price, Portland

DAVID Attenborough tells us that seals and walruses eat fish. But judging by the size of them they must have a shit load of chips too. They don't show you that on *Blue Planet* do they?
Dave Gibbs, Biscuit Mowbray

TODAY, to my amazement, I farted out a sunflower seed which must have come from the muesli I had for breakfast yesterday. I've planted it in the garden and I can't wait to see if it grows. Then I'll have my very own special sunflower.
Peter Hall, Dorking

BK 4 4 5 4 8 1 3 06-27-95
LOS ANGELES POLICE: HWD

LOOKING at that famous mugshot of Hugh Grant recently made me realise how the upper classes take the good things in life for granted. On the very rare occasion that I get noshed off, I'm grinning like a Cheshire cat for weeks, but he looked like a right miserable bastard.
Boyd Pointless, London

GILBERT RATCHET

YONDER STAR FOLLOWER-O-MATIC

D.T. '18

CHRISTMAS EVE AT THE VICARAGE.

I'M HELPING THE REVEREND NIPSY TO DECORATE HIS CHRISTMAS TREE, READERS.

MUNCH!

SMASH!

AND MY MECHANICAL 'CHILD ASSISTANT-O-MATIC' IS BREAKING THE BAUBLES AND SCOFFING ALL THE CHOCOLATE SANTAS AS FAST AS THE VICAR CAN HANG THEM UP!

KNOCK! KNOCK!

HELLO - WHO'S KNOCKING AT THE VICARAGE DOOR ON CHRISTMAS EVE?

GILBERT, LOOK! A TINY INFANT HAS BEEN LEFT ON MY DOORSTEP!

IT... IT MUST BE THE SECOND COMING OF THE BABY JESUS!

HAW HAW! WHAT A PUNY LITTLE SON OF GOD!

HUNH? IT'S REVEREND PECKERSNIFF, FROM THE NEIGHBOURING PARISH CHURCH!

JUST LOOK AT THE SIZE OF THIS BABY JESUS THAT WAS LEFT ON MY DOORSTEP...

IT'S A WHOPPING ELEVEN-POUNDER AT THE VERY LEAST, AND IT MAKES YOURS LOOK RUBBISH!

BAH! REVEREND PECKERSNIFF ALWAYS HAS TO OUTDO ME!

DON'T WORRY VICAR - I'LL SEE TO IT THAT OUR BABY JESUS IS THE BIGGEST!

BABY JESUSES NATURALLY FEED ON CHRISTMAS DINNERS...

ROAST SPUDS

TOOLS

AND MY FESTIVE DINNER GENERATOR WILL CRAM OUR DIVINE TOT FULL OF EXTRA HELPINGS UNTIL HE'S BUILT LIKE A BRICK SHITHOUSE!

IT'S WORKING, GILBERT!

MINCE PIES

GRAVY

AT THIS RATE WE'LL HAVE THE BIGGEST BABY JESUS IN FULCHESTER!

NOT IF I CAN HELP IT!

SPROUT CONTROL HIGH LOW

I'LL INCREASE THE CHRISTMAS DINNER "SPROUT RATIO" TO 100%!

EH? YOUR MACHINE IS JUST STUFFING THE MESSIAH WITH SPROUTS!

UH-OH! ANY MINUTE NOW HE'S GOING TO...

FFTHHBRAP!

... BLOW OFF!

HAW HAW! YOUR BABY JESUS IS LOOKING A BIT DEFLATED!

WHEEEE

GET A LOAD OF THE BRIGHTLY SHINING HALO AROUND THE HEAD OF MY HOLY ANKLE-BITER!

IT PUTS YOUR DRAB LITTLE SPECIMEN IN THE SHADE!

NOT FOR LONG, REVEREND PECKERSNIFF!

ON OFF

I'VE RIGGED UP THIS HALO OF FAIRY LIGHTS, USING SEVERAL 800 WATT BULBS! STAND BY...

FLASH!

AARGH! MY EYES!

OOPS! MAYBE I OVERDID OUR JESUS'S HALO WATTAGE!

THAT FLASH HAS TEMPORARILY BLINDED ME - I CAN'T SEE A THING!

ROLLER SKATE

OPEN CESS PIT

SKID!

YOW!

OPEN CESS PIT

SPLOTCH!

JUST THEN...

I'VE COME TO SEE THESE BABY JESUSES WHICH HAVE BEEN LEFT ON DOORSTEPS IN THE AREA.

COO! IT'S THE ARCHBISHOP OF CANTERBURY!

UGH! THIS BABY JESUS IS ALL COVERED IN TURDS!

BEING HUMBLE AND LOWLY IS ONE THING, BUT THAT IS JUST FUCKING MINGING!

AH! THIS IS MUCH MORE LIKE IT!

C OF E BANK PAY ONE THOUSAND POUNDS £1000

CONGRATULATIONS - YOU WIN THE CHURCH OF ENGLAND'S FIRST PRIZE FOR BEST SON OF GOD!

THAT THOUSAND QUID PAID FOR THIS SOLID GOLD MANGER AND MINK SWADDLING CLOTHES FOR OUR BABY JESUS, PLUS A DIAMOND-ENCRUSTED STAR OF BETHLEHEM!

BAH!

1st   24-CARAT

MERRY TRUE MEANING OF CHRISTMAS, READERS!

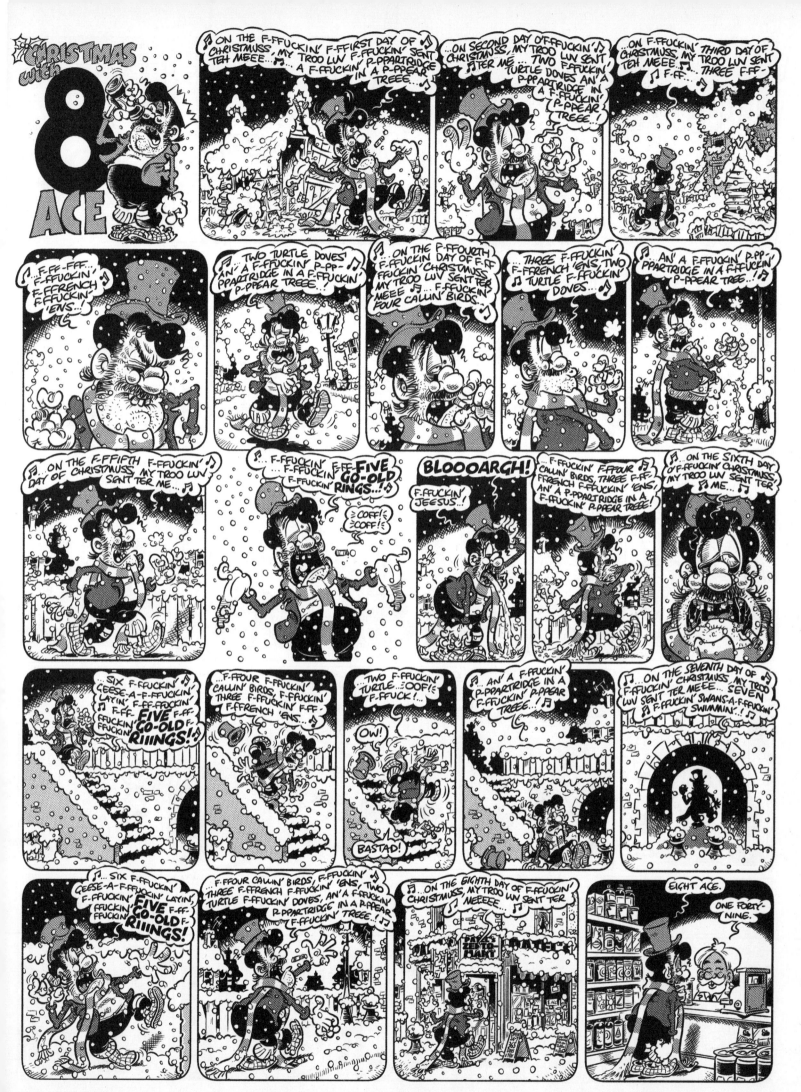

FAMILY PLOT

SOURCES close to the Scrumptons of Hull have refused to confirm or deny leaked details of the family's Christmas Day episode.

As ever, information about the hotly anticipated bumper festive instalment is being kept tightly under wraps, but it is believed that an overheard conversation between two of the Scrumptons in Aldi may have given away crucial details of what's in store for fans.

It is understood that villainous character Uncle Barry is set to make a shock return to the family's two-up two-down terraced house in Haydock Garth following his release from prison on Christmas Eve.

Scrumpton fans have long loved to hate bad boy Barry, who got next door neighbour Janice Toftsock pregnant and left her at the altar, and it is thought that his surprise reappearance will give the family a festive ratings boost.

romance

Additionally the leak also hints at a possible rekindling of the on-off romance between long-running characters Mr and Mrs Scrumpton.

Details of the scene are sketchy, but it is thought that after one too many glasses of sherry on Christmas afternoon, the couple will engage in a embrace on the settee, only to be interrupted by Mrs Scrumpton's mother, Ida, who is looking for her glasses.

Episode: Could there be a domestic brewing?

Xmas Special surprises in store for fans

piles

Anticipation is already rising among seasoned Scrumptons-watchers, with high hopes that this year's festive offering will outshine the Mukers at number 23, who are believed to be planning a Christmas Day divorce revelation and a controversial piles plotline that is expected to run into the new year.

Mrs BRADY OLD Lady

WHERE ARE WE GOING AGAIN, ADA?

I TOLD YOU, DOLLY.

WE'RE GOIN' TO SECURE USSELVES THE BEST VIEWIN' POINT.

OH YES, THAT'S RIGHT.

BEST VIEWIN' POINT FOR WHAT, EXACTLY, ADA..?

FOR HARRY AND MEGHAN, DOLLY...

THEY'RE COMIN' PAST, LOVE, RIGHT PAST 'ERE... MAKIN' THEIR STATELY REGAL PROGRESS!

OOH, FANCY! 'OW EXCITIN'!

NICE T'GET A GOOD VANTAGE POINT, THEN, T'SEE ALL THE ROYAL POMP AND PAGEANTRY.

I ALLUS SAY, ADA, THAT NO-ONE DOES ROYAL POMP AND PAGEANTRY LIKE US BRITISH.

YOU'RE NOT WRONG, DOLLY.

WE LEAD THE WORLD IN IT, ROYAL POMP AND PAGEANTRY, NO DOUBT ABOUT IT.

SO WHAT'RE THEY 'ERE FOR, ADA?

THEY'RE OPENIN' A B&M 'OME BARGAINS, DOLLY...

I'VE NOT SEEN OWT ABOUT IT IN THE PAPER.

THAT NEW ONE ON THE FODEN SUMP RETAIL PARK? ARE YOU SURE? HARRY AND MEGHAN? ...I'D'VE THOUGHT THEY'D GET SOMEONE A LITTLE MORE LOW RENT IN T'OPEN THAT...

...Y'KNOW, YER JOE SWASHES, YER RYLAN CLARK-NEALS, OR YER DUCHESS OF YORKS.

NO, IT'S DEFINITELY THEM, DOLLY. I 'AVE IT ON THE BEST AUTHORITY. A WOMAN IN THE QUEUE AT THE POST OFFICE TOLD ME.

OOH, SO IT IS TRUE, THEN. FANCY!

YES, AND YOU AND ME ARE GOIN' T'AVE FRONT ROW SEATS FOR ALL THE ROYAL POMP AND PAGEANTRY!

OOH SMASHIN'! 'OW LONG D'WE 'AVE T'WAIT?

LET ME SEE... WHAT TIME IS IT NOW, DOLLY?

FIVE-AND-TWENTY PAST EIGHT, ADA.

THREE DAYS, SIX HOURS AND FIVE MINUTES, LOVE.

Y'WHAT?!

WELL, YOU'VE GOT T'GET IN EARLY T'BAG BEST POSITION, DOLLY. Y'DUN'T WANT T'BE STOOD BEHIND SOMEONE IN A BIG 'AT WHEN PROCESSION COMES PAST...!

I SUPPOSE... I WOULDN'T WANT T'MISS ANY OF TH' ROYAL POMP AN' PAGEANTRY...

RIGHT THEN, 'APPEN I'LL SEE YOU THURSDAY AFTERNOON THEN, DOLLY.

EH?! WHERE Y' GOIN', ADA?

WELL I'M OFF 'OME, AREN'T I, DOLLY? THERE'S NO POINT IN US BOTH SLEEPIN' OUT, IS THERE? NOT AT OUR AGE.

IF ANYONE COMES TELL 'EM THESE SPACES ARE TAKEN.

THURSDAY AFTERNOON...

...AM I IN TIME, DOLLY? I THOUGHT THERE'D BE MORE FOLK OUT T'CELEBRATE TH' OCCASION!

NO, ADA... IT'S VERY QUIET ALL WEEK.

OOH, NO...'ERE THEY COME NOW, DOLLY! I CAN SEE THEIR MAGNIFICENT 'ORSE-DRAWN GOLDEN STATE COACH ROUNDIN' THE CORNER!

THREE CHEERS FOR THEIR ROYAL HIGHNESSES... HIP-HIP! HOORAY! HIP-HIP! HOORAY! HIP-HIP! HOORAY!

RAGGLY BOOOOO! RAGGLY BOOOOO!

OILY OILY OILY RA-BOOO!

Drunken bakers

You can't knock a bacon butty and a cappuccino for two quid.

FRESH BREAKFAST

FRESH COFFEE

Bargain.

See, what did I tell you?

Raking it in.

DREGGS movement

BASTARDS!

COFFEE TEA SAVOURIES CAKES

DREGGS movement

We could do that.

Yeah, all we'd need is a coffee machine.

Oh, and every other fucking thing.

We're a bakery not a cafe.

We ain't even got a fuckin' kettle.

Yes we fuckin' do.

No, we fuckin' *did*.

Soon

Is somewhere, I've had it.

Got binned. *Years* ago.

You tried mulling gin in it, set light.

Aha.

Fuck off.

You having another can?

Yeah – oh you dirty *fucker*.

That ain't one of mine, I been liquid for years.

Looks ancient.

BOP BOP

It's baked on alright.

Maybe that's how we put out the fire...

Ahh, is crumbling up nice and easy.

We was due a bit of luck.

Good as new.

Fuckin' reeks.

A few hot shit crumbs.

I'll nip ADLD for coffee, tea, milk, sugar... sausages, marge, bacon... chairs, tables, them hot lamps...

We have 40 quid.

By the way, I think the good rum deal is still on...

The litres.

YOU'LL FUCKIN' SEE!

DREGGS movement

ADLD

RUM RUM RUM SIX LITRES £40 RUM RUM

RUM? YUM YUM!

RUM DEAL STILL ON

Shortly

We're not a cafe.

No...

PLASTICS CRISIS LOOMS!

Crate expectations: Marriage guidance counsellors anticipate marriage break-up upswing if traditional milkmen start having it off with UK housewives again.

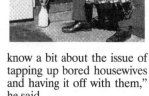

Delivering Milk And Much More !

THE UK's marriage guidance counsellors are bracing themselves for a huge spike in demand for their services as the government's forthcoming plastics ban begins to bite. For experts fear that once single-use plastic cartons are banned, milk will once again come in glass bottles delivered by traditional randy milkmen.

"Just like back in the seventies, lonely housewives will find themselves unable to resist the cheeky doorstep patter of these crate-toting lotharios," said Relate spokesman Sidney Bliss. "Affairs will be the inevitable result, and Britain's married couples will need our services more than ever to patch up their shattered relationships."

dairy

"Over the past few decades, people have increasingly bought their dairy produce in the supermarket, and consequently there has been a downward trend in marriage break-ups, which are now at an all time low," said Mr Bliss. "However, once plastics have been made illegal and housewives find themselves engaging in daily, innuendo-laced smalltalk with a cocky milko, it's not going to be long before they're giving him the glad-eye and inviting him in to make a another sort of delivery."

"And I'm not talking about a pint of gold-top," said Mr Bliss, placing his left hand into the crook of his right elbow and forming a raised fist.

train

The government are understood to be aware of the problem, and a Downing Street spokesman yesterday told us they are actively working to enlist more marriage guidance counsellors.

He said: "The use of plastic milk containers is a real problem that threatens our environment, and it is important that we act now to prevent further damage being done. However, we do realise that these urgent measures will inevitably have a knock-on effect that will put a strain on many marriages."

Government acts to head off national disaster

"We are therefore recruiting extra staff to cope with the expected raised demand for relationship-saving advice when the nation's housewives start falling for their milkmen's glib patter and inviting them in for a bit of the other."

milk

And the spokesman also announced the appointment of seventies *Confessions*-film actor Robin Askwith to the brand new post of Single Use Plastics and Affairs with the Milkman Tsar, to make sure that couples will have access to the help they need once the new environmental laws come into effect.

Askwith told reporters: "I feel very honoured to have been invited to take on this important and challenging role."

two sugars

And he vowed to bring to bear all his experience of playing nookie-bonkers tradesmen in his new position. "Back in my cheaply-knocked-out-sex-romp-comedy heyday, I played everything from a milkman to a driving instructor to a window cleaner, so I know a bit about the issue of tapping up bored housewives and having it off with them," he said.

"So if any women who are affected by the issues covered by official remit want to access government counselling services and need some advice on how to do it, I'll be happy to pop round while their husband is out and give them a bit," he added, placing his left hand into the crook of his right elbow and forming a raised fist.

GOTCHA! YOU'VE CAUGHT!

Holier-than-thou revealed as fuckin

Shocking undercover Viz report by undercover Viz reporter
Mahatma Macaroon

Rubbish reporter: Mahatma went under deep cover to expose green stars' hypocrisy.

IT SEEMS you can't turn on the television these days without being lectured by some holier-than-thou celebrity about how we have to clean up our act to save the world from ecological disaster. Whether it's jumped-up pop singers telling us not to fly on planes, celebrity chefs slagging us off for not wanting to buy wonky-shaped carrots, or some two'penny ha'penny actor telling us not to flush when we've had a piss, only when we've had a shit, it makes you sick.

But do these self-righteous celebrity arseholes live up to the standards they deign to set for the rest of us? *Viz* undercover reporter *Mahatma Macaroon* decided they didn't and went undercover to see if he was right. What he found out about this band of sanctimonious cunts will shock every right-minded person in Britain.

Casefile 1...
Sir David Attenborough

LOVED by millions thanks to his countless awe-inspiring documentary series, the veteran TV naturist has been a national treasure for decades. Now well into his nineties, Attenborough shows no sign of slowing down, and continues to use his unique place in the country's heart as a platform to campaign on environmental issues.

It's a shame he doesn't take some of his own advice. Under cover of darkness, I crept up the drive of Attenborough's swish, detached Richmond home - all bought and paid for by hard-working BBC licence payers - and located his wheelie bins. Tipping them over onto the lawn, I then made a detailed forensic investigation of the veteran *Life On Earth* presenter's rubbish.

Nestling in some beans amongst the food leftovers and general waste for landfill, I found the smoking gun I was looking for; the plastic lid from a tube of Smarties.

These things are made of 100% recyclable PET (polyethylene terephthalate), yet the self-proclaimed "environmentalist" had tossed it into the wrong bin without a thought for the environment.

citizen

It was left to me to do the decent thing and put the lid into the mealy-mouthed presenter's recycling bin, which - good citizen that I am - I duly did. Then I did a shit on the lawn to make it look as if a fox had been through his rubbish and made my escape.

The Living Planet may have won this shameless old hypocrite a shelf-full of awards, but our Blue Planet won't be living much longer if he's got anything to do with it.

Casefile 2...
Ian Hislop

THE *Private E* editor makes a b deal about his rag mission to expose t rank hypocrisy of pub figures and politician *But have I got news you* ... when it comes hypocrisy, he is the wo offender of them That's because, whi he accepts that glob warming is a fact, own actions are maki the problem worse.

Wearing a black morph s I approached Hislop's swar Little Venice mews house three in the morning, using b cutters to gain access to immaculately manicured ba garden where he stores

BIN

ebrities pocrites

eelie bins. Neatly stacked in glass recycling bin I found ee Champagne bottles, their urent-Perrier labels clearly ible by the light of the pen-ch gripped in my teeth.

rotary

ou might think that Hislop erves praise for his recycling rts, but you'd be wrong. For gross act of selfish disregard the planet's wellbeing, he l left remnants of the foil aps round the neck of each tle. It would have been the rk of just a few seconds to nove the foil completely and p it into the metal recycling . But the Oxford-educated tirist" was clearly too busy king on defenceless corrupt iticians and dishonest loid journalists to give moment's thought to the ironment.

pudding

did a shit on Hislop's patio make him think it was a that had been through his s. As I did so, I reflected t as a father of two, you'd ect Hislop to understand t we do not inherit the net from our parents, we row it from our children. t that might be expecting ittle too much from such slap-headed, short-arsed pocrite.

st like Private Eye, his sphere-wrecking actions are hing to laugh about.

Casefile 3... JK Rowling

AS FAR as I can tell, the billionaire *Harry Potter* author has never made any public pronouncements on environmental issues. However, if she did, she's exactly the sort of sneering, toffee-nosed leftie who'd be telling everyone else to ditch their smoke-belching diesel 4x4 or stop giving their kids turkey twizzlers. And, of course, this would be all well and good if she maintained a squeaky-clean environmental audit for herself.

I'm no snitch, but following my exhaustive investigation of the bins outside Rowling's swanky Edinburgh mansion, I can exclusively reveal that Rowling's carbon footprint is as big and dirty as Hagrid's underpants.

In the early hours of the morning, I donned an army surplus ghillie suit and scaled the back wall of Rowling's palatial Murrayfield estate. Dodging the security cameras, I made it round to the back of the house, where I swiftly and deftly tipped over her green mixed recycling bin.

mail

I rummaged through the contents - paper and unwanted mail, cardboard and drinks cartons, clean plastic bottles, tins, foil and envelopes. Every item had been neatly arranged in its correct place. It was exactly the same with every other bin I overturned; the blue box containing glass, small electricals and batteries, ditto the grey landfill bin.

express

But still I smelled a rat, and I found it when I kicked over the grey waste food caddy. There, nestling on top of the potato peelings and dinner scraps, was evidence of Rowling's disgusting and arrogant disregard for the environment: an avocado stone.

thompson

Everyone knows that these bulky fruits can only be grown on the other side of the world, and they go off so quickly that they can only be transported by air. They may be tasty, but they are an environ-mental disaster, with each one leaving a carbon footprint on

the atmosphere that is five times as big as a banana.

Before leaving, I did a shit on the steps by Rowling's French windows to make her think a fox had been through her bins. As I pulled up my trousers, I reflected on the sickening contrast between what I imagine her public statements about environmental issues would be, if she made them, and her private actions.

The Harry Potter author ought to be ashamed of herself, but sitting in her ivory tower filling her face with guacamole, she frankly couldn't give a Hufflepuff.

Casefile 4... Joanna Lumley

THE *Paddington 2* star is a 24-carat national treasure, and has campaigned tirelessly on behalf of orang utans, tigers, gurkhas and polar bears. But does she love these endangered species enough to actually change her own habits? I decided to find out.

After drugging her next door neighbour's dog with some meat to stop it barking, I scaled the garden wall of her elegant Notting Hill pad. I quickly found the bins in the side passage, and tipped them over to unearth evidence of her hypocrisy.

But then I hit a snag: the bins had been collected that morning and were as clean as a whistle.

proof

However, a good investigative journalist doesn't give up until he discovers the proof that he wants, and neither do I. I knew that Lumley wasn't in, as she was doing the BAFTAS with all her luvvie pals that night, so using a jemmy that I had found lying at the bottom of my inside pocket, I quickly forced the kitchen window and let myself in.

sixpence

Once inside, the evidence of the famously fragrant actress's stinking hypocrisy was everywhere. A bottle of extra virgin olive oil with the damning label "Recyclable in some areas. Please check with your local authority"; a bunch of six bananas only one of which bore a Fairtrade sticker; a single-use capsule coffee machine - perhaps the most environmentally irresponsible thing a person could own.

I ventured upstairs into Lumley's bedroom, and everywhere I looked, my suspicions were confirmed even more. A plastic light switch; a plastic clock radio; a plastic comb on the bedside table... all of which would one day end up in landfill and take 10,000 years to break down.

I quickly performed a sex act into her underwear drawer to make her think a fox had broken in and performed a sex act into her underwear drawer, before leaving. As I vanished into the Notting Hill night, I felt stick to my stomach.

Joanna Lumley may be the darling of the eco-set, but there's nothing "absolutely fabulous" about the damage she is single-handedly doing to our precious planet.

NEXT WEEK: *"How I posed as a Moscow hotel cleaner to expose the shameful skidmark secrets of Gareth Southgate's 2018 World Cup heroes"*

An ethical new magazine for people who are doing everything they can, within reason, obviously, to cut down on their use of plastics for a bit...

Middle Class Plastic Eschewer

August 2018 £29.99
Mauritius, Seychelles, Bahamas: $50

Eau Dear

"I only buy my Perrier in glass bottles these days. It's more expensive, but what price my children's future?"
A Hampstead gallery owner's sacrifice

Time for Change

"I won't have my Araminta wearing disposable nappies. The nanny, the au pair and the cleaner don't like it, but we all have to make sacrifices"

Save Our Soles

A TV commissioning editor's guilt:

"When I found there were plastic aiglets on the laces of my yacht shoes, I couldn't look my children in the face (when they came back from boarding school)"

An Inconvenient Tooth

"Yes, my toothbrush is plastic. But I've only got one, and I take it with me when I go to stay at my five weekend houses"

REALITY BITES

"When a crisp bag washed up in front of my Maldives beach retreat, I knew the time had come for us all to act"
~One Notting Hill Advertising Executive's Epiphany

Consumer Advice
The 5 Best Linen Shopping Bags Under £2000

Ethically Sauced
Top Ten Balsamic dressings that only come in hand-blown recycled glass flagons

Heroic Tale
"At last summer's regatta, we sipped our Mojitos through paper straws... We're all in this together"

ON SALE NOW

IT'S IN OUR HOMES, it's in our streets and it's in our shops, and mankind has found it indispensible for more than 100 years. But it's also choking our oceans, strangling our puffins and clogging up our turtles. It's *plastic*, and the world is only just waking up to the true enormity of its horrors. But how much do we really know about this cheap and useful nightmare substance? Here's ten fan-plastic nuggets of information about this wonderfully adaptable and durable material that is destroying the planet.

10 Things You Never Knew about PLASTIC

Holy smoke: Non-degradable plastic easily disposed of on a tyre bonfire.

1 **AN** ordinary plastic bag discarded and thrown into a landfill site will take more than 1,000 years to break down. If you find it hard to visualise a thousand years, think of it this way: It's enough time to play *Three Lions (Football's Coming Home)* by The Lightning Seeds featuring David Baddiel and Frank Skinner nearly 135 million times.

2 **IF** all those records were stacked onto an old-fashioned Dansette-style automatic-changer turntable, the resulting pile of singles would be more than 250 miles high, and would almost certainly break it.

3 **THE** world's first plastic was patented in 1909. Its inventor, Leo Polyoxybenzylmethylen-glycolanhydride, wanted to name it after himself, but after being advised that 'polyoxybenzylmethyl-englycolanhydride' wasn't a snappy enough name to become commercially successful he decided to call it his mother's maiden name - *Bakelite*.

4 **DESPITE** what you might think, 'plastic surgery' doesn't involve any plastic at all. It's actually a sort of operation in which middle-aged American actresses have their faces stretched behind their ears so that they can't blink any more and look like they're riding a motorbike without a helmet.

5 **MANY** pop acts have been named after plastic, including Plastic Bertrand, the Plastic Ono Band, and many, many more.

6 **AS** well as being a type of thing, 'plastic' is also a thing that another thing can be. According to the dictionary, a plastic thing is a thing that can be 'easily shaped or moulded'... ironically, a bit like plastic!

7 **PEOPLE** say they are paying for s o m e t h i n g 'on plastic' when they use a credit card in a shop instead of cash. However, what such people probably don't realise is that modern banknotes are actually printed on biaxially oriented polypropylene, so all money is technically plastic! Except coins, which are printed on metal.

8 **MANY** environmentaly minded people criticise plastic, complaining that it takes centuries to get rid of. However, nothing could be further from the truth, for unwanted plastic can actually be disposed of very quickly by burning it on a big pile of tyres, when it simply vanishes into a big cloud of black smoke.

9 **MIDDLE** class people don't like their children to play with plastic toys, deeming it 'common'. As a result, expensive toy shops now sell all manner of plastic-free wooden train sets, wooden dolls' houses, wooden Stretch Armstrongs and wooden Hungry Hippos.

10 **PLASTIC** macs - cheap, lightweight black or khaki PVC raincoats - were the clothing of choice for dirty old men back in the 1970s. These days, however, dirty old men no longer exist, having been re-branded during the Cool Britannia days of the 1990s as 'sex offenders', with a much more stylish and varied wardrobe of casual wear to match.

No Shoes is Bad News for Vegans

Britain's vegans have put their foot down and slapped a ban on shoes of all kinds. For many years, the plant-chomping radicals have been refusing to wear leather shoes, preferring instead to don 100% plastic footwear such as Crocs, jelly shoes and flip-flops. But now, thanks to growing awareness of the harm that synthetic materials are doing to our environment, they have now decided to forego footwear completely.

"As a vegan, the idea that my plastic Crocs could end up choking a turtle to death in the sea really upset me," said vegan River Stardust, 22. "As a vegan, that thought simply broke my heart. And I think that all vegans, and that includes me, would think similarly, being vegans."

creature

River's partner, Leaf Rainforest, 23, also a vegan, agreed. She told us: "As a vegan, I agree completely with River, who is also a vegan. As vegans, we could not countenance wearing anything on our feet that could harm a single

Sabotage: Some brightly coloured plastic clogs laying waste to the environment yesterday.

Lettuce-nibblers take firm stand on footwear

living creature in any way, because we are vegans."

"I think that all vegans, of which we are two, would wholeheartedly agree with our decision," she continued. "As a consequence, and as vegans, from now on we will not be wearing anything on our feet."

Meanwhile shoe scientists have been working on developing footwear that contains neither animal products or any other synthetic materials that are unacceptable to vegans.

banshee

However Professor Stanley Jordan from Timpsons College Cambridge, said the project was not making particularly good progress at the moment. He told us: "The only thing we can think of that isn't leather or plastic is glass, and for a number of reasons, glass is not a very good material for making shoes."

"We constructed an experimental pair of glass flip-flops, but our test subject only managed a couple of steps in them before they shattered and we had take him to A&E."

bob marley

But even if boffins somehow manage to produce a pair of flexible glass shoes, they may still face objections from vegans. "As a vegan, I would refuse to wear glass shoes," said Rainforest. "Glass is made out of sand, and that is where lugworms live, and as a vegan I couldn't bring myself to wear shoes that were made out of a worm's home."

"Did I mention I'm a vegan, and so is my girlfriend?" he said. "She is a vegan too."

"We're both vegans," he added.

23

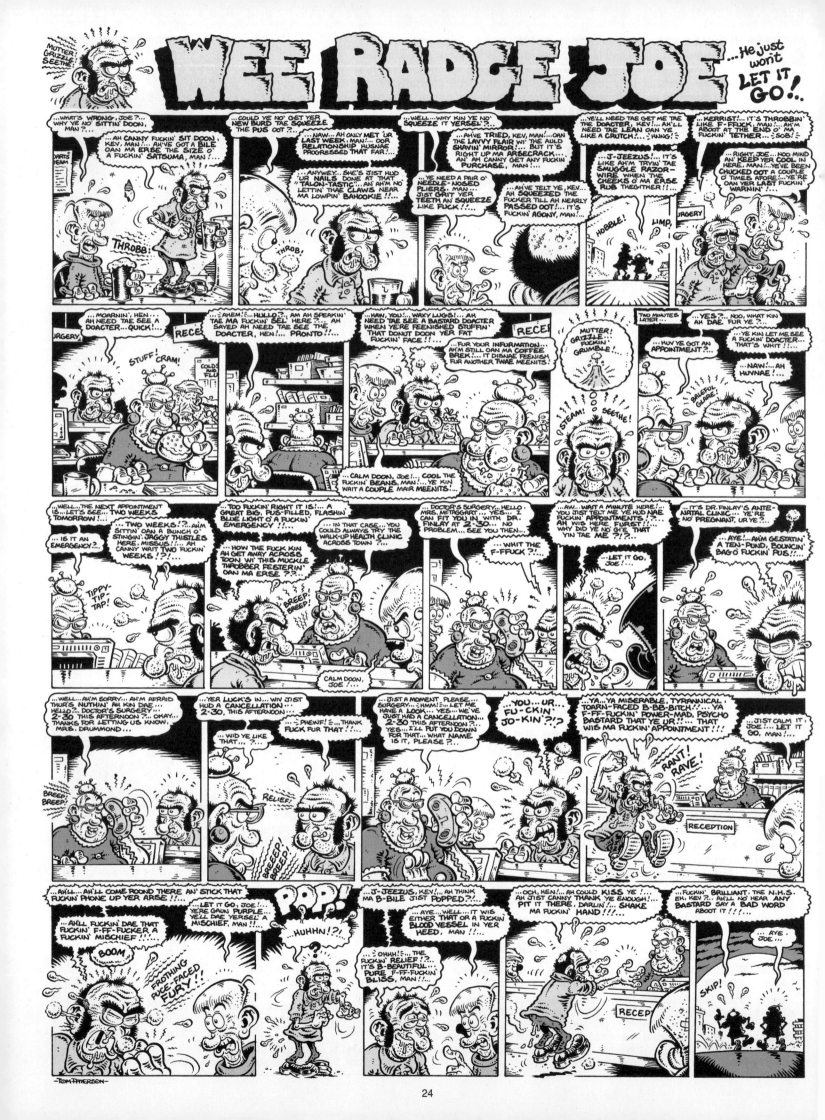

IT'S THE HAPPIEST DAY of any couple's life, as their friends and family gather together in the sight of God to witness them being joined together in holy matrimony. For the vast majority of us, it's the only time we ever step into a church unless someone's carked it, and as a result we dread being invited, for we know only too well what misery and torment lies ahead. Two hours of repeatedly standing up and sitting down, and mouthing our way through hymns we've never heard before while trying to stop our arse cheeks going numb.

It's a painful duty that we must all endure from time to time, but it needn't be such a chore. For the seasoned observer, those two hours can feel like a mere one hour fifty minutes, as the marriage service flies by in a whirl of interesting people, fascinating happenings, and remarkable situations. So let's step inside a typical British parish church and ask…

What Can You Spot at a Family Wedding?

● **THE GROOM**, eyeing up the bride's sister's arse, and realising that he may have gone for the wrong one.

● **SOMEONE** who hasn't said the Lord's Prayer since he was at Primary School, mouthing the words like John Redwood singing the Welsh National Anthem.

● **THE BRIDE'S** uncle with an earpiece connected to his phone, attempting to listen to the football.

● **THE WEDDING CAR** - an open-topped, "vintage"-style fibreglass tourer built on the chassis of a Ford Granada, that looks like Cruella de Ville's car as half-remembered by someone who can't draw and has no sense of proportion.

● **THE GROOM**, eyeing up the bride's mother, and realising he may possibly have made an error of judgement.

● **THE BEST MAN** doing a final read-through of his speech, which is a mish-mash of jokes and one-liners lifted from a Chubby Brown video.

● **THE VICAR**, delivering a delightfully witty, yet wise and thought-provoking lesson, giving the congregation the impression that he's given the task some thought, even though he's just printed it off from Sermons.com.

● **AN OWL** with the wedding ring tied round its neck on a ribbon, up in the church rafters where it has seen a bat.

● **A BLOKE** from the local bird of prey sanctuary, attempting to lure the owl down from the rafters by swinging a dead rat round on a piece of string.

● **THE GROOM**, eyeing up the bride's grandmother, and deciding he has made the biggest mistake of his life.

● **THE BRIDE'S** mother's brother stood behind the vicar in order to video the ceremony on his ipad.

● **THE GROOM'S** younger brother, still worse for wear from the stag night, being sick into his rented top hat.

● **THE VICAR** bollocking the groom's grandmother for throwing a handful of confetti at the happy couple, demanding an extra £150 on top of the £500 church-hire fee to pay for the verger to sweep the steps

● **THE BRIDE'S** mother's sister staring like a hawk at the bride's stomach, trying to work out whether she's pregnant or not.

● **THE USHERS** looking uncomfortable in their rented morning suits, gold flock wallpaper waistcoats, cravats and top hats that might have momentarily looked fashionable at a premiership footballer's wedding in OK! magazine twenty years ago

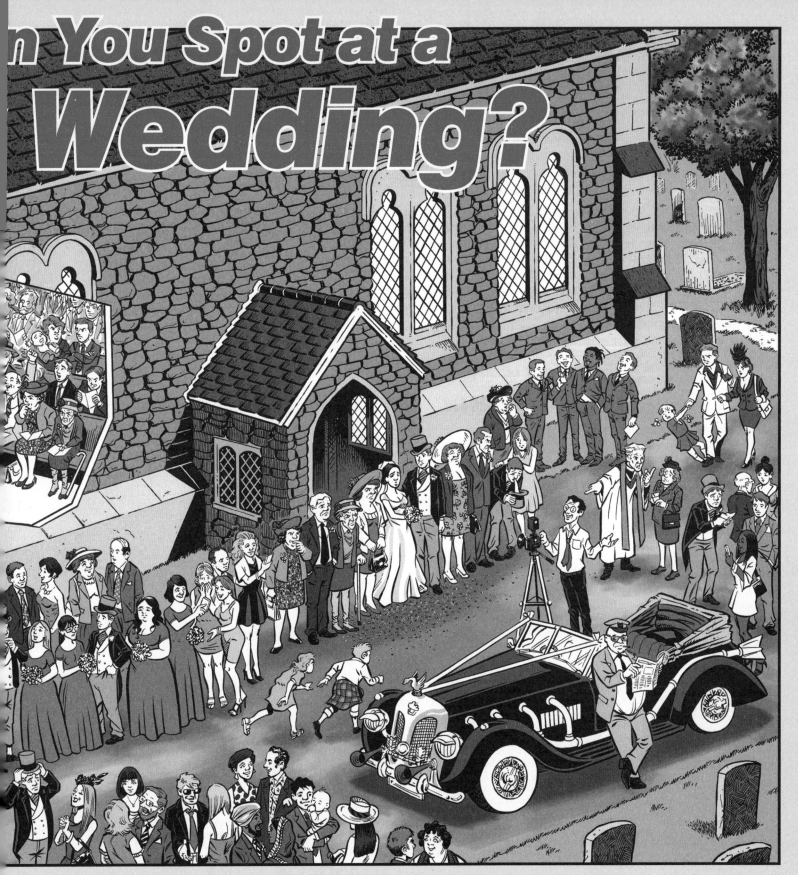

n You Spot at a Wedding?

● **THE PHOTOGRAPHER**, with his top button undone to show that - whilst his job is mainly to get a reasonably well-exposed picture of more or less everyone smiling with their eyes open - he's actually a bit of a Bohemian artist.

● **THE GROOM** with his top hat brim carefully angled to disguise the fact that his mates shaved off one of his eyebrows while he was passed out in a strip club last night.

● **THE BRIDE'S** father ruefully calculating what model of Porsche he could have bought brand new for the what this wedding is costing him.

● **THE BRIDE'S** mother looking daggers at the groom's mother because she's turned up in a bigger hat.

● **THE BRIDESMAIDS,** chosen not because they are the bride's best friends, but because she deems them fatter and less attractive than herself so as not to outshine her on her big day.

● **A DISTANT COUSIN** checking the order of service for the fiftieth time, trying to work out how many more bits there are to go before they can go to the reception and start getting hammered

● **ONE OF THE GUESTS** showing his mates pictures of the groom with his face pushed into a lapdancer's tits on his stag night.

● **ONE OF THE BRIDESMAIDS** showing her mates pictures of the bride pulling off a male stripper on her hen-do.

● **THE GROOM'S** younger brother being sick into his rented top hat again.

● **THE BRIDE**, breathing a sigh of relief that she has performed oral sex for the very last time.

Next Week: *What Can You Spot at the Fucking Reception?*

27

MEET CAPTAIN

Pulling off the writs: Crompton Allsorts QC aka Captain Loophole.

CHRISTMAS is fast approaching, and it's not just Santa Claus who will be kept busy over the festive period. For, as the days count down towards December 25th, the annual celebrity drink-drive season is already well underway. And that means that the phone never stops ringing for legal eagle CROMPTON ALLSORTS QC – better known to over-the-limit A-listers as Captain Loophole.

"I've lost count of the number of household names I've got off," he told us from the swish office-cum-bedsit he keeps above a Burnley fish and chip shop. "And it's not just on drink-driving charges neither. I've kept the stars out of chokey for all sorts of crimes, including burglary, armed robbery... *and even murder.*"

Allsorts – who amazingly has no formal legal training or any other qualifications whatsoever – is set to lift the lid on his sensational career as the stars' go-to brief. He is currently looking for a publisher for his scarcely credible tell-all memoir *Allsorts of Bother – My Life and Times as a Celebrity Lawyer.*

Now, in a series of exclusive extracts from his book, Crompton tells all and names names. He told us: "My clients might not like me spilling the beans about their brushes with the law, but they'll never dare sue me."

"They know only too well that if we had our day in court, I'd wipe the fucking floor with them."

Brian damages: Cox walked free thanks to Loophole.

EXCLUSIVE!

COX'S ORANGE NICKIN'

" It was a quiet afternoon and I was sitting in my chambers above the chip-shop watching the racing on Channel 4 when my phone rang. 'I'm in a bit of a pickle, and I need your help," said a familiar voice. It was TV astrologer **PROFESSOR BRIAN COX**. "They're going to do me for shoplifting," he continued. "I don't want to go to prison. A pretty scientist like me wouldn't last five minutes in there."

I told the mop-headed telly boffin to calm down and stop blubbing, and to come round to my chambers immediately. Shoplifting law is one of my specialities, as I have done time for it myself on a number of occasions, and I know every arcane twist and technicality of the legislation like the back of my hand.

Minutes later, a nervous Cox was perched on the end of my bed as I reviewed his case. Apparently, he'd gone into a sweetshop near Manchester University to buy a Terry's Chocolate Orange. Then, in a moment of madness that he now bitterly regretted, he had slipped the orange into his blouson pocket and left the premises without paying. Unfortunately, the shopkeeper had spotted what he was up to and had grabbed him on the street. Even worse, he had then called the filth on him.

My first question to Cox was one that could make or break his case: Had he said anything to the coppers who arrested him? An admission of guilt at this point would have made my job in court doubly difficult. He said he hadn't; this was good news.

The legal definition of stealing is permanently depriving someone of their property. As long as Cox maintained that he had merely taken the Twix outside to examine it in a better light, and that he had had no intention of depriving the

shopkeeper of his property by taking it back to his laboratory and eating it, he was in the clear.

Of course, they don't call me Captain Loophole for nothing. If Cox had fessed up to his crime when the pigs nabbed him, it wouldn't have been the end of the road; a number of legal channels would still have been open. For example, he could have stood up in court and told the jury under oath that the coppers had knocked him about to force a false confession out of him.

In the end, the case never went to trial. The prosecution knew only too well their case would fall to pieces under my forensic cross-examination. Professor Cox walked free, even though he and I both knew he was guilty as hell. "

DANNY'S DYER STRAITS

" Most of my legal casework involves defending the stars for relatively minor, victimless offences, such as speeding, drink-driving and having been a bit handsy in the seventies. But occasionally, a really serious crime arrives on my desk. And one that really sticks out in my mind is the time *EastEnders* star **DANNY DYER** found himself on the wrong end of an Attempted Murder charge.

For a man looking at an easy ten years to life if he was found guilty, the Queen Vic landlord was surprisingly calm as he sat in my chambers and explained what had happened. Apparently, the window cleaner had just done the windows of his Essex home, when Dyer noticed he had missed some birdshit on the conservatory roof. The tradesman maintained that he had cleaned it properly and a bird must have shit on it during the last couple of minutes. Dyer pointed out it was dry, to which the window cleaner replied that bird shite dries in seconds, especially during hot weather.

Dyer wasn't having that, and called him 'a fucking melt'. An argument ensued that rapidly escalated into a physical altercation on the doorstep, during which the hardman *Straightheads* actor pulled out a knife and stabbed the window cleaner in his side, leaving a deep wound that later required ten stitches.

The scuffers were called, Dyer had been arrested, and he was presently on bail after spending the night in the cells at Paddington Green. He was looking at a serious helping of porridge, but luckily he had come to the right place. I'd got Dot Cotton off a charge of assault with a deadly weapon a couple of years previously, and she'd given him my number.

As it happens, violent crime is one of my specialities. I've been done for

28

LOOPHOLE

GBH more times than I care to remember, and I know all the loopholes back to front and inside out, and I knew I could get Dyer off on it. Believe it or not, for a legal eagle like me, this case was as easy as piss.

You see, the window cleaner had had a wet chamois leather in his big pocket. Had he pushed that over Dyer's mouth and nose and held it there for a few minutes, the *EastEnders* actor would have suffocated. To all intents and purposes – and, most importantly, in the eyes of the law – that chamois was a deadly weapon. If the case came to trial, I would argue that, in pulling a knife on the window cleaner and stabbing the bastard up, my client had merely been acting in self defence.

Danny done it?
Dyer's chamois story held water.

When the filth saw the strength of my legal argument, they knew it would be pissing in the wind to pursue the case. But Danny had had a close call. He vowed that from now on, the only bars he would be finding himself behind would be the ones in the Queen Vic, and the only things he would be pulling on anyone in future would be pints of beer! "

ROLLING IN THE DEEP TROUBLE

" Benefit fraud costs this country millions of pounds every year, and the authorities are keen to bring those responsible to justice and make examples of them. And they must have thought they'd hooked themselves a big fish when pop singer **ADELE** was charged with fraudulently claiming Housing Benefit.

The *Rolling in the Deep* pop diva turned up at my chambers and explained to me the scam she had been

Benefit of the court:
Adele's housing benefit scam required sorting by Allsorts.

running. For the past four years, using a series of aliases, she had been claiming housing benefit on six council properties in the Greater Manchester area. Whilst living 200 miles away in a swanky Surrey mansion, she had been subletting these properties out to families of illegal immigrants, charging them exorbitant rents and threatening to dob them in if they didn't keep up their payments.

I've been convicted of benefits fraud a few times myself over the years. So, as a poacher turned poacher's lawyer, I knew from the outset that it was a particularly tricky area of legislation and it wasn't going to be straightforward to get Adele off. After she left, I spent several hours poring over my legal textbooks. When I finally found the loophole I had been looking for, I realised it had been staring me in the face all along.

A few weeks later, I accompanied my client to Burnley Court. Even before proceedings began, I approached the bench and slapped the charge sheet down in front of the magistrates with a flourish. "May it please your honours…" I began, theatrically. "I would like to refer you to the Christian name entered into the box on the charge sheet, to wit 'Adele'."

"I would further draw your attention to the box on that same document for the defendant's surname," I continued. "You will see that it has been left blank." There were audible gasps in the courtroom. The prosecution lawyer exchanged anxious looks with his clerk.

"Ladies and gentlemen of the jury, I put it to the you that the prosecution case is built on an incomplete, and therefore legally inadmissible, document." I sat down, and there was a moment's silence before the judge banged

his gavel. "Case dismissed," he intoned. "Adele, you may leave this court without a stain on your character."

That trial was a landmark case, and it was to prove a pivotal moment for countless other single-named stars. These days Sting, Bono, Lulu and Morrissey – to name but a few – are all running the exact same housing benefit scam as Adele was, and there is literally nothing the nash can do to stop them. Thanks to Captain Loophole, they know that any attempt to bring them to justice will simply be laughed out of court. "

BLEAK OUTLOOK FOR CAROL

" With her twinkly girl-next door image and butter-wouldn't-melt manner, BBC *Breakfast* meteorologist **CAROL KIRKWOOD** is loved by viewers. But her national treasure reputation would be shot to fuck in an instant were she to be charged with breaking and entering a house, stealing £200 cash and a wedding ring, and shitting on the floor.

But this was exactly the litany of criminal charges that were facing Carol when she arrived in my chambers one morning. And the famously cheery weather girl was far from a ray of sunshine as she perched on the end of my bed, anxiously puffing on her vape like a cooling tower. Kirkwood explained that it was merely an opportunist crime. "I'm not a real criminal," she insisted. "I just gave into temptation."

At first glance, the case against her looked strong. Neighbours had called police after seeing Kirkwood acting suspiciously in the back lane, and officers had apprehended her in the house – with the stolen property in her pockets – while she was pulling up her scads after curling one off on the hall rug. On the face of it, it was an open and shut case. Any lawyer would have advised her to plead guilty and throw herself on the mercy of the court.

Unfair weather?
Captain got Carol off scot-free.

But I'm not just any lawyer. Over the years, I have done time for burglary more times than I've had hot dinners, so I know every sneaky backdoor trick in the legal book … and a few more besides. "Carol," I reassured her. "We're going to fight this case, and what's more, we're going to win, and here's how."

Firstly, as I explained, she had had her collar felt before she had a chance to leave the house with the swag; technically, the ring and the cash had not been stolen, simply moved. As for the shite on the carpet, I instructed her to testify that she had been intending to wipe it up, but the titheads had rocked up before she'd had a chance to find a cloth.

These were all good legal arguments; probably enough on their own to sway any judge or jury Carol's way. But my coup de grace was the charge of breaking and entering. Carol had merely reached through an open porch window and flicked the latch on the door. In the circumstances, as she had caused no damage, the most she could be charged with was trespassing on private property – a minor civil misdemeanour rather than a criminal offence.

Needless to say, when the trial day arrived and the prosecution barrister got a gander at the legal elegance of the defence case I was about to present, he quickly decided to drop all charges.

When Carol first came to see me, it had looked like a decidedly gloomy forecast for the nine-times Weather Presenter of the Year. Now, thanks to Captain Loophole's timely intervention, she had nothing but sunny spells ahead. "

NEXT WEEK: Britpop star Jarvis Cocker is caught on CCTV wielding a sawn-off shotgun during an armed raid on a Sheffield sub-post office, during which a have-a-go hero member of the public is shot in the foot. Crompton has to call of his legal nous to stop the Pulp frontman going down for life.

THE Male Online

Beryl? *BERYL?!* *What is our salt situation?!?*

What is our what?
Salt! Salt!
Quickly! This is a matter of life and death!

I think we've about half a tub.
GAH! Not enough!
We need at least a pound a day *to beat Alzheimer's.*

Are you *sure* about that?
An English national newspaper has just said so, Beryl –
– in huge letters on their front page!

Now, do you seriously think these august institutions would stake their good name on *any old medical claptrap?*
Yes.

But
Thank *GOD* we got here ahead of the panic-buyers!

That's not near enough salt, Beryl.
Up the dose or risk one day forgetting I'm your husband!

I for one, however, will *not* go mental into that good night.

Six months later
B-Beryl! Beryyy!!!
The salt! *Gasp!* The salt!

No more today! You already ate a whole tub and your blood pressure –
Gaaah...
Mail Online
NO SALT EVER!!
Oh my *word,* you look dreadful!

I'll get your tablets!
Yes! Then we must purge our bodies of salt!
To beat Alzheimer's!!

Soon
Are you *insane?*
You need a little bit on fish and chi–
You soon will be!

I shall dine at my desk.
There's a risk your *sodium cloud* will settle on my meal.

Six months later
BERYL!

Who would believe that salt *does* make you immune from Alzheimer's after all?

Teatime
Don't come running to me when you've no idea who I am.

Six months later
GAAAAAAAAAAAAAAAAAAAAAAAAAAAAAAAAAAAAAAA–
Please! My friend is here!

BANG!

30

31

LETTERBOCKS

Viz Comic, P.O. Box 841 Whitley Bay, NE26 9EQ : letters@viz.co.uk

ST★R LETTER

IF it's unlucky to see a solitary magpie, then why didn't God invent them so they were always strapped together in twos like Siamese twins, or just not invent them at all? Or, if he really wanted magpies, then why didn't he just invent them so that they weren't unlucky? It's not rocket science, is it?

Gustav Fox, Chodchester

I SAW a toilet paper company say they will plant three trees for every one cut down. That's too much if you ask me. It's political correctness gone mad.

Daryll Buchanan, Glasgow

I WAS not in the least pleased when I received a hefty fine from the police after making an illegal right turn along Newcastle's Quayside, so I decided to get one over on them. Little do they know that prior to paying online, I slotted my debit card down the crack of my arse.

Graham Flintoft, Gateshead

IF you look at it from the animal's perspective, it's hard to see why David Attenborough is so revered. Imagine if you were having your dinner and some

posh bloke let himself into the kitchen and started whispering about you. Or even worse, if you were having a shag and he walked in and started filming you at it. Alright, my mate Dave did do that, but I asked him to because we were doing something for *Reader's Wives*.

Bartram Fibreboard, Hull

OLYMPIC high jumpers shouldn't waste money on expensive drugs, they should just get a dog to sniff their nipsy just before they jump. I'm pretty sure there's no rule about it and it certainly works. My dog sneaked into the bathroom and plunged her nose in for a good snort while I was drying my toes the other day and I nearly jumped through the fucking window.

Piston Reeling, Ealing

I WAS born in 1969. Two of those numbers are the same and another one is the same as those two, but inverted. Can any of your readers beat that?

Nobby, Doncaster

✱ *Well, readers, Nobby has well and truly thrown down the gauntlet. Maybe you were born in a year where two of the digits are odd and the other two even. Perhaps three of the digits of your birth year add up to the other one. Or perhaps one of the digits cubed is equal to the square of the product of the others. Write in and let us know.*

"I HAVE my books and my poetry to protect me," sang Simon and Garfunkel on their song *I Am a Rock*. I'd like to see how far that got them on a Saturday night out in Derby.

Dave Evans, Nottingham

AFTER watching *Match of the Day* last night, I had the thought that people tend only to choose their favourite sports from the relatively small number that are popular in the nation where they live, and in fact we delude ourselves into believing that our choice is based upon the empirical merits of 'our sport' over and above any others from different parts of the world. After a bit more thought, I realised this could also be said for religions, and food, and systems of government, and morals, and ethics and pretty much anything else that we like to think of as our own personal choice or we believe to be the truth. The logical extension of this thesis is that we are doomed to live and die by a narrow set of guidelines defined either actively or passively by our society, and that freedom and free will are nothing more than an illusion. Then I had a wank and fell asleep.

Mike Tatham, St Andrews

I SUPPOSE in the current climate we should expect that bloke who kissed that bird's arse to resign from whatever it is he is now doing, as a result of his historical inappropriate behaviour. Perhaps only then will any other birds who got their arse kissed off of that bloke be able to come forward as part of the #MyArseToo campaign.

Julian, email

THE artist who painted that picture of dogs playing snooker that you used to see in pubs years ago obviously didn't give it much thought. Everyone knows dogs can only see in black and white. It would have been impossible for them to play as they wouldn't be able to tell the difference between the colours, particularly the reds and the green. Or hold a cue.

Steve Bond, Castleford

MY mate has spent the last 12 months trying to convince me that ducks don't float and when you see them sat on top of the water then they are really just stood up and have really long legs which extend out of their bodies but are hidden by the water. He also predicted Donald Trump would become president about 10 years ago so, to be honest, I'm half inclined to believe him.

Tim Buktu, Timukt

I DON'T understand why so many people are obsessed with finding out who Jack the Ripper was. Even if they did discover his identity, he'd probably be really old now and not fit to stand trial, or even dead. Move on, I say.

Hector Bland, Tootin

I THOUGHT would be fun to stick a recorder up my arse and play *Blowin' in the Wind* on it. But the nurse in A&E didn't see the funny side, and my daughter insisted I buy her a new recorder. Honestly, some people are so miserable.

Dominic Twose, Leamington Sp

IF you ask me, the Bayeux Tapestry is fake news. It's not even a tapestry, for fuck's sake. Pardon my French.

Tim Tusling, Cottingha

WHY is it acceptable to binge-watch *Game of Thrones*, for instance, but when you do the same with continental pornography, you get all sorts of shitty looks? It's double standard pure and simple.

Gavin Forknif Wednesbu

FOR THE LOVE OF GOD

YOUR Valentine's Day theological questions answered by the Archbishop of Canterbury, Justin Welby

Dear Justin,

I NIPPED out to buy a big box of Ferrero Rochers for my husband Dennis for Valentine's Day. Unfortunately, when I returned home, I found that he had dropped dead of a heart attack. You can imagine my devastation, as I'm not keen on Ferrero Rochers since the nuts give me loose foulage, and I couldn't take them back as I didn't get a receipt. I was wondering, if I put them in Dennis' coffin, will they make it through to the afterlife with him, or will they be confiscated during some kind of ethereal security check?

Ada Callous, Doncaster

Justin says: "The chocolates will certainly make it through to the afterlife, Mrs Callous, but I'm afraid that your late husband won't get the chance to enjoy them. If Dennis ends up in Heaven, he will have unlimited access to celestial foodstuffs such as milk and honey and Manna, not to mention Ambrosia. Next to these rarefied otherworldly comestibles, a terrestrial Ferrero Rocher would taste foul. Alternatively, if your husband has lead a sinful life and is bound for Hell, the chocolates will melt instantaneously for all eternity."

Dear Justin,

ON FEBRUARY 14th last year, I spent half an hour praying to Saint Valentine for my wife to give me a blow job. However, when I floated the idea to her later that day, she simply laughed in my face as usual. I wonder if you could tell me where I went wrong as I am looking to give it another shot this year, with (hopefully) a little more success.

Martin Deathbed, Ackling

Justin says: "As you can imagine, February 14th is Saint Valentine's busiest day of the year - he receives upwards of 13 million prayers inside 24 hours, so you'll understand if a few slip between the cracks. My advice this year would be to squeeze your palms together extra tightly when you're praying. This is the prayer equivalent of the red exclamation mark on an email - it marks the prayer as 'urgent' and sends it straight to the top of the Saint's request pile. However, it's also worth mentioning that God is ultimately responsible for vetting every granted prayer, and He tends to take rather a dim view of blow jobs - even when performed by a spouse. With that in mind, you might be better off praying to a more sexually liberated deity, such as Bacchus or Satan."

Have YOU got a question about the most romantic day of the year that's also linked - no matter how tenuously - to the Anglican faith? Why not write in to: 'For The Love Of God', c/o Dr Justin Welby, Viz Comic, PO Box 841, Whitley Bay, NE26 9EQ

I UNDERSTAND that the Dutch are the tallest people in the world. Yet the Netherlands is almost completely flat with no mountains or even hills to peer over. This is a complete waste of height in my opinion, and typical of the profligacy of the European Union.

Graham Degg, Ashtead

WHEN I was a boy we used to have a little terrier called Scamp. He was a right randy little fucker. His lipstick was out all the time and he was always trying to shag the neighbours' dogs. One day we had posh relatives visiting and we were all sitting in the living room making small talk when Scamp came in and started rubbing his lipstick on the carpet right in the middle of the room. My dad, while trying to remain inconspicuous, tried to kick Scamp's arse and slipped off the couch and did his back in. How we laughed. Do any other readers have any cute pet stories of their childhood?

Gillboy, Glasgow

WHY is it that all red-blooded men love watching steamy girl-on-girl bongo films, yet their wives aren't in the least interested in seeing two blokes at it like knives. Yet another example of there being one rule for them and another for the rest of us.

Rogie Bogan, email

IF funeral directors stopped crawling along and drove around at normal speed like everyone else, then they could easily fit in a few more funerals a day, thereby increasing their profits. I've worked that out and I'm as thick as fuck.

Gareth Lynch, Huddersfield

I'VE just sent you a Top Tip about sending starving polar bears to Antarctica to feast on penguins. It's so good you're bound to print it to the right of this letter, and you should also print this letter to guide readers to it. Particularly as Christina Martin can't be arsed to write anything now.

Pard, Bridgwater

We're sorry, Mr Pard, but your Top Tip about sending polar bears to the Antarctic to feed on penguins failed to make the final cut.

IT has been alleged that playwright Noel Coward operated as a spy during World War II. I suppose if he'd been caught he would have been charged with *thespianarge*. Thank you, I'm here all week.

Ross Lewis, L' ton Spa

ROGER Federer won the 2017 Men's Singles at Wimbledon, yet it turns out he's married. If he had any shred of decency, he'd hand back the prize money immediately.

Ed O'Meara, London

I KNOW you don't ordinarily publish lonely hearts letters, but I'm choking for a shag right now. Thank you.

Peter Busby, Australia

I FOUND a great picture for Up-the-Arse Corner, but as there's no way to submit it on your website, you can go fuck yourselves.

Antwistle Goocher Huddersfield

Thank you Mr Goocher. There is no facility to upload pictures to our website. But if you send an email to letters@viz.co.uk, and click on that little thing at the top of your screen that looks like a paper clip, then click on the picture that you want to send, then press the send button, it should work. If it doesn't, let us know and we'll go fuck ourselves.

IT'S said that beef production contributes massively to global warming due to the methane emissions from cattle. Yet I've been a veggie for a week now and I haven't stopped trumping. It appears we're in a lose-lose situation.

Mr P. Rant, Southsea

I READ recently that Gwyneth Paltrow recommends pumping coffee up your arse to live for ever, or something. I don't doubt the methodology, but I wish celebrities would enlighten us on topics other than health now and again, such as bricklaying.

Dr. H.S.E. O'Hurlighy, Dublin

Kramer vs. Gamer

MOMENTS OF MADNESS

CAT-BIN woman, that politician who got sucked off on Hampstead Heath while looking for badgers, the Moto GP bike racer who pulled on his opponent's brakes at 140mph, Prince Harry in his Nazi armband, Theresa May doing her fucking stupid dance… at some point in our life, every single one of us has experienced a Moment of Madness that we have lived to regret. We've all done something completely out of character which, if we had our time over, we would not do again. And that includes the stars…

A-list celebs reveal all about the things they did that they now wish they hadn't

Fiona Bruce BBC presenter

I ONCE done a shit in Tomasz Schafernacker's shoe. I drove in one morning and his car was in my parking space, so I went down to the weather forecast department to have it out with him and saw his shiny brogues outside his office door. There was nobody around so I just squatted down and curled one out. Unfortunately, my moment of madness was caught on CCTV, and I was called in to see the Head of News and Current Affairs who gave me a proper dressing down. In my defence, it was the end of a very stressful week and I'd been under a lot of strain recording an episode of *Antiques Roadshow* at Blenheim Palace. I suppose I just flipped. I know it's no excuse, and if I had my time over, I certainly wouldn't do it again. That said, Schafernacker hasn't nicked my parking space since.

Gerry Adams Ex Sinn Fein leader

I ONCE stole a penguin – not one of the chocolate-covered biscuits ones, but one of the flightless birds. Back in the eighties, me and a few of the lads from the IRA went on a day trip to see the animals at Edinburgh Zoo, and I absolutely fell in love with the penguins. They were just so cute and funny; they looked like little waiters waddling about in their enclosure. I don't know what came over me, but during a moment of madness I leaned over the barrier, grabbed one of them, and stuffed it in my rucksack. I can't imagine what I was intending to do with it when I got it home; I hadn't thought that far ahead. I haven't got a pond in the garden, so I suppose I would have had to keep it in the bathroom or something. Anyway, I never got that far because when I was in the gift shop it started squawking and flapping about in my bag, which alerted the security guards. The police were called and I was given a caution, and because I was in the public eye, the press had a field day. I made a statement, apologising and saying that my actions had been completely out of character although, because it was the eighties, my words were voiced by an actor to starve me of the oxygen of publicity.

Una Stubbs Actress

I STUCK a banger up a cat's arse. I had been invited to a *Give Us A Clue* bonfire party at Michael Aspel's house, and we'd all had quite a bit to drink. To cut a long story short, Lionel Blair, Liza Goddard and Bernie Winters kept daring me to shove a banger up Michael's cat's bottom. I can't imagine what I was thinking – my only explanation, and I know this is no excuse whatsoever for what I did, is that I was very drunk, but in a moment of madness I agreed to do it. Michael went in the house and got his cat – a beautiful pedigree Persian – and I inserted the firework. It sounds awful now in the cold light of day, but everyone was laughing their heads off as I lit the blue touchpaper. Luckily, the cat ran off and the banger fell out of its arse before it went off. The poor thing was unharmed, but I still shudder to think what would have happened if I'd pushed it in a bit further.

Mark Carney Bank of England Governor

I STOLE a car and wrecked the green at my local golf course. I had booked myself in to tee off at quarter past four, but when I arrived I was told I was five minutes late and had missed my slot. I was absolutely furious, and as I made my way through the car park, I saw a Jag that had the keys left in the ignition. To cut a long story short, in a moment of madness I twocced the car and drove it onto the course, revving the engine and doing wheelspins and dough-nuts on the ninth green, really churning up the grass, before trying to do a handbrake turn and crashing it into a bunker. At a hearing in front of the full club committee, I explained that I had had a very frustrating week at work, trying to adjust the Exchange Rate Mechanism, which had kept going wrong. I had to write a formal letter of apology to the captain and my fellow club members, and pay a fine of £250. My foolish actions of that day are something that I will regret until the day I die.

Mary Beard Classicist

I CLIMBED onto the roof of a moving train. I was on my way to give a speech about the Emperor Trajan at the British Library, and I was sitting in the first class compartment of the Cambridge-Kings Cross express. Literally out of nowhere, I was struck by thought of how thrilling it would be to climb up onto the roof of the carriage and run down the length of the train as fast as I could, like in a James Bond movie. Before I knew what I was doing, I had made my way into the vestibule by the toilets and lowered the window. Then, in a moment of madness and without a thought for my own safety, I clambered out of the window and scrambled up onto the roof. Once there, the enormity of my predicament suddenly hit me and I came to my senses. I was absolutely petrified, frozen to the spot as I clung to a vent in the 125mph wind. Luckily, the guard had seen me climbing out and he alerted the driver, who applied the brakes. For the next five miles, the train pottered along the track at 10mph until it reached Finsbury Park station, where the fire brigade and British Transport Police were waiting with a ladder to get me down. To this day, I can't explain why I did it, and I have never again felt the need to perform such a dangerous and foolhardy stunt.

★ Are **YOU** a celebrity who has experienced your own Moment of Madness? Write in to the usual Viz address and let us know about the shocking, out-of-character behaviour that you now bitterly regret. There's a Cheap Viz Pen worth up to 19p for the best celebrity Moment of Madness we receive. Mark your envelope or email submission: 'Celebrity Moment of Madness'.

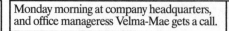

That does sound good. Perhaps I'll take one out myself!

Plans start from less than £5 a month, and as long as you're between 50 and 80, you're guaranteed to be accepted without a medical, and you get this free car sponge just for applying.

You can wash mine next!

Ho! Ho! Ho! Cheeky cunt!

The Beauregards are Tennessee's *Dukes of Dung*, and they're following a tip-off about a heap of ordure that could see them pocket a pile of cash…

…but first, Bubba's got to strike the toughest bargain of his life!

I'll give you a hundred fifty bucks, and me and Bobby-Joe'll take it away today. Do we got a deal?

Mister… y'all got yourself a deal.

Alright!

Yee-haw!

When he said yes, I was as happy as a possum with two tails. There's a mushroom farm in Bayou County will pay us top dollar for this load of foulage.

BUBBA BEAUREGARD
CEO

Hi Ma. Could y'all call the DuBois mushroom farm and tell 'em me and Pa's got two ton of prime beefstock stools for a good price.

Sure thing, Bobby-Joe.

BAR-B-Q RANCH

Everything looks like it's coming up smelling of roses, but disaster strikes as Bubba and Bobby-Joe hit the West Tennessee backroads…

Pa! Look out for that pothole!

CLUNK!

Oh BLEEEP! The BLEEEP! BLEEEP! axle's snapped.

BLEEEP! BLEEEEEEP!

With the nearest truck repair shop over 200 miles away in Wisconsin, a broken axle is the last thing that Bubba and Bobby-Joe need…

If that axle's bust, we'll have to call a tow truck.

And they sure ain't gonna want us on the back if we're hauling two tons of ripe cow bobs… We'd have to dump 'em.

Everything depends on the results of Bubba's examination of the underside of his pick-up…

No, everything's fine. It ain't broke.

Up next on Quest: *All New Outback Piss Hunters*

Back on the road, the Redneck Shit Salvagers start their 35-mile drive to the DuBois mushroom farm. But then Velma-Mae comes on the radio, and she's got bad news…

Boys, I got something to tell y'all…

What is it, ma…?

I just spoke with DuBois mushroom farm…

…and they ain't buyin'!

They just bought a wagon-load from Lafayette Horseshit. Three tons for a hundred bucks!

BLEEEP!

Next time on Redneck Shit Salvage, it's take-it or leave-it for Bubba and Bobby-Joe…

A hundred-fifty for the whole load.

Sorry boys. I ain't payin' a cent over seventy-five.

BAYOU MAGGOT FARM

BLAZE DESTROYS LOCAL BUSINESS

A FULCHESTER man is facing financial ruin after his business was destroyed... *by the Great Fire of London!* And self-employed Ronnie Fletcher is now warning others to be vigilant after the second hand car showroom he has run for 25 years was reduced to ashes by the historical conflagration yesterday.

Hot wheels: Fletcher watched as business went up in smoke.

"I was just shutting up shop when I became aware of some kind of wormhole in the space-time continuum opening up in the showroom," Fletcher told reporters.

"I could see all old-fashioned people and wooden buildings through it, and everything was on fire. I immediately knew I was looking at 1666 and the Great Fire of London," he continued.

"I didn't know what to do but I wanted to help, so rushed into the toilets and got some water to throw through the wormhole."

showroom

But disaster awaited brave Ronnie when he returned to the showroom.

"The inter-epochal portal had closed, but some of the Great Fire had obviously made it through into our time, because the showroom was ablaze," he said.

In the end, Ronnie could only stand and watch as his successful business empire burned. A member of the public called the fire brigade, but by the time they arrived the showroom, and all the cars in it, had been destroyed.

"The fire chief asked me what I was doing in the smoking remains of my business in the early hours of the morning, holding an empty petrol can," Ronnie recalled.

tack

"I explained that I had been working late due to how well the business was doing at the moment, and that I'd filled the petrol can with water to put out the Great Fire of London."

"It's devastating," he continued. "You might think the Great Fire of London burned itself out on the morning of 5th September 1666, but it could strike at any minute and deprive you of your successful business in otherwise inexplicable circumstances."

muncher

Asked to respond to rumours that the insurance on Ronnie's showroom had been trebled the week before the blaze, a spokesman for Fulchester police said: "We haven't ruled anything out at this time, including that the fire may have been started deliberately."

"We are appealing to members of the public with any information, including anyone in 1666 who might have seen a wormhole pop up with a 21st century car showroom on the other side of it, to come forward," the spokesman added.

London's burning: A Viz artist's impression of how the wormhole may have looked if someone had done a painting of it at the time.

39

ON MY BACK TO THE FUTURE
with Stormy Daniels

THE YEAR IS 2525. Adult actress Stormy Daniels has been in cryogenic storage for more than 500 years after being frozen in the wake of her affair with US President Donald Trump. Now finally thawed out in a future that is beyond her wildest imaginings, a world where everything is not as it seems and nothing is how she remembers it, it is time for her to explore the future.

This week, Stormy gets down on all fours to look at...

CARPETS IN THE YEAR 2525

" **THE FIRST** thing that strikes me about carpets in the year 2525 is the amazing variety of colours on offer. Of course, the old-fashioned neutral tones that were popular back in the 21st century when I let the future 45th POTUS fuck me - shades such as Oatmeal, Sand, Dark Beige and Light Beige - are still on sale. But now you can also choose carpet in a myriad of exotic space-age hues, such as Silver Tobacco, Irridescent Barleycorn and Radioactive Champignon, which are a bit like normal carpet but with silvery tinsel woven in.

Carpet is also available in a brand new colour that simply didn't exist before I was frozen in liquid nitrogen half a millennium ago. Colorex-3000 is a hue that scientists discovered hidden within the spectrum, and it is impossible to describe without actually seeing it. Colorex-3000 is a fashionable choice in the smartest homes of 2525, but such exclusivity comes at a cost: It's 29.99 Space Credits per square yard, and that doesn't include underlay or fitting. "

" **BACK BEFORE** I was put in cryogenic storage, I had my Los Angeles condo completely re-carpeted, using some of the $130,000 that Donald Trump gave me to keep schtum about letting him have it off with me. On the advice of my attorney Michael Avenatti, I went for a blue and pink Regency stripe pattern in an 80%/20% wool/polyester mix. Just like letting The Donald have a go on my twat, it was a decision I immediately regretted. It didn't really go with the curtains or the sofa, and because my lounge isn't exactly square, one of the stripes looked like it got wider as it ran along the skirting. But once it was down, I was stuck with it.

Here in 2525, that's no longer a problem. Using liquid crystal technology, the pattern on a carpet can be changed electronically to suit the shape and decor of your room. If you decide you don't like stripes, a single press of a button on a sleek, wrist-mounted carpet remote control, can instantly make it Paisley, zig-zags, tartan, polka-dots... or any one of billions of other stylish designs. Using a mobile phone 'app', you can even upload your favourite photo from your Instagram account and put that on your carpet too. The possibilities are endless. I only wish that this technology had been available 500 years ago!" "

"**FIVE CENTURIES** ago, I appreciated a carpet that had a thick, soft pile, as it was very forgiving on my knees when Donald Trump was trying to push his weird-shaped cock up me from behind. But on the other hand, that same comfy deep pile was a terrible trap for crumbs, pet hair and cigarette ash; it was a nightmare to keep it properly vacuumed. To solve this problem, the carpet makers of 2525 have turned to state-of-the-art science.

The fibres of today's deep-pile Axminsters are made of self-reproducing 'nano-bots' that utilise advanced AI technology to constantly adjust their length to exactly match your immediate needs. A 3D 360˚ camera mounted in a discreet podule fitted to the ceiling monitors what you are doing and adapts the pile-height accordingly. For example, if you are shooting a spitroast video, the fibres will automatically increase their maximum length to keep your knees and elbows comfy. On the other hand, if you are having a game of marbles, the same fibres will instantly shrink themselves down to practically nothing. "

"**ONE PRINCIPLE** that hasn't changed over the 500 years I've been in a super-cooled torpor is that a carpet can be made or broken by the quality of its underlay. Money skimped on this vital element of the fitting process is a false economy, just as it was back in the day when - against my better judgement - I gave Trump a shot on my snatch. But here in 2525, the risk of picking the wrong grade of underlay is happily a thing of the past. Woven into every modern carpet's hemp backing are billions of molecule-sized neodymium magnets. A current passed through a special metalised coating painted onto the floorboards creates an electromagnetic charge that repels the carpet, causing it to hover 1cm above the floor on a luxurious cushion of invisible flux. "

"**BACK IN** the 21st century, having a carpet fitted meant dragging all the furniture out of the room before a fat man with a sweaty Dagenham smile slashed at your brand new Tufted Wilton with a Stanley knife before kneeing it roughly into place. Put simply, just like lying under Donald Trump as he heaved himself to a dribbly climax, it was an ordeal.

But that's no longer the case. Because here halfway through the third millennium, carpets no longer come on a roll hanging out the back of a van. These days, they come in a tin … in liquid form. Your new liquid carpet is simply poured onto the floor, where it spreads out evenly, under your furniture and around your chair legs until it meets your skirting boards. A catalyst is then added, which initiates a chemical polymer chain reaction that turns the liquid into solid carpet. All that remains is to tack it down in the corners to stop it riding up when you're vaccing. "

NEXT WEEK: Stormy is On Her Back to the Future reporting on ceiling tiles in 3030

PAISLEY TUFTED WILTON 25 SQ YDS

41

JOKER AVOIDS JAIL

A **SERIAL** prankster who has raised thousands of pounds for good causes has narrowly avoided a prison sentence after one of his charity stunts went wrong.

Big-hearted fundraiser, Mick Halibut has built up a small reputation in South Yorkshire after playing a series of pranks that primarily target brothels in Doncaster and Sheffield.

"I've always found that people working in the sex industry are bit straight-faced and take themselves far too seriously," he told the *Doncaster Cyst and Embolism*.

"Playing tricks and poking a bit of fun at them is just my way of getting them to lighten up, while highlighting some of the hypocrisy in the industry, especially in terms of pricing and time-keeping," he added.

practical

Ever the practical joker, Halibut's hilarious pranks have included pretending to have misplaced his wallet after having full sex with a prostitute and climbing out of the window and, following oral in his car, asking a good time girl to get out and check if his brakelights were working before driving off.

In another classic gotcha, after getting executive relief, Mick set off the fire alarms in

Knocking shop down ginger: Hard-hearted magistrates didn't see funny side of Halibut's sexy japes.

a Sheffield massage parlour and promptly disappeared down the fire escape without paying. "It was absolutely hilarious," he said.

"The look on their faces when they eventually turned the alarms off and got back in the building must have been priceless," he recalled.

"It's a pity I was long gone and couldn't see them."

amateur

"All the money I save on the sexual services is donated to local charities, so it's all for a good cause," he added.

However, back in July, one of his stunts in a lap dancing club was rumbled, and Mick ended up being arrested.

wedding

Magistrates heard that Halibut had spent the night in Doncaster's Peppermint Hippo club, running up a three-figure bill which included drinks and a private dance in the specially curtained-off area.

When it came to paying, in typical Halibut style, the inveterate joker feigned a heart attack and ran off whilst the girls went to call an ambulance.

town

Unfortunately, he was caught just outside the club by bouncers. He tried to explain he was fundraising for charity, but his pleas fell on deaf ears and the police were called. And yesterday, hard-hearted magistrates handed him a £300 fine and a six months suspended sentence.

But Halibut vowed that his conviction would not stop him raising money for good causes. "Many of the brothels' owners and employees fail to see the funny side of my pranks," he told reporters outside Doncaster Magistrates Court. "I have often been chased down the road for miles by these humourless killjoys armed with makeshift weapons."

"But they won't stop me doing my charitable deeds," he promised.

Halibut told reporters: "When I'm doing a stunt and, for example, getting pulled off by an uninterested masseuse, I tell myself it's all for charity and that really helps me get through it."

barry

Indeed, such is Mick's reputation in South Yorkshire knocking shops that he has been forced to be ever more inventive, becoming a master of disguise in order to prevent the sex workers twigging on to his wacky stunts. To this end, he has created a set of zany characters that he uses to pull his pranks including:

- *Stan Molehusband - A Sheffield-based truck driver who loves blowjobs*
- *Barry Fibreboard - A Doncaster-based plasterer with a thing for threesomes*
- *Doug Twelvetrees - A Glossop-based painter and decorator with a penchant for getting smacked on the arse*

And these characters are something Halibut takes

great pride in: "I've worked hard developing them; each has their own unique back story which adds a layer of credibility when getting past notoriously stringent brothel receptions," he said.

"Generally, dressing up as these people gets me through the door and past security," he continued.

"The only thing they have in common is that they all have a hard-on in need of relief, but other than that they give me a great deal of creative freedom to stay one step ahead of the madams."

novelty

And Halibut believes that one day his charitable work will be recognised at the highest levels. "You see people getting gongs all the time for their work with charities," he said.

biscuit

"I've honestly lost count of the amount of money I've saved and donated to charity with my practical jokes. Maybe one day someone in the community will put my name forward to the palace."

"But that's not why I do it," he stressed. "In a way, I hope I'm passed over for an award, as the fame might make it difficult for me to play my practical jokes."

Halibut says that next week he is going to attempt a tour of all the Sheffield massage parlours in one afternoon dressed as an Otley-based carpet fitter, to raise £350 for the dialysis unit of a local hospital.

HOT WEATHER SPLITS COUNTRY IN TWO

FROM Land's End to John O'Groats, this year's sizzling summer has left Brits with just one topic of conversation … The drought. Now, as the scorching weather finally cools and the country's depleted reservoirs slowly begin to refill, scientists are issuing dire warnings that, as the climate changes and global warming begins to bite, even worse droughts are headed our way in the years ahead.

EXCLUSIVE!

"There's no doubt about it. Next time we have a prolonged spell of nice weather, the country's lakes and rivers will simply boil dry," said Met Office forecaster Dr Zsa-Zsa Grenouille. "And that will be bad news for anyone who likes water, or who depends on it for their living."

ponds

"For example, aquarium keepers and people who own ponds will be hit particularly hard by a catastrophic drought of the sort I am predicting, as they will have no fluid medium to keep their fish in," said Dr Grenouille.

"Likewise, swimmers such as Duncan Goodhew, Adrian Moorhouse and Sharron Davies will find the parched earth very much not to their liking," she continued. "And Tom Daley will have to find something else to fill his pool with, such as bubblewrap, cotton wool, or Quavers, before jumping thirty foot off the top board into it."

skateboards

Canoeists, rowers and water-skiers are also expected to find conditions challenging in a post-water Britain. "Pottering about in my boat on a dried-up river or canal bed isn't going to be nearly as much fun as doing it on water, I'll admit," said four-times Olympic gold medallist Sir Matthew Pinsent. "In fact I'll probably have to screw a couple of skateboards on the bottom of it so I can get around a bit.

"On the other hand, I won't have to put my life jacket on any more, so it's swings and roundabouts really," he added.

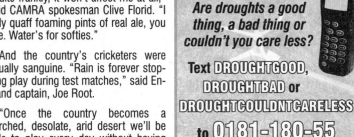
Spray away? With future water availability uncertain, meteorologists are investigating how it may affect people such diver Tom Daley and cricketer Joe Root (above inset).

Others were even less worried about a future drought desiccating the UK. "Quite frankly, it won't affect me at all," said CAMRA spokesman Clive Florid. "I only quaff foaming pints of real ale, you see. Water's for softies."

And the country's cricketers were equally sanguine. "Rain is forever stopping play during test matches," said England captain, Joe Root.

"Once the country becomes a parched, desolate, arid desert we'll be able to play every day without having to go back into the pavilion, except for when we stop for lunch, tea, orange squash or bad light."

WHAT DO YOU THINK?

Are droughts a good thing, a bad thing or couldn't you care less?

Text **DROUGHTGOOD, DROUGHTBAD or DROUGHTCOULDNTCARELESS**

to **0181-180-55**

Texts cost £2.50 plus another £10 and then another £5 plus your standard network rate, plus another £10

NO DROUGHT ABOUT IT

Bono Saves Planet yet AGAIN!

THE recent spell of unseasonal summery weather saw Britons stripping off in their droves as the UK sizzled for week after week. But according to some experts, those high temperatures could easily spell disaster, with the country's reservoirs boiling dry under the baking sun. And a lack of water could prove disastrous to human beings, dogs, cats and plants, as all living things rely on the tasteless see-through liquid for survival.

But as scientists scratch their heads wondering how to save life on earth, it has once again been left to pint-sized pop star Bono to come to the planet's aid. And according to the U2 frontman, who tips the height chart at 5'3", the answer was glaringly obvious.

"As our rivers, reservoirs and lakes dry up, we could simply drink the sea," he told reporters at a press conference held in the Channel Islands for tax reasons.

"It's made out of water and it's absolutely huge. It's a no-brainer. If everyone on the planet had four glasses of the sea every day, it would still last for millions of years," he added.

> From our BONO correspondent
> **Bo Nolan** in Dublin

And the singer's ludicrously simple life-saving suggestion has left boffins with egg on their egghead faces.

ludicrous

"I can't believe we missed this one," said Professor Hector Cravat, a climate change scientist from Oxford University. "We were so wrapped up with trying to produce water by somehow fusing gaseous hydrogen and oxygen, or extracting the organic component from fossil hydrocarbons, that we forgot that two thirds of the planet is covered in the stuff," he continued.

"I feel a right dickhead."

Other scientists also could not believe how stupid they had been. *"Facepalm! Talk 'bout not seeing the wood 4 the trees,"* tweeted BBC *Science Today* presenter Dr Adam Rutherford.

And CERN particle smasher Professor Brian Cox was equally embarrassed. "The sea. Of course! Is there no limit to the number of ways this short-arsed bellend can save the planet?" he said. "Honestly, he's made us scientists look proper fools," he added.

Sea moves in mysterious waves: Bono's watery solution could save billions of lives worldwide.

hat

But although he is responsible for saving the earth's entire population, the tax-averse warbler was being characteristically modest last night. "I daresay that many people would like to thank me for saving the earth, perhaps with some medal or award, but that's not the reason I did it," he told *Majesty* magazine.

"Many may go so far as to suggest that the planet's name be changed from Earth to Planet Bono in my honour. But that's not for me to say, that's for other people to decide," he opined.

However, web server hosts Cardiac Internet confirmed that they had yesterday sold the domain names Planetbono.com, Planetbono.org and Planetbono.co.uk over the phone to an anonymous buyer for £19.99 per year with automatic renewal.

"I don't know who he was, but he had an Irish accent," said a Cardiac Internet telesales operator. "And he sounded like he was about 5'3", with sunglasses and a hat," he added.

FLASH BANG WALLOP! WATER PICTURE!

PEOPLE who take photographs of water board spokespeople standing on the cracked surfaces of dried-up reservoirs are working round the clock to keep up with demand from local and national newspapers. As the hot weather continues and the drought bites, editors around the country are said to be finding it difficult to source enough of the clichéd images to accompany their formulaic and alarmist reports.

"Business hasn't been this brisk since the summer of 1976," said Burnley-based veteran water-board-spokespeople-standing-on-the-cracked-surfaces-of-dried-up-reservoirs photographer Frank Smudger.

Boom time for people who take photographs of water board spokespeople standing on the cracked surfaces of dried-up reservoirs

Reservoir dreggs: This year has seen record demand for photographs like this one of a waterboard spokesperson standing on the cracked surface of a dried-up reservoir, says snapper Smudger.

demand

"Last year, I didn't take a single picture of a water board spokesperson standing on the cracked surface of a dried-up reservoir, but this year I've been rushed off my feet," he told us. "In fact, I've had to take on four extra members of staff just to keep up with the increased demand."

"Even so, photographs of water board spokespeople standing on the cracked surfaces of dried-up reservoirs have been flying off the shelves faster than we can take them," he added.

realistic

Mr Smudger said that the water-board-spokespeople-standing-on-the-cracked-surfaces-of-dried-up-reservoirs business has always been a very seasonal one. He told us: "I've got to be realistic. This drought isn't going to last forever. Sooner or later, the heavens are going to open again and the reservoirs are going to fill up again. At that point, there simply won't be any dried-up, cracked reservoir beds for me to take take photographs of water board spokespeople standing on, and I'm going to have to lay off some or all of my newly hired employees."

inflatable

But Mr Smudger was cautiously optimistic about the future. "If it keeps raining and we get some good floods again, I've got a friend who specialises in taking pictures of old ladies and their cats being carried to inflatable dinghies by firemen, and he might be able to offer me a bit of seasonal work to tide me over until next year," he said.

CACTUS COSTS SPIKE

Buyers prickled by unscrupulous sellers

AS the country wilted in the scorching temperatures of the hottest summer since 1976 since records began, one major industry was slammed for cashing in and making a killing while the sun shone. Responding to increased demand for their spiky, drought-loving plants, Britain's cactus growers stood accused of more than **DOUBLING** their prices, leaving desperate customers fuming.

"A barrel cactus from my local garden centre would have cost me £2.99 last year when I didn't want one, but this summer the price for that same cactus had gone up to more than a fiver," fumed Surbiton mum-of-three Audrey Steaming. "They are ripping us off simply because there is no water to keep our other houseplants alive."

"I had some ferns, but as soon as the taps in the house ran dry they just shrivelled up and died," Mrs Steaming continued. "I went to buy some cactii to replace them, but the robdogs had stuck the prices up on account of the drought. And it was the same story with the prickly pears and all the other xerophytes."

"It's an absolute disgrace," she added.

But Digby Lithops, chair of cactus growers' trade body the UK Succulents Guild, refuted suggestions that his members had been cashing in on the catastrophic, superheated state of the planet's climate. "Nothing could be further from the truth," he told us. "The fact is, my members have a responsibility to their shareholders to maximise profits, and if that means cashing in on the catastrophic, superheated state of the planet's climate, then so be it."

However, Mr Lithops promised that costs would remain stable for the foreseeable future. "I can guarantee that cactus plant prices will now remain pegged at their present level on a permanent basis," he told us. "Unless, of course, we have further droughts in forthcoming years, in which case we may have to, and indeed will, increase them again and again."

Sharp practice: High prices for cacti is leaving consumers sore.

BOWSER! BOWSER! BOWSER!

Drought spells sales for dull books

DICTIONARY publishers are looking forward to record sales, and it's all thanks to the summer drought. As our reservoirs dry up and the news starts reporting that bowsers are being deployed on Britain's streets, the public are expected to flock to the shops in their thousands to buy dictionaries in order to look up what the word "bowser" means.

Word up: Dictionary sales look set to soar with the temperature.

OED lexicographer Susie Concavity told us: "It's the same every time there's a dry spell. The first thing the authorities do is instigate a hosepipe ban. Our sales don't move because everyone knows what a hosepipe is."

"The next stage, once the reservoirs start to get a bit depleted, is to set up standpipes," she continued. "We sell a few more dictionaries then, but it's only when they reach the 'bowser' stage that our sales really go through the roof."

However, when asked what the meaning of the word "bowser" was, Concavity was playing her cards close to her chest. "No spoilers," she teased. "You'll have to buy the book to find out."

NORMAN THE DOORMAN

LADIES AND GENTLEMEN, HELLO, GOOD EVENING AND WELCOME TO THE GRAND BALLROOM OF THE GROSVENOR HOUSE HOTEL FOR THE 2018 NATIONAL DOORMAN OF THE YEAR AWARDS...

THIS PRESTIGIOUS HONOUR - THE EQUIVALENT OF A NOBEL PRIZE FOR BOUNCING - RECOGNISES A DOORMAN WHO HAS ACHIEVED CONSISTENT EXCELLENCE IN THIS FIELD OVER THE PAST TWELVE MONTHS.

WELL, WITHOUT FURTHER ADO, IT'S TIME TO ANNOUNCE THIS YEAR'S WINNER, WHO WILL RECEIVE £10,000 AND THIS MAGNIFICENT GOLD TROPHY...

LADIES AND GENTLEMEN THE WINNER OF THE 2018 NATIONAL DOORMAN OF THE YEAR AWARD IS...

...NORMAN BOORMAN FROM RITZY'S AT KING TUT'S NITE-SPOT IN FULCHESTER!

COME UP HERE AND COLLECT YOUR PRIZE, NORMAN!

...WOAH-WOAH-WOAH! WHERE THE FUCK D'YOU THINK YOU'RE GOING, PAL?

ERM...UP ON STAGE TO COLLECT MY...

STOP YOU THERE, SON. NO YOU'RE FUCKIN' NOT.

FANCY YOURSELF, DO YER,? DO YOU WANT SOME? I EAT CUNTS LIKE YOU FOR DINNER, SUNSHINE.

...AND THAT BOW TIE'S CASUAL AN' ALL.

CAMERON'S DAUGHTER STILL IN THE PUB

Cameron: Probably in his hut.

EX-Prime Minister DAVID CAMERON still hasn't been back to pick up his daughter from that pub, after inadvertently leaving her there following a Sunday lunch in 2012.

The child, who was 8 years old at the time, is now 16 and has been sitting by the bar of the Plough Inn, Cadsden, with a glass of lemonade and a bag of crisps for nearly a decade. The landlord told us: "Every time someone comes in the door, she looks up hopefully. But her hopes are always dashed. It's quite sad, really."

A spokesman for the former premier told us: "It's a simple mix-up. Mr Cameron thought his wife had gone back to the pub to pick her up in 2012, while she in turn thought that he had gone."

"Mr Cameron has probably now phoned the pub to make sure his daughter is safe and well, and will be driving straight over there to get her," said the spokesman. "Just as soon as he has finished writing his memoirs in his £25,000 Farrow & Ball-painted shepherd's hut."

"Either that or Mrs Cameron will go and get her if she's not too busy doing them handbags. One or the other, anyway," added the spokesman.

A LITTLE CAVALIER WITH THE FACTS

OH CRAP. "WHAT'S THE CAPITAL OF BOSNIA?"

I DON'T KNOW THAT!

PSSST.

"SARAJEVO."

CHEERS, MATE!

OI!

FUCKING CHEAT.

WRITE! SCRIBBLE!

HANDS UP!

Think the Stars are as honest as the day is long? *Well think again!* Because here are a few well known names who have been caught being naughty on camera. Can *YOU* spot the stars in our identity parade of A-List blaggers?

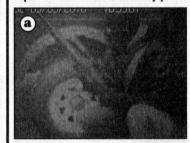

a

This former Rear of the Year was hoping for a 'Good Life' on the proceeds of a violent security van heist which left two guards severely concussed after they were hit in the face with the butt of a shotgun.

A. Felicity Kendal

Springwatch out! There's a thief about! A 'wildlife' behind bars awaits this Bonnie & Clyde-style pair of telly presenters who were recently caught on CCTV, blowing the safe at the Slimbridge branch of the Nat West.

b

A. Chris Packham & Michaela Strachan

c

Order! Order! Bedfordshire Police would like to 'Speaker' to this eminent parliamentarian, who they want to question with regard to the theft of £8 million of gold bullion from a bonded warehouse near Luton Airport.

A. John Bercow

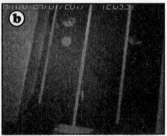

46

The Lowdown on...
Joke Shop FLIES

with Professor
Frank Lowdown
Churchill College, Cambridge

JOKE SHOP FLIES are big business. It is estimated that more than 95% of the global population regularly put joke shop flies on their friends' food for a laugh. The international joke shop fly market is worth more than $2 trillion a year, and is a vital cog in the world's economic engine.

Let's spend a day with the boss of a joke shop fly manufacturing corporation to get the lowdown on this amazing multi-billion dollar business.

IT'S 6.30 am and Lance Bateman, CEO of one of the world's biggest joke shop fly businesses, *Global Joke Shop Fly Corp*, arrives at his company's palatial glass and steel headquarters in Manhattan's swish Joke Shop Fly district. He makes his early start because the joke shop fly business is a truly international, 24-hour-a-day one.

AS Bateman enters his office suite on the 88th floor, his secretary brings him up to speed on the day's scheduled appointments and meetings. But before he does anything, he checks his company stock on the Asian Markets before they close in order to ward off hostile takeover bids from other joke shop fly multinationals on the other side of the world.

BATEMAN has his first coffee of the day at a briefing meeting in the boardroom. His directors bring him up to speed on any overnight fluctuations in joke shop fly futures. This morning brings good news: initial sales of the company's latest product, a half-inch plastic bluebottle that retails for 30p for a bag of 5, have been encouraging.

8.30 am and it's time for a working breakfast with the owner of an injection moulding plant in China, hoping to secure an order for 30 billion joke shop flies. He wants 3.05p per unit, but that would mean that *Global Joke Shop Fly Corp* would have to sell them for 55p for a bag of 6. Bateman is reluctant to go higher than the psychologically important 50p per half dozen pricepoint. In the end, the two businessmen shake hands at a cost of 2.75p per joke shop fly.

BATEMAN calls an emergency video conference with his legal team. One of his company's bestselling designs - a housefly - is being pirated in South America. The copycat joke shop flies in question are of inferior quality, with moulding burr left on the legs and their wings too thick, and threaten to damage *Global Joke Shop Fly Corp*'s reputation. It's a clear-cut case of intellectual property theft, and the lawyers are instructed to take the pirates down.

AFTER a working lunch snatched at his desk, during which he reviews several ambitious design proposals for a new range of joke shop flies, horseflies and wasps, Bateman rushes across the city to address a high-powered conference of joke shop fly manufacturers. The topic under discussion - *Whilst using a single staple on the folded cardboard bit at the top of a bag of joke shop flies reduces manufacturing costs, is it worth the risk of some of the flies falling out?*

IT'S 8.30pm, the end of another busy day at the office, and Bateman makes his way up to the roof of his headquarters to catch the company helicopter. But his working day is far from over. During the 30 minute flight to his home in the Hamptons, he will sign several high-powered contracts to export his products to joke shops around the world.

NEXT WEEK: *The Lowdown on the Worrying Escalation of Stink Bomb Production in North Korea*

FAKES TO FORTUNES

Undercover Viz reporter tricks the stars in Great Art Fake-Off

Art of Deception: Viz's undercover reporter, Mahatma Macaroon, forged a new identity as A-list art dealer.

ANYONE who reads the newspaper knows that art connoisseurs and collectors regularly hand over dizzying amounts of cash for paintings and sculptures by their favourite artists such as **VAN GOGH**, **MONET**, **PICASSO** and **CONSTABLE**. At a New York auction last year, an anonymous buyer forked out an eye-watering **$450 MILLION** for a painting by **LEONARDO DA VINCI**… *enough money to buy 150,000 top-of-the-range 64" flatscreen tellys!*

Not surprisingly, an international art market so saturated with money is also awash with fakes. And while experts can obviously spot a bootleg Botticelli or a counterfeit Canaletto a mile off, it is feared that many inexperienced collectors have been duped into unwittingly paying big money for worthless forgeries.

Increasingly, unscrupulous crooks posing as respectable art dealers are targeting the showbiz stars with crude fakes. With their shallow tastes, big houses and seven-figure incomes, these deep-pocketed celebs are simply asking to be taken for a ride. *Viz* investigative reporter **MAHATMA MACAROON** decided to create his own knock-off masterpieces to see if he could tempt a series of household names to buy them for big money. What he found will shock every right-thinking celebrity lover in the country.

CASEFILE NO. 1

Celebrity: Gary Barlow

Artwork: Leonardo da Vinci's Mona Lisa

I DOWNLOAD a high-resolution image of the world's most iconic masterpiece off the internet and take it along to a local printshop. For just £10, they print it out A3-size onto canvas-effect paper. In a nearby charity shop, a fiver buys me a gold-effect picture frame, into which I pop my "original" Leonardo da Vinci. my next stop is the doorstep of a swish Cheshire mansion, the home of Take That! star and art lover **GARY BARLOW**.

Affecting a strong French accent, I introduce myself as a top Paris art dealer who is in the area for the day, selling artworks from the Louvre Gallery, which is holding a closing-down sale. I explain that I have had a busy day, and the only painting I have left to shift is the Mona Lisa, which I take out of a binbag with a Gallic flourish.

As Barlow studies the painting, examining the frame, I can tell that he is interested. He has clearly been taken in by my patter and my 'Faux-na Lisa', and whistles as I tell him that masterpiece in his hand has been conservatively valued at half a billion pounds. I explain that my bus back to Paris leaves in half an hour, and for a quick sale it's his for a £150. Barlow once again looks at the Mona Lisa, taking in the enigmatic smile that has charmed countless art lovers since the Renaissance, and then looks at me. "I'm not sure," he says. "It's a nice picture, and it would look nice in the hall."

When I tell him it's his for a hundred quid and I'm cutting my own throat, the deal is done. "Put it there," says Barlow, proffering his hand, and we shake on the deal. He goes back in the house and returns with four twenties, a ten, a five and some shrapnel. "Take that," he laughs, as he hands over the money.

But it's me who's really having the last laugh, as I take his hard-earned money and hand over a picture that is worth less than a fifth of what he's just paid for it.

CASEFILE NO. 2

Celebrity: Lewis Hamilton

Artwork: Michelangelo's Statue of David

FEW STATUES are as instantly recognisable as David - the giant marble nude originally sculpted by the Italian artist Michelangelo in 1504. At a local car boot sale, I hand over a couple of pounds for a crudely cast Action Man-sized resin replica of this iconic Renaissance masterpiece. The seller wants £3, but I knock him down because the end of his cock been chipped off.

A few days later, I find myself in the paddock of the Monza Grand Prix circuit, knocking on the door of a luxury Mercedes motorhome belonging to F1 world champion **LEWIS HAMILTON**. Her off the yoghurt adverts answers the door, and, affecting a convincing Italian accent, I introduce myself as Dr Enrico Palazzo, chief curator of the Galleria dell'Accademia in Florence.

"I was wondering if Señor Hamilton would like to buy one of our art treasures?" I ask, and at the words 'art treasures', the F1 champion's familiar chinstrap-bearded face appears round the door of the chemical toilet. He tells me to come in and wait. Twenty minutes later, I hear the toilet flush four or five times and Hamilton enters the living area, wiping his hands on the back of his logo-plastered racing overalls.

I explain that we are having a bit of a re-vamp in the gallery, and are selling off some of our older stock. Flattering him, I tell him that I think Michelangelo's statue of David would make a great addition to the already impressive collection of art he keeps in his Monaco apartment. "Hmm, I thought it was bigger than that," he says as I take the statue out of its carrier bag and free it from its newspaper wrapping.

"No," I reply. "It's always been this small. It's just that all photos of it are taken really close up." My quick-thinking seems to allay the F1 star's suspicions, and he quickly cuts to the chase. "I've got to have it," he says. "How much do you want for it? Name your price." I realise that I'm in pole position, so I go in high, pointing out that David is regularly voted the world's most iconic statue, so it's not going to be cheap.

"I couldn't let it go for less than five hundred," I say. "Done!" he replies, immediately handing over a wad of high denomination notes. I quickly make my excuses and leave.

Lewis may be a whizz on the racetrack, but when it comes to art connoisseurship, he's clearly the Formula 1 pits.

CASEFILE NO. 3

Celebrity: Jamie Oliver
Artwork: Picasso's Les Desmoiselles d'Avignon

MODERN art provides a rich seam for art forgers to mine, because unlike the work of the old masters, it requires no talent or drawing skill to do. With a folder containing a crude drawing made by my four-year-old daughter under my arm, I turn up at one of the Naked Chef's restaurants and book a table. After eating my meal of tempura turkey spirals in sourdough breadcrumbs and twice-fried pommes-de-terre batons, I tell the waiter that I'd like to pay my compliments to the chef in person, and I am taken to the kitchens and introduced to Oliver, who is busy removing a Dr Oetker pizza from its wrapper.

Reaching into my folder, I remove the toddler's incompetent daub and show it to him. "It's a genuine Picasso," I tell him. "Les Demoiselles d'Avignon - one of his most famous works." The millionaire pan-jiggler, who is well known for his love of modern art, looks interested. "Yes, it's definitely genuine," he bluffs. "I'd know a real Picasso anywhere, and I'd love to add this work to my collection. Do you have any provenance?"

I explain that I bought it off Picasso's sister during a recent holiday in Benidorm. For a moment, he looks doubtful, but when I swear on my three kids, he is finally convinced; as a father himself, Jamie knows that such a cast-iron promise is as good as it gets. "How much do you want?" he asks, reaching into his apron for his wallet. I tell him it's his for just £200. "One hundred and the meal you've just ate," the mockney chef comes back, and we shake hands.

As I leave, I decide to leave Oliver a tip. And it's this: Make sure you really know your onions before you decide to dish out big money on modern art, or it could be a recipe for disaster.

CASEFILE NO. 4

Celebrity: Janina Ramirez
Artwork: LS Lowry's Matchstalk Men and Matchstalk Cats and Dogs

YOU'D think that a professional art historian would be the last person to be taken in by a crudely faked work of art. But you'd be wrong, as I discover when I decide to flog a 'genuine' LS Lowry to BBC4 academic **DR JANINA RAMIREZ**. Settling down at the table next to her in the reading room of the British Library, I adopt a thick Lancashire accent. "Are you in th'market to buy a reet champion Lowry painting?" I ask her, doffing my cap which is even flatter than my vowels. "Why? Have you got one to sell?" she smiles. "Because if you have, I'd definitely be interested."

Lying through my teeth, I explain to the credulous telly brainbox that I used to be Lowry's milkman, and the painter once couldn't pay his bill so he gave me a one of his trademark matchstalk men oils instead. Then I show her my undiscovered 'masterpiece' - in reality a cheap paint-by-numbers I found in a Cancer Research shop and knocked up quickly last night. Some of the colours aren't even dry yet, but with the pound signs already flashing in her eyes, does Ramirez notice? Does she bollocks.

"I only want £150 for it," I tell her, and she can't believe her luck. After all, genuine Lowrys rarely come on the market these days, and when they do they can easily fetch ten times that amount. Two minutes later we are at the cashpoint on Euston Road. She types in her PIN number - 1234 - and the notes are spat out into her eager grasp. "Here you go," she says, handing over seven twenties and a ten.

Highly qualified Dr Ramirez may boast a string of letters after her name, but after my visit she can add six more - S.U.C.K.E.R.

CASEFILE NO. 5

Celebrity: Dame Judi Dench
Artwork: Tracey Emin's Shitted Bed

THE ONLY thing easier to fake than Modern Art is Installation Art; literally anything goes in this Emperor's New Clothes world. A dead shark in a tank for a million quid? Ker-ching! A load of elephant shite rubbed on a canvas for another million? Ker-ching! A pile of bricks or old tyres? Ker-ching!

And one celeb who's an absolute sod for this sort of rubbish may well be actress **JUDI DENCH**. Dame Judi regularly thrills movie-goers with her portrayal of 'M' - James Bond's boss and the head of British intelligence. But just as I suspect she will, she throws intelligence right out of the window when I offer to flog her an iconic piece of Installation Art - Tracey Emin's Turner Prize-winning *Shitted Bed* - for just fifty quid.

Posing as international art dealer Charles Saatchi, I join the crowds waiting outside the stage door of the Garrick Theatre, where Dame Judi is currently wowing West End audiences with her portrayal of Lady Bracknell in *The Importance of Being Earnest*. When the autograph hunters finally leave, I step forward to introduce myself and make her an offer that's literally too good to be true.

"How would you like to own a work of art that's won the Turner Prize?" I ask, putting on a plummy accent like I've got a mouthful of Elgin marbles. "And the best part is, I just want fifty nicker for it." Her eyes widen and I can tell I've piqued her interest. It's time to reel her in and seal the deal. "It's Tracey Emin's shitted bed," I whisper, and she trembles with excitement. "I've just bought a load of brand new modern art, and I'm selling it off cheap because I need to free up some space in my gallery." "Oh my God. Emin's Shitted Bed is my favourite piece of Young British Art," Dame Judi trills. "It's such a brave and exciting piece; it's so full of energy and beautifully shitted. I've always dreamed of owning it!"

She gets in my car and we drive to a dingy back lane behind Custom House DLR station. We walk across some waste ground to a dark railway arch, where I point out a half-burnt, soiled mattress leaning up against some binbags in the gloom. "There you go," I say.

Dench looks puzzled. "I thought it was a whole bed and a bedside table, not just the mattress," she says. Thinking quickly, I explain: "Like Van Gogh with his many paintings of sunflowers, throughout her career Tracey has shitted numerous versions of her bed, variations on a theme, if you will. This particular impression is number six out of twelve."

Dame Judi clasps her hands together with glee. "It's simply wonderful, Mr Saatchi!" she gushes as she hands over my fifty pounds. She even starts to cry a little as the 'masterpiece' moves her. She asks if I will give her a hand getting her purchase home, but I take the opportunity to make my excuses and leave, claiming that I am already running late for a cheese and wine party at Simon Sebag-Montefiore's house.

As I drive away, I take a last look in my wing mirrors as the 83-year-old grande-dame of British theatre sets off dragging the stinking, charred mattress the 6-miles back to her Greenwich Mews home.

At least now I know what the 'M' in her Secret Service designation stands for ... MUG.

NEXT WEEK: *Just how vulnerable to fraud are our OAPs? Mahatma Macaroon poses as an unscrupulous rogue builder and fleeces them of their life savings in return for unnecessary work on their houses to find out.*

RAFFLES THE GENTLEMAN THUG

MONKEY TRAGIC!

DARWINIST egghead Professor *Richard Dawkins* was left red-faced yesterday after embarrassing details about his ancestry came to light. Because despite his outspoken belief that mankind came from monkeys, experts investigating his family tree unveiled not one single ape!

Dawkins, 77, was filming for the new series of BBC genealogy show *Who Do You Think You Are?* when the humiliating discovery was made.

Series producer Merton Chemicals told reporters: "A week ago, my research team took some of Richard's DNA and a selection of his family correspondence and went off to trace his roots."

monkey

"Due to Richard's well-known evolutionary theories we all assumed that once we got a few hundred years back, it'd just be wall-to-wall monkeys. But when they unveiled their findings, they told a very different story," he added.

Chemicals revealed that his team had tracked the blasphemous boffin's lineage all the way back to 938 AD - and discovered not one single simian in his bloodline.

pigsy

"It was just human after human after human," Chemicals chuckled. "To be honest, we're almost too embarrassed for Richard to show him the results. He's going to be absolutely mortified."

It is not yet known wheth-

Godless Boffin left red-faced as family tree reveals ZERO apes

er Dawkins will give the go-ahead for the episode to air. However, the Archbishop of Canterbury, Dr Justin Welby, this morning expressed his sympathy and amusement at the Professor's predicament.

tripitaka

"One hates to say 'I told you so', but I'm afraid poor old Richard has made himself look rather foolish here," Welby told the *Canterbury Prolapse and Argos*.

"He's spent his entire life quacking on about how he's directly related to chimps, and now it's been conclusively proven that he was talking utter shite the whole time," he continued.

"God made man in his own image. Simple as. End of," added Welby.

MEDDLESOME RATBAG

DJ '18

"ARE YOU COMING INTO THE SEA, DADDY?"

"SOON AS I GET CHANGED INTO MY TRUNKS, KIDS!"

BUZZZZ

BUZZZ

SNATCH!
BUZZZ

WHISK!
BUZZZ

"SNFF! SOB! AND THEN, OFFICER, HE... HE EXPOSED HIMSELF TO ME!"

"I WILL NEVER FEEL SAFE COMING TO THE BEACH ON MY OWN AGAIN!"

NOBEL SAVAGE!

Write on! Savage shocked by literary achievement.

FORMER Blackburn Rovers midfielder **ROBBIE SAVAGE** was celebrating last night after being awarded the 2021 Nobel Prize for Literature.

Savage, 45, is the first ex-professional footballer to bag the top prose gong, whose previous winners have included Jean-Paul Sartre, TS Eliot and Pablo Neruda.

At a glitzy ceremony in Stockholm Concert Hall last night, the former Birmingham City winger looked pleased and confused as members of the official Nobel Committee took turns to heap praise on his 2015 tome *I'll Tell You What... My Take On The Modern Game Of Football.*

Top lit gong for soccer ace Robbie

Speaking to journalists after the event, Savage confirmed that he was astonished to have received the prestigious literary accolade.

aback

"I was a bit taken aback just to get the invite, to be honest," the ex-Derby man chuckled. "I was supposed to be doing an after-dinner in Llandudno with Tony Cascarino, but in the end, I thought, 'Sod it - how often do you get asked to a bash like this?'"

The platinum blonde Welshman added: "I thought it'd be a bit of a giggle and a free buffet. I certainly wasn't expecting to win anything. When the Swedish bloke read out my name onstage you could have knocked me down with a feather."

affront

At a press conference in Oslo this morning, the head of the Nobel literary judging panel, Ulvaeus Dvalla-Knubbig, outlined the committee's reasoning behind its controversial choice of recipient.

aside

"You wouldn't believe the amount of dreary old shite I have to read in this job," Dvalla-Knubbig told reporters. "So, when I happened upon *I'll Tell You What...* at the airport last month it was an absolute godsend."

atop

The 69-year-old Harvard professor continued: "Honest, I was proper pissing myself at the chapter where Robbie talks about leaving

Roy Keane a voicemail that began 'Whazzzaaappp!' like off of the Budweiser ads. The wife thought I was having a seizure."

"It was wise, brave, crucial prose," Dvalla-Knubbig added.

abottom

And it seems that the trend for prestigious literary awards embracing former journeyman footballers is set to continue.

At time of press, the Man Booker Prize judges have announced the inclusion of *The Romford Pele: It's Only Ray Parlour's Autobiography* on their 2018 shortlist.

NEW! The SHED of ETERNAL YOUTH

Direct from the Amazonian Jungle

| 6' x 10' ~ 10 years younger |
| 8' x 10' ~ 15 years younger |
| 10' x 12' ~ 20 years younger |
| 12' x 16' ~ 25 years younger |

Shed of Eternal Youth comes with 2 coats of creosote. You must enter the shed on a regular basis for its rejuvenating properties to work.

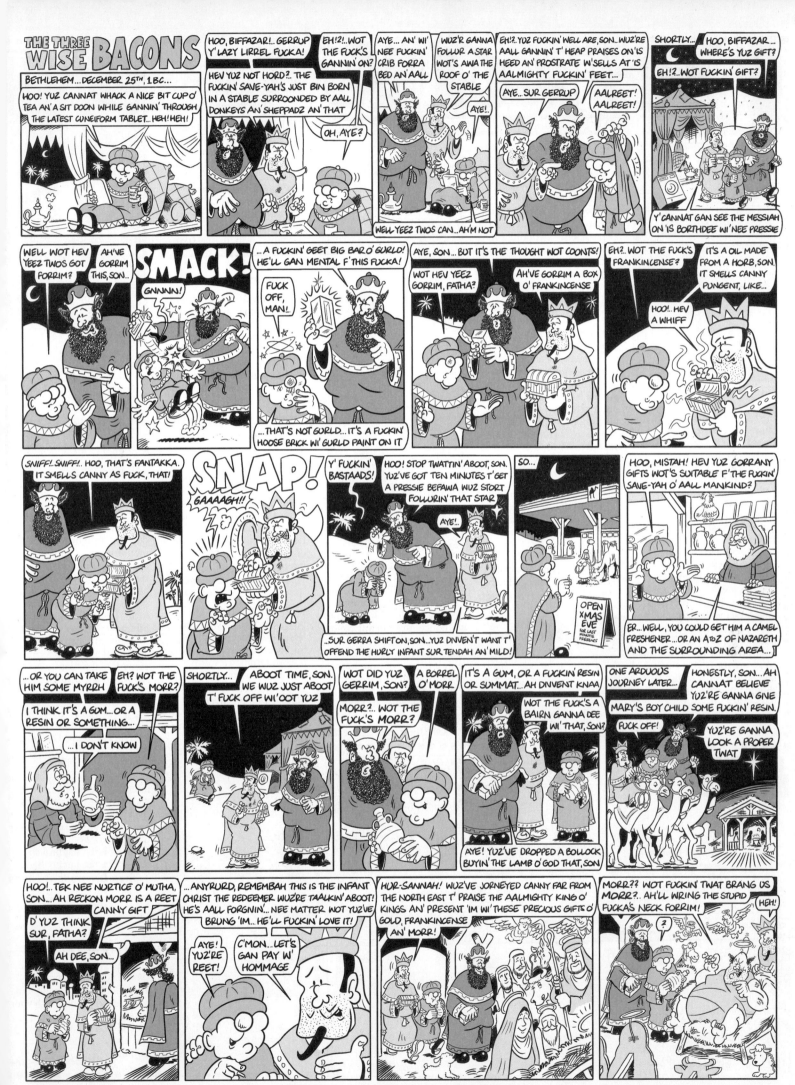

LetterbOcks

Viz Comic, P.O. Box 841 Whitley Bay, NE26 9EQ : letters@viz.co.uk

IF you try to torrent ten TV series at once, it takes forever. But if you stagger them one by one, you can blitz through it. Perhaps we should do that with research for diseases and get every scientist working on the same one, one at a time, until they're all cured. It's worth a try.

Stan Cross, London

THE other night I dreamt that I was looking for a Micro USB cable to charge a tin of beans with. I'd like to read Sigmund Floyd's analysis of that one.

Frankie Mince, Cardiff

IT'S typical of the perpetually pessimistic remoaners at the BBC that traffic news on the radio is little more than a tedious list of setbacks and problems. Instead, why not read out the names of the many places and roads where there are no problems? If you don't hear your area mentioned, you can draw your own conclusions, but the rest of us can be happy because decent British roads are the best in Europe, and probably the world. We should take pride in them, not keep talking them down.

Philip Kitching, Isle of Jura

WHY do people insist on saying "I might get run over by a bus tomorrow?" Why not a car, or a lorry? As a bus driver, I want to assure your readers that we are no more responsible for running people over than drivers of other vehicles. I think I have only run over one or maybe two people in the entire thirty years I have worked for my local bus company.

Bus Driver, email

MY teenage daughter just described the roast chicken dinner I cooked her as "the pengest munch." Do any of your readers know whether this meant she liked it or not, because, honestly I haven't got a fucking clue?

Steve Crouch, P'borough

STAR LETTER

THE ongoing extinction of bees worries me deeply. As a manufacturer of allergy-treatments and anti-histamine creams, bee-stings are about 30% of my business. Could scientists perhaps genetically engineer flies so they have the stinger of a bee, or even better, a wasp? Then I could even open another factory and it would be great for the economy.

J Crease, Cambridge

AT the age of 6, or 42 in dog years, my dog's reflexes are still spot on. She can catch any ball thrown at close-range with virtually no notice and can anticipate the angle of bounce with exact precision. I think it's only a matter of time before scientists isolate the specific genes which code for this ability and splice it into goalkeepers.

Kai Sheldrake, Leicester

IF everyone drives on the left, then what on earth is the point of having the right hand side of the road?

D Williams, Donegal

WHEN I was young, comics often showed people leaving pies on the windowsill to cool. But looking at the size of my windowsills, I think I would struggle to balance a pie on it. Maybe pies were smaller in those days because of rationing, perhaps. Or there may have been a fashion for larger windowsills. Who knows?

Grandad's cafe, Ventnor

I ONCE bet my friend Dave from Swansea that he couldn't down a pint of snakebite and black in under 30 seconds. I told him if he could do it, I would eat my hat. And he did! Luckily I was wearing a hat made of sausages.

Brian Wagalot, Ross on Wye

I DON'T know why those indigenous people in the Brazilian rain forests are always banging on about their trees being cut down. It's not as if it's costing them anything. When I had to have a couple of massive Leylandii cut down because of subsidence damage, it cost me nearly a grand.

Bartram Peasgood, Newcastle

WHY are they always sending David Bowie's *Space Odyssey* into space? Surely any alien hearing it would think we were a bunch of glammed-up, arty bisexuals. Hawkwind's *Masters of the Universe* would be a far better choice and would certainly get the message across that we are not to be fucked with.

Dave Brock, Trunch

LEADING the way with his fringe of hair around a bald dome, Prince William gave the nation high hopes for the return of the Great British comb-over. So, like many others, I was incandescent with rage when he shaved his head. Once upon a time, our Robert Robinsons, Bobby Charltons, Desmond Morrises and Arthur Scargills were the envy of the world. Come on, your highness, sweep your hair over your dome and make Britain great again.

Robert Nut-Flush, Bracknell

HOW come David Attenborough only gives cute, furry animals names in his increasingly dumbed-down natural history documentaries? If a lion cub is bitten by a black mamba, you might hear "Little Zimba has been bitten by a highly venomous snake." You'll never hear "Little Zimba has been bitten by Phil." It's one rule for cute cat-faced animals and another for the more cunty-looking types.

Eugene Ruane, Liverpool

I DON'T know why car manufacturers brag that their latest car can go from 0 to 60 in x seconds. The only place you can do sixty is on a motorway, and if your car is going from nought, then it must be stationary. And if it's stationary on a motorway, then it must be on the hard shoulder. And the only reason for a car to be on the hard shoulder is if it has broken down. Thanks, but no thanks.

Stan Dromedary, Leeds

I DON'T really get the expression "if the shoe was on the other foot." You'd look a right bellend if you walked around with your shoes on the wrong feet, people would just assume you had a bad case of the farmers.

Gillboy, Glasgow

DESIGNATED HAMSTER

SIGH...

RIGHT, LADS. MOVE IT! TIME WE GOT GOING. LAST ORDERS WAS HALF AN HOUR AGO.

YES, WELL. MAYBE YOU'D BE THE SPOILSPORT IF YOU WERE THE ONE WHO ALWAYS HAD TO DRIVE. COME ON.

AWWW. SPOILSPORT!

SWIG! GULP!

OKAYYY!

CAN YOU DROP MY MATE OFF? IT'S NOT THAT FAR OUT OF YOUR WAY! WHAT?!? NO! I HAVEN'T GOT THE ROOM, IF I GET STOPPED...

AW. GO ON. PLEEEASE!?

FINE. JUST HURRY UP AND GET IN THEN, WILL YOU?

AND SO... I NEED A WEE. I FEEL SICK. JESUS. SETTLE DOWN, WILL YOU?

BURP!

WASH THAT BLUE LIGHT?

AND... WOULD YOU MIND STEPPING OUT OF YOUR VEHICLE, SIR? SHIT. I KNEW IT!

TAP! TAP!!

☐ **I HAD** an old car that I needed to get rid of, but instead of dumping it in space, I stuck it on Gumtree and some bloke gave me £150 for it! Who's the smart one now, Elon Musk?

Simon Walker-Stewart, Mauchline

☐ **ORGANISERS** of relay racing in the Olympics really have missed a trick. If they supplied the competitors with a baton each, then surely this would speed up the whole proceedings and make for a more exciting event?

Ada Grime, Nottingham

☐ **HOW** about printing a picture of a turbot? I've heard of them but I don't know what they look like.

Sal Bundon, Bolton

✻ *No problem at all, Sal. Here you go.*

☐ **WHAT** is it with bees these days, getting all tired and needing to be fed sugared water to keep them going? Bees never got tired in my day. The lazy bastards.

Matthew Pymm, Hornsea

☐ **I DON'T** know what all this hoo-hah is about polar bears becoming extinct. There are plenty of brown bears knocking about from what I've seen. And if the inevitable does happen, what's so wrong with just bleaching a few of the brown ones? A bear's a bear when all's said and done.

Crawford Coldstream, Berwick

☐ **WHEN** visiting the supermarket, I always park in the disabled spaces because it reduces the risk of getting my BMW scratched. When people make unpleasant comments about it, I set my Alsatian on them. That tends to keep the nastiness to a minimum.

Ian Webb, Bury St Edmunds

☐ **THIS** week I've had two dreams involving North Korea. In the first, I had dinner with Kim Jong-un, and proceeded to tell everyone he is actually a sound bloke. Then, in the second dream I was hiding in terror from his secret police. I just don't know what to believe about the place any more.

Pete Beat, Newcastle

☐ **I VISITED** Hampton Court Maze today, and I am currently still lost somewhere inside it. I wonder if anyone can help me, as it's starting to get bloody cold and I could do with a shit. Could you please publish this appeal as a matter of urgency?

Cyril Prepuce, Hampton

☐ **THE** other day I worked out that toothpaste costs about £250 a gallon. Petrol is just over a fiver. If I was a scientist I know which one I'd be trying to replace with electricity.

Andy Mac, Derbyshire

☐ **LAWRENCE** of Arabia and Scott of the Antarctic were a pair of pretentious bastards, weren't they? They go somewhere once and suddenly they are 'of' the place.

Joseph of Bournemouth, Dorset

☐ **THEY** say that a watched kettle never boils. So imagine my dismay when my kettle failed to boil even though I wasn't even watching it. It was then that I realised that perhaps my wife had been watching it, causing it to remain unboiled. She denied this and a furious row ensued. It only calmed down when we realised that in fact it hadn't boiled because it wasn't plugged in. How we laughed when the mystery was solved.

Terrence Stoats, Barrow

☐ **WHY** are so-called geniuses always writing their big ideas on the back of napkins? They're clearly not so clever that they can carry a fucking notepad round with them.

Phil O'Meara, London

☐ **WHY** are people so out of order to ants? They take a couple of stale crumbs from under your fridge and you wipe out their entire city with boiling water. It's a bit of a fucking overreaction, isn't it?

Gustav Fox, Losechelsea

EVERYONE who isn't called Clive has wondered at some point what it would be like to be called Clive, and they're lying if they say they haven't. But with so many Clives to choose from, which would YOU pick and why? We rounded up three of our fave celebs who aren't called Clive and asked them one simple question: if you could spend a whole day as a Clive, which Clive would you choose?

Saddam Hussein, *deceased dictator*

I FAMOUSLY POPPED my clogs back in 2006, when I was hung from the neck until dead. As such, if I could be any *Clive For A Day*, I'd probably choose **CLIVE ANDERSON**, for the simple reason that he has no neck. I could then nip back to that fateful day 12 years ago, and bamboozle my would-be executioners, who'd all be scratching their heads, trying to figure out how to string me up! Plus, Anderson trained as a barrister before becoming a comedian, so I would be able to use my newfound legal nous to try and get myself off the hook. And if that didn't work, I would simply hurl light-hearted abuse at my lynch mob until they stormed off in fury, like The Bee Gees.

Prof. Brian Cox, *tousle-haired astrophysicist*

EARN MY CRUST by fannying about with complex, modern things like long-range telescopes, Large Hadron Colliders and electronic synthesizers, and occasionally I find myself yearning for a simpler time. So if I was *Clive For A Day*, I think I'd be **CLIVE DUNN**, whose 1971 hit single *Grandad* found him reminiscing fondly about Penny Farthings and phonographs and all that sort of stuff. I'd spend my day as Clive sat in a comfortable rocking chair, wearing a flat cap whilst melodically recalling the halcyon days of yore. And then, 24 hours later, I would return to my futuristic synth-stabbing and star-gazing with a newfound fervour and zeal.

Ice T, *gangsta rap icon*

IF I COULD BE any *Clive For A Day*, I reckon I'd be **CLIVE SWIFT**. I absolutely love *Keeping Up Appearances*, and Clive's hilarious performance as hen-pecked husband Richard Bucket has kept me chuckling away on many a long tour bus journey. Once I had transformed into Clive, I would invite a few pals over who are also fans of the show - such as P Diddy, Ice Cube and Ghostface Killah - and then I'd amuse them all by replicating the exasperated face Clive used to pull whenever Hyacinth shrieked, "The Bouquet residence, the lady of the house speaking!" We'd all fall about laughing until the clock struck midnight and I turned back into my normal self again.

☐ **WHENEVER** I see a cowboy film and one of them pays for three fingers of redeye or whatever, you never see the bartender giving any change. I'm beginning to understand why there were so many gunfights, hangings and saloon brawls in the wild west.

Bryan Golightly, Aberdeen

☐ **I'M** all for these new Swedish crime dramas, but I think we're being sold short. We put a lot of money into their economy by buying their pornography in the 70s and 80s, and now all of a sudden they won't even show us a bit of side-tit in things like *The Bridge* and *Jordskott*.

Hampton Cardboard, Hull

☐ **IF** you put a quid on a horse to win at 3/1, you stand to win £3. But if you put your quid on a horse to win at 25/1, then you stand to win twenty-five quid! I can't believe I'm the only person to have spotted such a simple way to beat the bookies.

Dave Winter, France

Billy Dobson
the Star Striker of
Barnton Rovers

Billy Dobson was the best striker in the history of Barnton football club, but a bad run of form meant that he hadn't scored a single goal for the last twenty years…

Watch him put this wide!

Told you so!

Ruddy Nora! He's missed again!

Ooh! That was a cherry ripe for the picking!

On the final whistle…

That's another game without finding the net, Mr Pangborn.

Don't worry, Billy. You know what they say… Form is temporary… Class is permanent.

Just remember, you're the best striker this club has ever had. Your goal drought will come to an end soon… isn't that right, Eddie?

Certainly is, boss… Don't you worry, Billy, you'll find your shooting boots.

But, as Billy left the pitch…

Oi, Dobson… You're rubbish!…

Yes!..you couldn't hit a cow's arse with a banjo!

Ho-ho!

In the dressing room…

Come on, Billy…don't let those idiots get you down.

But Eddie, I've gone eight hundred games without finding the net.

They said I couldn't hit a cow's arse with a banjo… *and they're right.*

No! They're not right, Billy. They're *wrong …dead wrong!*

You *could* hit a cow's arse with a banjo…and what's more you *will!*

What do you mean?

Next Saturday, we've got a cup tie against Gritley Town.

Before the match, we'll bring a cow onto the pitch…

…and you'll hit its arse with a banjo!

That'll shut those naysayers up, so you can go out there and do the job you do best… scoring goals.

That's a great idea. Let's do it!

Next morning, Gritley Town manager Stan Cassidy was reading the paper…

Have you seen this, Alfie?…

What's that, Mr Cassidy?

Is he?

Billy Dobson is going to hit a cow's arse with a banjo before our cup tie with Barnton.

Yes…and that is very bad news…

If he succeeds, his confidence will return…

…he'll regain his form, and he'll put a handful past our keeper.

We can't allow that to happen, Alfie… We've got to make sure Dobson's banjo doesn't hit that cow's arse.

Leave it to me, Mr. Cassidy.

On Saturday afternoon, there was only one topic of conversation amongst the crowd…

Let's hope Billy can hit that cow's arse before the game.

Yes. If he puts that banjo wide or over the top, he'll be handing the game to Gritley.

Five minutes before kick-off…

Right, Billy. You can do this. Just relax, okay?…

…just go out there and enjoy yourself.

Okay, Mr Pangborn.

56

A hush fell upon the crowd as, banjo in hand, Billy prepared to hit the cow's arse...

PHEEP!

Billy's started well... a good long run up!

Yes...he's on target so far!

But in the crowd...

Let's see how good your aim is with the sun in your eyes, Dobson!...He! He! He!

Aargh! My eyes! I can't see!

Oh no! He's missed!

Yes... and he's spooned that banjo into row Z!

What a farce!

Boo!

Hard lines, Pangborn. It was a good gamble but it didn't pay off.

There's still ninety minutes to play, Cassidy. Billy may yet find his form!

Don't kid yourself. He's a broken man...

...he's just proved he couldn't hit a cow's arse with a banjo.

Wait a minute... Look!...

...the banjo... It's curving round!...

...It's heading back! It's heading back toward's the cow's arse!

It might just...

SPANG!

Ooh! What a banana shot!

Yes! Right on the top corner of the arse!

Wa-hey! Game on!

Bah!

The game got underway, and buoyed up by his success hitting a cow's arse with a banjo, Billy's form returned with a vengeance...

What a shot!

Wow! A piledriver of a header!

Ha! The keeper stood no chance!

PHEEP!

Yes! We've won. Thirty-nil!...

Well done, Billy... Ten hat tricks! What a way to end your goal drought.

It's all thanks to you and Eddie, Mr Pangborn!

Next week: After another goal drought, cruel jibes from the crowd lead Billy to go into a brothel with a ten pound note tied round his chopper in an attempt to re-capture his form.

57

WHAT ON EARTH?

"Surely there must be something that I haven't done yet."
~Attenborough

SIR David Attenborough yesterday issued a desperate plea to biologists around the world: "Please tell me a group of animals I haven't done a landmark series about yet." The veteran TV naturalist said he had been racking his brains to think of a topic for a new 8-part series, but had so far drawn a complete blank.

"I've done them about birds, fish, mammals, insects, reptiles, the lot," he told reporters. "I've even done ones about the places they live, like the Arctic, jungles, mountains, deserts, up in the sky and under the sea and all that stuff."

planet

Attenborough, who even managed to get a whole big-budget series - *The Trials of Life* - out of the various stages of animals' life cycles, admitted that although he now fears that he may have exhausted every different type of life on the planet, there may still

EXCLUSIVE!

be something really obvious that he has overlooked. He said: "I'm hoping against hope that there's something staring me in the face; a big group of animals or an environment or something like that, that I haven't already made a ground-breaking series with stunning cinematography about."

earth

"Something like things that live under the floor, like worms and moles and stuff, or things like only come out

Natural selection: Attenborough admits to drawing blanks on ideas for ground-breaking new television series.

in the dark, like moths and them little monkey things with massive eyes," he continued. "I know they're no good because I've already done them, but something like them that I haven't done yet."

"Come on, everyone, get your thinking caps on," he added.

girls

Attenborough revealed that he wasn't limiting himself to life on earth. "If NASA give me the nod, I'll happily go and make a series about life on Mars or Jupiter or the Moon or somewhere like that," he said. "I'm really not fussy. Tell us a planet where we can film a beautifully composed and edited sequence of something laying an egg, having a fight or crawling on a rock, and me and the lads will be on the next rocket."

However, leading mem-

bers of the science community were pessimistic about Attenborough's prospects of discovering a fresh topic. "I've been sat here thinking and thinking, and I can't come up with a big life-based topic of any sort that Sir David hasn't already covered in a landmark series," said Dr Stanley Jordan, head of Cambridge University's Natural Sciences department. "I can't remember if he's done one about viruses and phages yet, but there's still some debate about whether they're actually alive or not."

on film

"And even if they are alive, he's not going to screw a series of eight fifty-minute episodes, plus the same number of ten-minute making-of segments tacked on the arse end, out of them, because they're really tiny and boring as fuck," added Professor Jordan.

NOBBY'S PILES

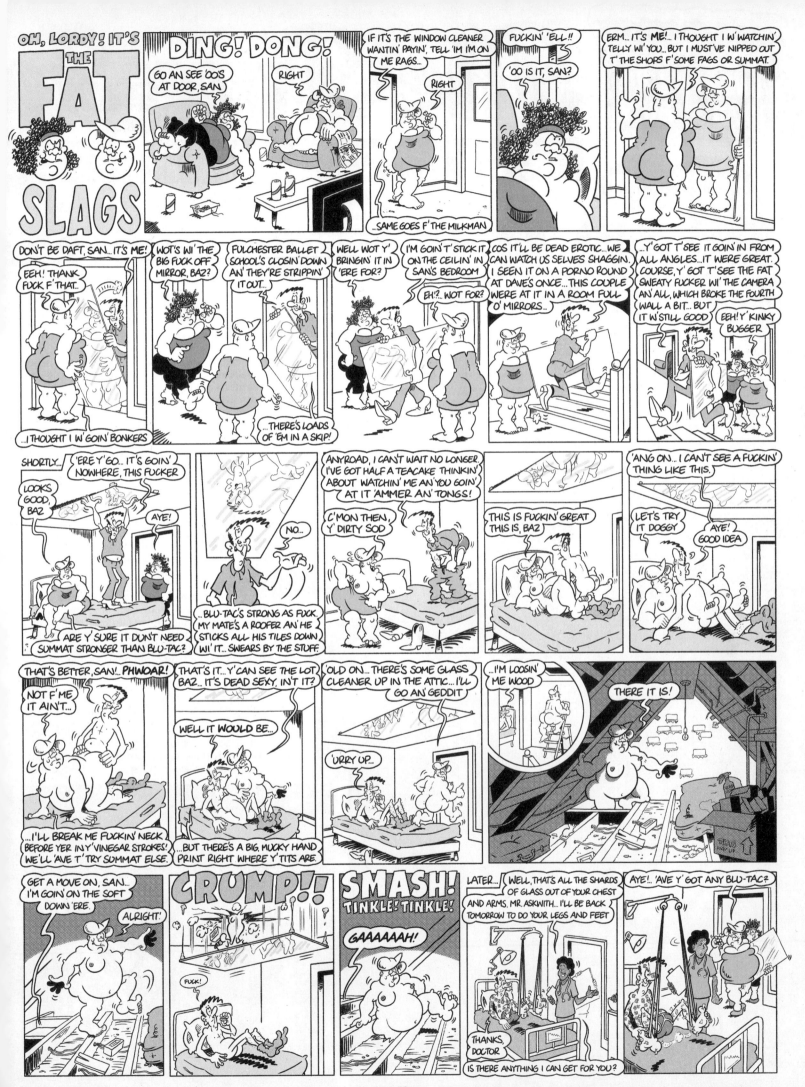

The True Fa

with Dr Adam Rutherford off of BBC Radio 4's Inside Science

ASK ANYONE in the street to describe Father Christmas, and they'll say he's a ruddy-faced man with a scarlet tunic and a big white beard. However, the REAL Father Christmas could not have been more different from Santa Claus, and he lived thousands of miles from the North Pole. Shy, unassuming, and slight of build, the world's greatest scientist Sir Isaac Newton was born near Grantham, Lincolnshire, on December 25th 1642. It is entirely thanks to him and his invention of Gravity that we enjoy the festive season we know and love today.

And if you think that's an over-exaggeration of Isaac Newton's importance to the festive season, then let us imagine what a typical family Christmas would be like if the force of Gravity had never existed.

Every Christmas Eve, excited children leave a mince pie and a glass of sherry for Santa, and a carrot for his magic reindeer (*Rangifer tarandus*). But if Newton had never come up with his gravitational equation $F=GMm/r^2$, these Yuletide offerings for St Nick wouldn't stay on their occasional table by the fire. They would simply bob around in mid-air, just like they would in a space capsule floating through the gravity-free vacuum of space. Even worse, the occasional table would be bobbing round as well, floating annoyingly in front of the telly.

Decorating your tree in the run-up to a gravity-free Christmas would be infinitely more difficult. The baubles we are familiar with in our post-Newtonian world are pulled towards the centre of our planet by a powerful force that is proportional to the product of their own and the planet's enormous mass. Without gravity to hold them in place on the branch, they would instead be pushed upwards with an equal and opposite force, shattering on the ceiling and showering everyone with shards of broken glass.

Without Gravity, we would have no point of reference to tell us which way was up or down, so it would be impossible to leave presents "under" the tree on Christmas Eve. Likewise, the tree itself would not have a "top" on which to put the fairy. In an absence of geotropism – the phenomenon that makes roots grow downwards and stems grow upwards – our Christmas trees (*Picea abies*) would evolve into bizarre, hovering spheroids, with branches radiating from a central apical growing node, and an infinite number of tops where the fairy could be stuck. On the plus side, there would be no needle drop; although your tree would still shed its needles, they would simply remain floating in mid-air instead of falling on the floor and going in your socks.

But it wouldn't all be bad news. Believe it or not, if Isaac Newton had never invented gravity, your Christmas dinner would be bigger than ever… *and cheaper*. Despite the best efforts

her Christmas

of present-day poultry farmers, who pump their livestock full of steroids and exogenous pulsatile growth hormones to plump them up in readiness for the festive season, the size to which a traditional turkey (*Meleagris gallopavo*) can grow is limited by the strength of its legs. Freed from the constraints of gravity, these birds could be made to reach truly colossal proportions, meaning there would be plenty of meat left over for sandwiches and curries well into the new year and beyond.

Also, because they wouldn't be restricted to living on the floor, gravity-free turkeys could be crammed into their rearing sheds in three dimensions. A typical 10 yard x 10 yard coup that accommodates 2,000 free-range turkeys at the moment could easily accommodate 20,000 or more in the absence of gravity. This would push production costs down, and turkeys would become much cheaper in the shops.

One of Britain's best-loved Christmas traditions is the Queen's Speech on the afternoon of December 25th, but this could be another tragic casualty of a gravity-free world. After all, if her majesty were to float off into space and suffocate due to a lack of Oxygen (O_2 – a colourless and odourless diatomic gas in the Chalcogen group of the Periodic Table that is essential for her majesty's survival) while making her annual address to the people of the Commonwealth, it would cause a constitutional crisis.

Accordingly, some means of holding the Queen down for the duration of her speech would have to be employed. She could be tethered by monafilament carbon fibre guyropes that would be invisible on screen. Perhaps she could wear lead deep-sea divers' boots, or she may simply elect to jam her knees under her desk and grip the sides of her desktop tightly.

There is no more welcome sound at Christmas than a band of merry carol singers on the doorstep. Old favourites such as *God Rest Ye Merry Gentlemen*, *Silent Night* and *Hark the Herald Angels Sing* are all guaranteed to instil a warm, festive glow in a householder's heart. However, hiding behind the settee until they stop ringing the bell and go away would be much more difficult without Gravity. Either you or your sofa could drift upwards off the ground at any moment, revealing that you were in to any

wassailer peeking in through the front window.

Also, carol singers would sound very different. At the moment, we rely upon the force of gravity to hold the earth's atmosphere firmly in place, providing us with air to breathe at a pressure of approximately 101,325Pa (1.01325 Bar). In its absence, much of our breathable air would simply disappear into the trackless void of outer space, leaving our atmosphere painfully thin. As a consequence, the carol singers' voices would be much higher pitched, making them sound like Pinky and Perky or Joe Pasquale.

Since it relies on chemically based visco-elasticity rather than gravitational attraction for its adhesive properties, the Sellotape used for wrapping presents would

be one of the few things to remain relatively unchanged in a gravity-free Christmas. In fact, one would be hard-pressed to tell the difference between a gift that had been wrapped in the world as we know it from one wrapped in a world where Sir Isaac Newton had never existed. However, if you picked up the present and shook it to guess what was inside, the difference would immediately become apparent. Whilst we, in our Gravity-filled world, can instantaneously tell whether a package contains something heavy, such as a coffee machine or a big socket set, or something light like some fucking socks or fucking hankies, in the absence of Gravity both presents would have exactly the same weight… zero lbs ($0.000kgms^{-2}$ in SI units).

No Christmas is complete without a visit to church for the Midnight Service on Christmas Eve. It's a delightful event that brings the whole community together, only spoiled when the vicar asks for donation to pay for repairs to his leaky vestry roof. But without Isaac Newton's universal force attracting the rain earthwards from the

clouds with an acceleration of approximately $9.81ms^{-2}$, there would be no need for him ever to get his leadwork fixed. However, it's unlikely this would stop him handing round the plate, although it would have to be fitted with a powerful electro-magnet to stop the coins floating off and getting lost in the rafters.

Perhaps the most satisfying part of Yuletide is the hour each of us spends on the toilet enjoying our Boxing Day stool while perusing a new book. But this pleasurable annual episode in the smallest room is only as relaxing as it is thanks to Newton's 1686 discovery that every point mass attracts every other point mass by a force acting along a line intersecting both points. For it is Sir Isaac Newton's Gravitational Constant (6.674×10^{-11} $Nkg^{-2}m^2$) that does the hard work of pulling the dense, figgy-pudding-rich foulage out of our anal sphincters and down into the toilet. If this figure were to be reduced to zero, as it would be had Newton not come up with it, our turds would float upwards and ricochet endlessly from pan to cheek to taint, soiling everything in their path.

Rather than being one of Christmas highlights, our December 26th lavatory visit would be an unhygienic, semi-farcical nightmare. To alleviate this problem, every home would have to be fitted with an aeroplane-style, vacuum-operated toilet that would use negative air pressure to do Gravity's job.

NEXT WEEK: Dr Hannah Fry looks at Quantum Physicist Max Planck - the True Easter Bunny.

THE GREAT WALL OF TIPTON
Guthrie plans West Midlands rival to Chinese spectacle

TIPTON Town Council has given the green light to an ambitious building project that is set to put the West Midlands town on the map ... a 14,000-mile-long wall. It is hoped that the massive, 40-foot-high stone structure will attract visitors from as far afield as Wolverhampton, Warley and Tettenhall. Tourist boss Hugo Guthrie told local paper the *Tipton and Sandwell Meatus:* "The wall will begin at the corner of Victoria Road and Mayfair Gardens, and run roughly north west for roughly 14,000 miles."

"Just like its famous Chinese counterpart, the Great Wall of Tipton will be visible from the Moon. It's something that will put the town firmly on the map and give all Tiptonians something to be proud of," he continued. "Once it is up and running, we have high hopes that our Great Wall will push Dudley Leather Museum off the coveted number one spot on the list of Things to Do in Tipton."

Mr Guthrie is confident that the project will bring in much-needed revenue to the town. "Tickets will be £1.50 for adults and 75p for children and pensioners," he told the paper. "There will even be a gift shop at the exit 14,000 miles away, where visitors can buy a souvenir of their day out, such as a pencil sharpener, a leatherette bookmark or a fridge magnet bearing the Tipton town crest."

"I have no doubt that the Great Wall of Tipton will pay for itself within a few months of opening," said Mr Guthrie.

erecting

The task of erecting the immense fortification has been given to local builder Stan O'Reilly, who quoted £450 cash for the job, which he reckons will take him and

his lad about six weeks. Mr O'Reilly has already dropped a mixer and four bags of Blue Circle cement off at the site. Mr Guthrie said: "He was supposed to start last Monday, but unfortunately his plans have been unexpectedly delayed due to his mother being diagnosed with cancer."

"He's having to take her for her appointments in his van," said Mr Guthrie. "But he says he'll definitely be starting next Tuesday or Wednesday, if the weather's alright."

Wall I never!: An artist's impression of how Tipton's Great Wall might look if finished.

Hugo undertaking: Guthrie hopes wall will pay for itself within a few months.

VOX POPS
We went out onto the streets of Tipton to see what local population had to say about Hugo Guthrie's ambitious project.

"ANYTHING THAT brings people to the town is good, and a 40-foot-high, 14,000-mile-long castellated rampart certainly fits that bill in my book."
Richard le Scrope, consultant proctologist

"IF THEY go ahead with it, I hope they put some gates in, because I live on Davis Avenue and I don't want to have to walk thousands of miles every day just to get to me ciggies from the Spar on Peel Street."
Henry Bowet, chartered turf accountant

"I'VE JUST paid the thick end of £150 to have my back kitchen wall repointed, and that's just ten foot long. I shudder to think how much it is going to cost the local ratepayers to have the mortar on a 14,000-mile wall titivated every few years when the frost's got in."
Samuel Harsnett, jazz trombonist

"I THINK it's a wonderful idea, as people could abseil down it to raise money for animal charities, such as rescued donkeys, blind dogs or seagulls with all oil on them."
Edna Grindal, grandmother

"I THINK it's an utter waste of money. They should spend the cost of this pointless wall on something the town really needs, like a Sphinx, a Machu Pichu, or a Hanging Garden of Babylon."
Janice Sandys, HR consultant

"THEY COULD hold an annual Great Wall of Tipton Marathon, where people run along the top as far as Codsall Wood and back. Or they could do a Half Marathon where they turn around when they reach the Sainsbury's at Raglan Street in Wolverhampton."
Ada Sentamu, wool shop owner

MOON'S POPULARITY BOOMS!

...but it's not all good news

Astronomical ratings: The moon (right) yesterday and (below right) some Apollo astronauts walking on it in its 1970s heyday.

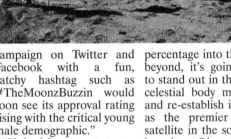

A scientist yesterday.

FOR THE first time in its 4-and-a-half billion year history, the Moon's Approval Rating has topped three quarters, with 76% of the public saying they think the earth's natural satellite is *Good*, *Very good*, or even *Excellent*. The same survey found that just 16% of people questioned disapproved of the Moon, with 8% undecided.

"This is great news," said Lunar expert Maggie Aderin-Pocock. "Even during the Moon's 1960s heyday, when the Americans were sending rockets up to it left, right and centre, it was never this popular."

"All these lunar eclipses, supermoons and stuff we've been having lately must of really put it back centre stage and in the forefront of people's minds where it belongs," she added.

moon

According to the survey, the Moon is now particularly popular with women, 83% of whom rated it positively, compared with just 69% of men of all age groups. Amongst women aged 45 and over, the result was even more pronounced, with 92% giving the crater-pocked, 2,500-mile-wide spherical rock the thumbs-up.

harris

However, the Moon was less popular with young males. A disapointing 12% of men aged 25-34 rated it Very good or Excellent, while 56% - well over half of the surveyed sample - said they though it was Poor or Extremely Poor. Of those aged 16-24, the trend was even more pronounced, with approval figures dropping to a mere 4%, and 82% rating it Below Average or Poor.

TV boffin Professor Brian Cox welcomed the overall

Moon enters brightest phase ever

Waxing lyrical: Satellite's popularity put down to recent lunar eclipses and supermoons.

improvement in the Moon's popularity, but despaired at the lack of approval it presently receives from young men. "I just don't understand it," he told us. "The Moon provides us with waves, tides, and a bit of light at night. It also stops the earth from wobbling off its axis and crashing into the Sun. I mean, what's not to like?"

richards

Marketing guru Beasley Bogleby says that the Moon is suffering from a PR problem. "The man in the street associates the Moon with Draculas, werewolves and witches, and these things don't play well with the millennial demographic," he vouchsafed.

"The Moon is a heritage brand, and the kids these days aren't interested in heritage brands," he continued. "They're too busy playing Space Invaders or riding round on their BMX bicycles."

burtons

Bogleby thinks the key to successfully re-positioning the Moon is social media. He told us: "A targeted campaign on Twitter and Facebook with a fun, catchy hashtag such as #TheMoonzBuzzin would soon see its approval rating rising with the critical young male demographic."

"If the Moon wants to re-position its positive rating percentage into the 80s and beyond, it's going to have to stand out in the crowded celestial body marketplace and re-establish its position as the premier planetary satellite in the solar system brand tent," he added, while sniffing every few seconds.

Bryan May, out of Queen's

MOON Factfile

Everybody's talking about the Moon these days, and none of us want to get shown up by our lack of lunar knowledge. Now you can keep up with the conversation thanks to this fantastic *MOON FACTFILE*.

We've teamed up with poodle-haired, plank-spanking Moon-rocker *Brian May* to bring you a handly double-sided credit-card-sized checklist of fascinating nuggets about everyone's favourite barren satellite. Keep it with you at all times so you can refer to it when the need arises.

Brian May out of Queen's

MOON FACTFILE

Name:	The Moon	Shapes:	Circle, lemon,
Orbital period:	27.32 days	half circle, banana, none
Diameter:	2159 miles	Colour:	Light grey with
Radius:	1079.5 miles	darker grey bits
Half radius:	539.75 miles	Cratered surface:	Yes

Lifeforms:	Unknown
Nearest planet:	Earth
Composition:	Moon rock and Moon dust
Sides:	2 (dark and light)
Mass:	$7.34767309 \times 10^{22}$ kg
Mass in 1lb bags of sugar:	$16.2200287 \times 10^{22}$ bags of sugar
Number of people what of walked on it:	12
Number of feet what of walked on it:	24
Number of toes what of walked on it:	119
Name in French:	La Lune
Name in Spanish:	La Luna
Name in Catalan:	La Lluna

Underwear Wolf!

"The Moon made me do it," says washing line pervert Preston

A Shropshire man sentenced to 200 hours community service following a spate of underwear thefts says that he is the innocent victim of a miscarriage of justice. Whilst warehouseman Preston Pontesford doesn't deny that he took over a thousand items of ladies' underwear from gardens in and around Ludlow, he claims that he was not responsible for his actions.

Entering a plea of mitigation, he told magistrates that although he was a respectable law-abiding citizen, a mysterious and sinister change overcame him whenever there was a full Moon. Pontesford, 59, described how, every 28 days

- *He would crouch over and become hairy*
- *His feet would burst out the end of his shoes*
- *He would go from garden to garden, stealing bras and knickers from washing lines*

Talking to reporters after his sentencing hearing, the twice-divorced father of six said that he felt let down by the legal system. "I am the real victim here," he said. "I can't help being as I am. Every time there's a full Moon, I turn into a beast I do not recognise. I become an animal whose ravening hunger for women's underwear can only be slaked by stealing it off washing lines."

sick

"Most of the time I don't even know I'm doing it. I feel sick to my stomach when I wake up in the morning to find my bedsit strewn with ladies' smalls," he said.

And he had this message for his victims: "You must believe me when I tell you that this is not who I am. I need help. I've tried locking myself in when there's a full Moon, but the monster inside me simply unlocks the door and goes out on his perverted quest."

comfort farm

"If anybody out there knows how to rid me of this terrible curse that blights me, I will be forever grateful," he added.

"Nothing would give me more pleasure than to be able to return the property which my alter-ego stole to its rightful owners," Pontesford continued. "Unfortunately, I appear to have masturbated into it after being possessed by the perverted spirit of the Marquis de Sade."

Line of defence: Pontesford claims that the full Moon (right) turns him into an uncontrollable knicker bandit.

Stars line up to throw light on hidden lunar secrets

IT'S a strange and inexplicable fact that the Moon spins on its axis in exactly the same time that it takes to orbit the earth. As a result, we only ever see one side of it - a barren, grey wasteland pock-marked with craters. *But what lies on the other side of the Moon that we have never seen, and will never see? What secrets does it hold? One thing is certain: whatever is there is beyond our imaginings*. But luckily, it's not beyond the imaginings of the celebrities. We asked a galaxy of stars to tell us what they thought was on...

THE DARK SIDE OF THE MOON!

Katie Price, *Polymathic ex-tit model*

I think it's like a magical world all covered in like Swarovski crystals and that and there's this princess what lives there in a castle made of Swarovski crystals only she's really sad because there isn't not no light there because it's on the dark side of the moon and everythink so while she's the richest princess in the world because she's got all them Swarovski crystals she's always like really sad.

David Attenborough, *Naturist*

I have spent my entire career studying all the diverse forms of life on earth, and if there is one thing that I have learned, it is that life can flourish in even the most inhospitable environments. At the bottom of the deepest ocean, at the top of the highest mountain, in the permafrost of the Arctic and in the bowels of the hottest volcano, life thrives. And there is no reason to imagine that the dark side of the moon is any different. If we ever ventured there, perhaps we would see dinosaur-size reptiles with three eyes, giant silver crabs walking upright on two legs, or maybe monkeys, ostensibly similar to those on earth, but with ten cocks. And the females would have about twenty fannies.

Gregg Wallace, *Fighty greengrocer*

I think that if you ventured to the dark side of the Moon, you might find a world that appeared at first sight to be a Utopia. It would look a bit like Ancient Greece, with marble fountains, all big bowls of succulent fruit everywhere, and all the people wearing togas and playing harps. It would only be after a few days living there that it would suddenly dawn on you that there were no old people and it was actually an authoritarian Dystopia where once you get to the age of 30 you get sent for "re-cycling". There may be a small band of renegades who have managed to escape and are now living in the drains, but because it's on the dark side of the Moon, I guess we'll never know.

Mark Carney, *Governor of the Bank of England*

As a full-time economist, Governor of the Bank of England and Chairman of the G20 Financial Stability Board, I get very little time to exercise my imaginative faculty. As a consequence, I envisage the Dark Side of the Moon to be very similar, if not identical, to the side that we see, that is to say, grey, bereft of interest, and pock-marked with craters from various meteoric impacts that have occurred during the last 4.51 billion years. Now, if you'll excuse me, I have to go and turn the Exchange Rate Mechanism up by a quarter of one percent.

Dappy, *Out of N-Dubz*

After the end of the film *Alien vs Predator*, I think the two species made a truce and decided to take over the earth together, pooling their resources. And what better place for them to set up their base than on the Dark Side of the Moon where we can't see them. They can see us, of course, because they've got a big periscope poking over the top.

Porking on the MOON

The barely legal has landed: Veteran porn actor Dover reassured fans that they will still be able to see it going in thanks to specially designed see-through astronaut suits.

PORN VID stalwart *Ben Dover* has announced an ambitious plan to film a hardcore sex video... *on the MOON!* The veteran cocksmith, 71, says is already in talks with tech billionaire *Elon Musk* about booking seats on the next SpaceX rocket for himself, a cameraman and three milfs in their mid-thirties from Nottingham.

He told reporters: "The film, provisionally entitled *Orbit of the Other*, will be all about three space housewives with big tits who live on the Moon. Their sink gets blocked and I play a randy astronaut plumber who they call out to fix it."

"One thing leads to another and the four of us end up having a zero-G gang bang in the weightless vacuum of the lunar surface," he said

flick

Dover, real name Linseed Honeypot, says he expects filming the triple-X flick on the Moon to present unique challenges. "Obviously, there is no air on the Moon, so myself and the girls will have to wear spacesuits at all times. But they'll be completely see-through so viewers will still be able to see all the tits and fannies, he said."

Blue Moon: Cast will be the first adult stars to visit the lunar surface since Apollo 17 in 1972.

"My suit will be designed with a special airlock on the front for my wotsit to stick out of," he added. "And the milfs' helmets will have a matching airlock on the front, so they can still suck me off as normal."

alexis

But the biggest problem he expects to encounter on the shoot is the lack of gravity in space. "I'm going to have

Stickman Dover to shoot scud vid on lunar surface

to keep a tight grip of the girls while I'm doing them, especially when I get to the vinegar strokes," he said.

"According to Newton's third law of motion, action and reaction are equal and opposite. If I'm not holding on, one big push as I go off could see me propelled upwards and out into space."

fallon

"With nothing to stop me or slow me down, I'd just keep floating further and further out into the solar system," said Dover. "After five billion miles, I'd eventually pass Pluto, still with my cock poking out the front of my spacesuit, and that's something I want to avoid if at all possible."

Dover says that the twenty-five minute movie will be the most expensive one he has ever made. "We're working with the Adult Channel and they've given us a huge budget," he said.

"The girls will be getting two hundred quid each, and the cameraman wants a hundred so that's seven hundred quid to start with. And on top of that there's the cost of flying us all to the Moon and back, which could run into the hundreds of millions."

williamson

However, Dover needs to put his plan into action quickly if he wants to be the first porn performer in space, as *40 and Naughty* star Lara Latex is currently in talks with NASA to send her, a cameraman and four unemployed Essex builders to Mars.

We have lift off: The Spacex Falcon Heavy rocket that will ferry Dover, his cameraman and the 3 housewives from Nottingham to Mars

Further, Higher, Faster

A timeline of landmarks in extreme porn flight

Ever since man first dreamed of flying, he has also dreamed of filming people having sex while doing it. Here's a brief history of pornographic manned flight.

1783. Joseph-Michel and Jacques-Étienne Montgolfier make the world's first ever airborne adult movie. *Up, up, and Have it Away* is filmed in the gondola of their "globe aerostatique" 2,000 feet above Paris. The plot features a bored Parisienne housewife with big tits who orders a pizza to her hot air balloon, but then finds she hasn't got enough money to pay the delivery man.

1903. The Wright Brothers film *Kitty Hawk Sluts 4* during a 150ft, 11-second hop in their aeroplane The Flyer. While Wilbur pilots the plane, Orville operates the hand-cranked camera, filming two local girls engaged in hot lesbian action on a bed fastened to one of the wings with rope.

1909. Pioneer aviator Louis Blériot films an X-rated movie entitled *The White Tits of Dover* during his record-breaking flight across the English Channel. In the POV flick, Louis finds a young woman stowed away in the footwell of his cockpit, and she volunteers to pay for her passage in kind.

1919. The pilots of the first plane to fly from America to Britain produce *Alcock & Brown's All Cock & Brown*. As well as being the first movie made while crossing the Atlantic, the movie is also notable as being the earliest cinematic depiction of a double-anal cream pie.

1947. Aboard his Bell XS-1 experimental aircraft, US Air Force General Chuck Yeager writes and directs *Mach Me Ragged* an adult movie which features the first bareback spitroast ever filmed at faster than the speed of sound.

Super, smashing, great!

How would you like to go home tonight with a little piece of Lunar history in your back pocket? Well believe it or not, that's what's on offer as the star prize in our fabulous new competition...

The DART side of the MOON!

We've got EIGHT pieces of priceless Apollo Moonshot memorabilia to give away. Let's take a look at these fabulous prizes....

In ONE! Step out in style in astronaut Neil Armstrong's spacesuit boots, the very ones in which he took that iconic "One small step for man" back in 1969.

In TWO! Take a turn for the best with the actual steering wheel off of the Apollo 17 Lunar Rover... the very last vehicle to ever drive on the Moon in 1971.

In THREE! Stone the crows! It's a super half-brick-sized piece of genuine Moon rock collected by Buzz Aldrin from the beach next to the Sea of Tranquility.

In FOUR! Be a bright spark with this state-of-the-art piece of electronic circuitry form the Apollo 14 Mission Control computer desk at Cape Carnival.

In FIVE! It's bendy, but it's not a Bendy Bully. It's a flexible hose that went from the side of astronaut Neil Armstrong's helmet and into his haversack.

In SIX! Any old iron? How about the actual pitching wedge which Alan Shepard took to the Moon ... AND the very golfball he chipped 27 miles into outer space.

In EIGHT! Have you got the write stuff? It's an actual biro that was sitting on the desk of NASA Mission Director Eugene Krantz when they went to the Moon.

In SEVEN! Get a grip on things with the handle from the door where the astronauts got in at the very top of Apollo 12's Saturn 5 rocket.

...and in THE BULLSEYE! Make a splash at the marina in this super lunar speedboat that they were going to take to the Moon before they realised there wasn't any water on it.

How to play: Cut out Bully's lunar dart board and stick it on a door with the bullseye at a height of 5' 8" from the floor. If you don't have a tape measure, ask a celebrity who is 5' 8" tall, such as Ed Sheeran, Charlize Theron or Lewis Hamilton, to pop round to your house and stand with their back to the door and make a mark level with the top of their head. On the floor, mark an oche exactly 7' 9¼" from the door. If you still haven't got a tape measure, get 7' 9" Chinese basketball player Sun Mingming to lie down with his head against the bottom of the door and mark where his feet come to. Then add an extra quarter of an inch, which is about the thickness of two pound coins. Find a friend who can't play darts and then take turns to each throw three darts at the board, with the non-dart player going first. Take your time. You've got all time in the world. Throw when you're ready. Each dart in the red wins that prize, but beware: A second dart in the same sector and you forfeit that prize. Remember: *Stay in the red and out of the black. Two in the same and we take your prize back.* When you have thrown all six darts, send the board with the holes showing where the darts landed to: *Dart Side of the Moon Contest, Viz Comic, PO Box 841, Whitley Bay, NE26 9EQ.* The first one out of the Viz space helmet will win all the prizes corresponding to the holes in their lunar dart board. The judges' decision is final. This competition is not open to professional darts players, NASA employees, their family, friends and relatives.

"I've saved the Earth... now I'm going to save the Moon" ~Bono

U2 front-bellend **Bono** has volunteered his services as the world's Goodwill Ambassador to the Moon. Addressing the United Nations, the singer, 57, said he had already saved the earth and he was now willing to do the same for its planetoid satellite.

He told delegates: "It is not yet clear what threats the Moon may face in the future. But what is certain is that it is standing on the edge of a precipice and staring into an unknown abyss."

comet

"It could get hit by a comet, maybe it will come under attack from a hostile alien civilisation that is technologically light years ahead of our own, or the threat may even be an environmental one. Perhaps its thin atmosphere will begin to heat up, leading to moonal warming and rising levels in the Sea of Tranquility," he continued.

"Whatever happens, I want the Moon to know that I am there for it, ready to step up to the plate at a moment's notice to raise awareness, tweet something or organise a charity MP3."

currys

"I will literally do anything to help the Moon, as long as I don't have to spend any of my own money on it," he added. And the singer had this message for those he dubbed "naysayers and doubters" who questioned his ability to save the Moon: "Look what I have already done here on earth."

"Poverty, gone. Famine, vanquished. Climate change, reversed. Disease, eradicated. The Moon is crying out for an inspirational rock star like myself to fight for it. I am passionate about taking on this role," he said.

chineses

However a NASA spokesperson last night said that Bono had yet to get in touch to offer his services, and in any case it was not clear what a Lunar Goodwill Ambassador would actually do. She told reporters: "The Moon is not under any imminent threat as far as we aware. If a situation arises where we feel that a self-important shortarse in sunglasses and a hat could be of any assistance, we'll let him know."

Meanwhile Bono insisted that he was ready and willing to do whatever he could for the Moon. "Believe me when I say that I have so much to give," he said. "Except, obviously, stumping up any of my own cash."

"As I said before, that's out of the question," he added.

JANET OF THE APES

WOTCHA! Nightmare flame-haired telly harridan **JANET STREET-PORTER** here. When I'm not screeching on *Have I Got News For You* or editing the *Independent on Sunday* between 1999 and 2002, you can probably find me obsessing about apes. I'm absolutely fascinated by all manner of non-hominoid simians - in fact, you could say that I'm *'monkey nuts!'* And judging by the size of my *Janet Of The Apes* postbag, *Viz* readers are as potty about primates as I am. So let's stop 'monkeying' around, and check out the best letters I've received this week.

Monkeyest regards, Janet xx

AS A life-long ape fan, I find it utterly sickening that every animal species has been granted a unique name for its babies - except monkeys. Baby kangaroos are called joeys, baby dogs are called puppies, baby cats are called kittens, and so forth. But baby monkeys are simply known as "infants" - the same word we humans use to describe our young. Come on OED, how about coining some brand new names for baby simians, such as "monkeyling", "apelet" or "chimpule"?

Oliver Reaction, Chipping Norton

"POP out and get us some monkey nuts, will you, love?" I asked my husband Derek the other day. And I had to chuckle as I pictured him driving over to the local zoo to castrate a chimp and return with its bloody, severed testes. You can imagine my disappointment and rage, then, when he didn't comedically misconstrue my request at all and came back a few minutes later with just a bag of peanuts still in their fibrous shells.

Mrs Ethel Vet-Cameron, Port Vale

MY husband used to make a very good living shooting wild monkeys in China and then selling their body parts to state-owned medical companies. However, he's recently chucked that job in to become a professional impersonator of the late, great British Formula One racing driver, James Hunt. So I suppose you could say - if you really wanted to - that he used to 'hunt apes' and now he 'apes Hunt'.

Deidre Dog-Breeder, Ambleforth

I MUST say I find it laughable that the French word for "monkey" is "singe". Don't those Gallic garlic-munchers realise that monkeys are entirely unable to 'singe' anything, since they've yet to discover the secret to man's red fire? Honestly, what are the French like? They make me fucking sick.

N Farage, Herts

THE atheist firebrand Richard Dawkins would have us believe that we are all related to monkeys. However, I have yet to witness Professor Dawkins inviting any monkeys over to his house for Christmas. Perhaps Professor Dawkins should practise what he preaches, or he may end up being accused of hypocrisy.

J Welby, Canterbury

THE church's official position is that the Theory of Evolution is nonsense and that God created us in his image. Fair enough, but then why oh why do they then insist that all their bishops are "Primates"? They can't have it both ways, and the sheer hypocrisy of this double standard makes me sick to my stomach.

Rampton Saxilby, Lincoln

AS the Poet Laureate, I didn't have a huge amount on this week, so I thought I might as well do a poem for World Monkey Day. Which does exist, by the way, I've looked it up. Anyway, here it is:

They scamper about and they live in the trees,
They pick through their fur with their fingers for fleas,
Some have got tails and others have none,
And at a chimps' party they might eat a scone,
They've been on the telly to advertise tea,
A favourite drink both for you and for me,
Make it by putting some bags in the pot,
Then add the water and drink it while hot,
Have it with sugar and also with milk,
While listening to music played by Acker Bilk.

I think it lost its way a bit in the middle and turned into a poem about tea, and I had a bit of a problem finding a rhyme for the word 'milk', but on the whole, I reckon it's certainly the best one I've written during my tenure. Also, there is also a World Tea Day, so I'll probably use it again for that and have the day off.

CA Duffy, Manchester

IT MAKES me sick to think of the number of pop songs we humans have written about monkeys, when they've never written a single one about us in return. *Monkey's Gone To Heaven* by the Pixies, *Monkey Man* by the Rolling Stones, *Brass Monkey* by the Beastie Boys, *Monkey Wrench* by the Foo Fighters... the list goes on and on and on. And still, not one single monkey-penned ditty about us *Homo sapienses*. I think we humans should refuse to write any more ape-themed hits until our non-hominoid ancestors have done us the common courtesy of immortalising us at least once in song form.

Agnes No-Changeling, Portsmouth

WHOEVER coined the term "ape" meaning to "copy or mimic" needs their head examined. According to the evolutionary biologist Charles Darwin, we humans evolved off the apes, so if anything, it was us who copied and mimicked *them*.

Benedict Hideous Replica, Port Merrie

WHAT is it with monkeys pulling our car aerials and windscreen wipers off in safari parks? This is why we can't have anything nice.

Anonymous, Longlea...

IF we're supposed to be descended from monkeys then why haven't we all got long tails? Until Professor Richard Dawkins and his like minded cronies can answer that one, the[y] should all just shut the fuck up.

Rev. J Foucault, Trur...

"MONKEY see, monkey do", or so they say. Well I was at Bristol Zoo yesterday and I watched a monkey masturbate in front of my wife and children before throwing his faeces at the wall. Well I don't know who he was copying, but it certainly wasn't me.

T Piles, Trin...

ZOOLOGISTS apparently insist that we refer to orang-utans, gorillas and chimpanzees as the "Great Apes". Well, I saw a gorilla in the zoo last week and I'm sorry, but fail to see what's so "great" abou[t] being sick into your own hand and then eating it up again. The "Need To Be Taught Some Rude Manners Apes" would be a more appropriate name for them, if you ask me. And that's swearing.

Dolly Bollock... Port Talbo[t]

Michael Burke's Monkey Moral Maze

TOP Beeb telly fave **MICHAEL BUERK** has mislaid a cheeky chimp in his iconic 'Moral Maze'. But can YOU help him lead the puzzled primate back out to enjoy his favourite teatime banana treat?

10 THINGS YOU NEVER KNEW ABOUT MONKEYS

1 The word 'monkey' is a composite of the Old Norse term 'Monn' (meaning to 'fling shit') and the Anglo-Saxon verb 'Kee' (meaning to 'tamper with a car aerial in a safari park').

2 Many of our favourite pop stars have been influenced by monkeys - whether it's Oasis funnyman **LIAM GALLAGHER** swaggering about like a pissed-up chimp, or deceased rocker **GG ALLIN** hurling his own excrement at the audience.

3 The smallest monkey of all time belonged to the world's smallest man - **CALVIN PHILLIPS**. The minuscule macaque - named **TINY KONG** - was born in Nha Trang, Vietnam, and was roughly the size of a small mouse on its hind legs. Phillips had it shipped to his home in Essex after he became obsessed with the 1978 Clint Eastwood comedy *Every Which Way But Loose*, and decided he wanted a cheeky primate pal of his own. The pint-sized pair got into all manner of scrapes, driving around the American west in a pick-up truck the size of a breadbin.

4 The current world record for the furthest distance of faeces flung against a wall by a primate was set by Urko, a 350 pound western lowland gorilla from the Democratic Republic of Congo. On 27 March 2005, with representatives from the *Guinness Book of World Records* in attendance, Urko successfully hurled a lump of his own excrement against a brick wall that was a whopping **175 FEET** away.

5 Despite numerous films featuring the giant 100 foot gorilla, King Kong could never exist in real life. That's because, according to monkey experts, as a gorilla gets bigger the tensile strength of its bones increases with the square of its height whilst the animal's weight - and hence the stress on its bones - increases with the cube of its height. As it grew past 33'8", a King Kong's legs would snap like matchsticks.

6 A Mighty Joe Young could exist, though, as he was only about 25' high.

7 Believe it or not, U2 frontman **BONO** adopted his famous nickname because of his long-standing admiration for the "bonobo" species of chimpanzee, merely dropping the final "bo". The short-arsed pop fave, real name George O'Dowd, told *Puzzler* magazine: "I saw a chimp's tea party at the circus in Dublin when I was a kid, and the bonobo monkey particularly stood out because he was wearing a cute little bowler hat. I was especially impressed because it turned out that he'd had the hat flown halfway around the world in a private jet from his home in Central Africa."

8 There are currently a whopping 264 different species of monkey, such as mandrills, macaques and 262 more. Celebs who cite mandrills as their favourite type of monkey include Fleetwood Mac rocker **STEVIE NICKS**, Middlesbrough FC manager **TONY PULIS** and *EastEnders* actor **DEAN GAFFNEY**.

9 Celebs who cite macaques as their favourite type of monkey include *Fifty Shades* hunk **JAMIE DORNAN**, snooker ace **WILLIE THORNE** and gangsta rapper **P DIDDY**.

10 Celebs who cite one of the other 262 types of monkey as their favourite type of monkey include Jam frontman **PAUL WELLER**, US Vice President **MIKE PENCE** and freelance ejaculator **PETER NORTH**.

Monkey Business

ALL the latest simian stock market news, brought to you **LIVE** by primate finance expert **ROBERT PESTON**

▶ **CAPUCHIN STOCK** was raised to Hold from a Sell at $20.25 this morning at opening bell.

Robert says: "BUY white-headed capuchins with a stop loss at Rs 211 for target at Rs 201. SELL robust tufted capuchins with a stop loss at Rs 333 for target at Rs 310."

▼ **INVESTORS** with stakes in larger Old World monkeys, be warned: Baboon stock slumped dramatically yesterday - down 16% against the mandrill — after swollen red arses were hit with industrial strike action.

Robert says: "Only gray-footed chacma baboon stocks were still showing growth at closing bell. Buy, buy, buy!"

▲ **THE MNKE 100** hit a record high last night as marmoset and tamarin stocks soared.

Robert says: "My advice is to invest heavily in flat-nosed New World apes. Golden-backed uakari securities opened at $178.89 this morning, so they look a good bet. If that's a little out of your price range, however, then the Ecuadorian squirrel monkey is a buy with a stop loss of Rs 919 ($39.51 at the bell)."

▼ **BONOBO BITCOIN** slipped below $100,000 at the opening bell yesterday. The simian cryptocurrency is currently trading at 8%, near $1,203 per coin.

Robert says: "Even given the monkey market's recent volatility, this is a sizeable drop for the pygmy chimp cryptocurrency. I would authorize your broker to hold bonobo bitcoin with a stop loss at Rs 419, selling immediately when the markets recover."

More money-minded monkey minutiae next time, folks!

Robert xx

Miriam

YOUR MONKEY AND APE PROBLEMS ANSWERED BY DR MIRIAM STOPPARD

Dear Miriam

MY husband is an adventurer and he recently brought a King Kong back from an expedition to the South Seas. Now I fear that this enormous monkey has come between me and him.

I am 36, my husband is 38, and we've been married for 12 years. He used to be a very attentive husband, buying me flowers, taking me out to restaurants and telling me he loved me. But as soon as he had this 100-foot gorilla chained up in the back yard, he started to become distant and no longer seemed to have any time for me.

One night last week, I cooked my husband a special romantic meal. I spent ages preparing it, cooking all his favourite dishes and getting the ambience just right, with candles on the table and soft music playing on the stereo. However, halfway through the first course, the King Kong somehow broke free from its iron shackles, stuck its hand through the dining room window and grabbed me out of my chair.

It carried me right up to the top of a nearby block of flats, where it sat and picked all my clothes off with its enormous fingers. In the end, someone called out the RAF who arrived in a Eurofighter and shot it dead. Ever since then, my husband has been cold and distant. Even though he won't admit it, I think he secretly blames me for the death of his King Kong.

I suggested to him that we go to a marriage guidance counsellor to talk things through, but he refused to discuss the subject. Please help me, Miriam. I'm scared that our marriage could break down if we don't sort out this problem soon. *Ada D., Portsmouth*

Miriam says: The loss of an enraged 100ft gorilla in such tragic circumstances would put a strain on even the strongest marriage. However, your husband should not be blaming you for the death of his King Kong, and you should speak frankly to him before this bone of contention begins to fester. Explain to him how upset you were when it carried you up them flats and picked your clothes off. If he really loves you, he will understand that there are two sides to every story, and a King Kong getting shot by a Eurofighter is simply one of the trials that every relationship must endure.

I am sending you my leaflet: 'King Kongs, Your Marriage and You.'

ROY'LL WATCH E II R

Hello?

Is anyone in there?

Good morning officer. How –

Could you step out of the tent please sir?

Right, now get *that* packed up and be on your way, or I'll run you in so fast your feet-

But I'm waiting for the Duchess.

Who?

The Duchess of Fulchestershire!

She's coming to open the new tourist information centre.

FULCHESTER TOURIST INFORMATION

That's not for a week!

Nine days, four hours, 20 minutes!

Cut it fine, really. Can't *believe* the spot I've got!

Your *spot* is blocking the pavement!

I blocked the pavement outside Kate's hospital for two months – *with no tent!*

Right through that 'Beast From The East'!

I only have two toes on one foot.

I'm sorry about your toes, but you still can't –

I've already rung all the newspapers.

What?

POP! SNAP! SNAP! CLICK! SNAP!

CLICK!

POP!

See?

Soon

THE Sunt

LESBIANISM: HOW TO CURE YOUR WIFE

Royal Fawning Exclusive

CROWDS BEGIN TO GATHER

Next day **FULCHESTER TOURIST INFORMATION**

POP!

SNAP!

CLICK!

And the next

FULCHESTER TOURIST INFORMATION

DUCHESS OF HEARTS

POP!

SNAP!

PRESS

That's great guys!

Kiss her again!

POP! SNAP! CLICK!

Hard, on the *mouth*.

Can I borrow her again later?

I suppose...

POP! SNAP! POP! SNAP! CLICK!

Later

This time sluice it out front *and* back.

Noon, the big day

OPEN IT

12:03

YAAAAAAYYYYYYY!

POP! CLIC!

CLICK! SNAP!

12:07

I love you!

Where you off next?

Down the hospital.

SCREEEE!

Rumour is, Prince Philip has an infected cyst on his anus.

TONY  PARSEHOLE

MANY tears have been shedded in my house in the last month, but none more so have been shedded than have been for the death of Sir Ken Dodd. And even none morer so for the death of Professor Stephen Hawkings.

For these two men were giants in their respective fields.

Fields of comedy and fields of something to do with science.

And although these two fields were miles apart, they were in fact closer together than we can ever know.

Because comedy is a science, and what is science but an attempt to explain the comedy of life?

Both men left behind them a legacy, committing their thoughts and ideas to print so that generations yet unborn could have the benefit of their genius.

Hawkings's *A Brief History of Time* re-wrote the world of science that hadn't been re-wrote since Isaac Newton discovered gravity in Victorian times, while Ken Dodd's 1977 book *Ken Dodd's Butty Book* is no less of a seminal work, containing as it does many sandwich recipes.

According to Hawkings, we inhabit just one out of an infinite number of parallel universes.

In one such universe, the Professor himself stood on the stage in a long overcoat and tall hat, waving his tickling stick while regaling his audience with his latest theories about space, time and the Big Bang.

In that same universe, Ken Dodd sat slumped in a wheelchair as his electronically synthesized voice spun fanciful tales about Diddy Men, jam butty mines and the broken biscuit factories of Knotty Ash.

And in that other universe, far, far away on the other side of the galaxy, I have already knocked out my 500 words, emailed it off to the features editor of the Sun and been paid.

Tragically, however, it is this universe that we inhabit, and I still have 202 words to go. 194 words to go now.

These two Titans of the age, so similar in so many ways, were equally different in many other ways too.

Doddy could sing with the voice of an angel, selling more records than the Beatles with songs such as *Love is Like a Violin*, *Happiness*, and *Tears for Souvenirs*. Cruelly robbed of the power of speech by the (subs check name of disease) that ravished him for half a century, Professor Hawkings talked like an old sat-nav.

We may never know whether, if he hadn't of been cruelly robbed of the power of speech by the (xxxx) that ravished him for half a century, Professor Hawkings would of been just as successful in the pop charts as what Ken Dodd was.

And whilst Professor Hawkings's knowledge of atoms and space and chemicals knew no bounds, Dodd knew nothing of science. But had he not spent his schooldays clowning around during his science lessons, perhaps he too could of unlocked the mysteries of the universe. Tragically, now that he has passed, we may never know that neither.

But in amongst the tears of sadness that we shed for these two great there thats 500 inv enc TP

I was discom-knockerated at Doddy's death. And Hawkings's death left a black hole in my heart

---

Billy the FISH

72

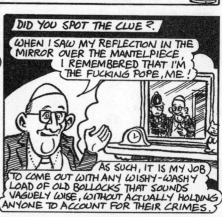

BAXTER BASICS MP

9.00 pm...

THE HONOURABLE MEMBER FOR FULCHESTER SUNNYSIDE...!

MR SPEAKER...

...I SHALL AIM TO BE BRIEF.

THIS BILL, WHICH SEEKS TO RELAX BAR OPENING HOURS ON CERTAIN BANK HOLIDAYS, IS THE START OF A SLIPPERY SLOPE, WHICH WOULD SEE THE MAJORITY OF HARD-WORKING BRITONS DESCEND INTO ALCOHOLISM...!

THE CONSEQUENCES WOULD BE DIRE, WITH CRIME RIFE AND VAGRANCY AT AN ALL-TIME HIGH ON THE STREETS OF OUR VILLAGES, TOWNS AND CITIES...

VILLAGES, TOWNS AND CITIES SUCH AS ABBAS COMBE, ABBERLEY, ABBERTON, ABBERWICK...

ABBETDALE, ABBEYSTEAD, ABBOTS BICKINGTON, ABBOTS BROMLEY, ABBOTS LANGLEY...

...ABBOTS LEIGH, ABBOTS MORTON, ABBOTS RIPTON, ABBOTS SALFORD, ABBOTSBURY...

11.30 pm...

LEECE, LEECHPOOL, LEEDS, LEEDSTOWN, LEEK, LEEK WOOTTON, LEEKBROOK, LEEMING, LEEMING BAR...

2.00 am...

...WACTON, WADBISTER, WADDESDON, WADBOROUGH, WADDINGHAM, WADDINGTON, WADEBRIDGE, WADSFORD...

TIME!

THANK FUCK FOR THAT, MR SPEAKER.

THIS DEBATE HAS BEEN TALKED OUT WITHOUT A VOTE. THE BILL IS THERE-FORE REJECTED...!

HERE! HERE!

SHAME!

SPLENDID FILLIBUSTERING, BAXTER, THAT BILL TO LIBERALISE LICENS-ING HOURS NEVER STOOD A CHANCE..!

ERM... YES.

AS YOU KNOW, IT'S A SUBJECT THAT IS VERY CLOSE TO MY HEART...

WHICH WAY'S THE MEMBERS' BAR..?

I MEAN, DO YOU HAVE ANY IDEA HOW MUCH THE NHS SPENDS ON DRINK-RELATED ILLNESSES EACH YEAR..?

HERE IT IS..! EXCELLENT! IT'S STILL OPEN!

ALCOHOL COSTS THIS COUNTRY A FORTUNE, BAXTER!

...A LARGE GLENMORANGIE OVER HERE.

...STICK IT ON MY PARLIAMENTARY EXPENSES WILL YOU..? LATE SITTING AND ALL THAT.

AH, BASICS! A LITTLE BIRD TELLS ME YOU'RE ON THE WHIPS' LIST..!

LIST!? WHAT LIST?

THE NAUGHTY BOYS' LIST. ALL THE MEMBERS WHO'VE BEEN DISLOYAL TO NUMBER TEN ARE ON THERE, Y'KNOW!

IT'S GOING TO BE LEAKED TOMORROW. ALL THE DETAILS OF YOUR SQUALID, INAPPROPRIATE BEHAVIOUR AND... A-HEM... BROWSING HABITS.

WH-WHAT?!

OH MY GOD!

YES. I WOULDN'T LIKE TO BE IN YOUR SHOES, BASICS.

THE HUMILIATION! STANDING AT YOUR GARDEN GATE, FAMILY BY YOUR SIDE DELIVERING YOUR MEALY-MOUTHED APOLOGY FOR PAST "MIS-STEPS"...

JUST THINK OF IT..!

SHIT A FUCKING BRICK.

OH DEARIE ME, IT'LL BE THE FULL MELLOR FOR YOU, BASICS, WHEN THAT LIST GETS LEAKED..!

NOT WHEN...

EH?

IF THAT LIST GETS LEAKED OLD BOY... IF..!

4.00 am THE CABINET OFFICE...

CHIEF WHIP

LetterbOcks

Viz Comic, P.O. Box 841 Whitley Bay, NE26 9EQ : letters@viz.co.uk

AS a strict vegetarian, I was heartened to see that Nasa selected Alan Bean as part of the Apollo 12 moon landing crew. However, since then there have been no other astronauts with surnames acceptable to veggies. Is this further proof, as if it were needed, of President Trump's fascist agenda?

Darvid Edwards, Bridport

IT strikes me that having a paddle wouldn't improve the experience of being up shit creek that much. You'd probably just end up flicking the stuff all over yourself whenever you tried to row.

Christina Martin, Bexhill-on-Sea

I DON'T know why everyone was moaning about the snow we had a few weeks ago. I got a lie-in in the morning, and because the missus was off work I got a shag too. It can snow every day as far as I'm concerned.

Timmy Fisher, Mansfield

THEY say that if you see a robin in your garden, it is in fact a visit from a dead relative. How preposterous. I saw a robin out of my kitchen window only this morning, and it did a massive shit on the barbecue. My grandmother would never have done that.

Jimmy C. Rocker, Stratford-upon-Avon

WHAT'S the big deal with Giant Pandas? You never hear or see anyone gushing about normal-sized pandas. Come on you wildlife people, size isn't everything, as my wife often reassures me.

Norman Breadboard, Hull

THEY say something lost is always found in the last place you look for it. Well, that's not true. I've lost my car keys and the last place I looked for them was down the side of the sofa, and they're definitely not there.

Daniel Lowbridge, Scunthorpe

WHY is it that when a man shags heaps of women he is a "legend", but when I do it I'm labelled a "lesbian"? Once again, it's one rule for men and another rule for women.

Edna Crowe, email

WHOEVER said laughter is the best medicine was talking out of their arse. I'm recovering from a hernia operation, and when my wife slipped on a wet dog turd recently and ended up sitting in it, I laughed so hard that I burst all of my stitches. Rather than aiding my recovery, this bout of laughter has set me back weeks.

Steve Crouch, P'borough

I RECENTLY spent almost £100 on a new trumpet, and I don't even know how to play the thing properly. Yet another example of 'Rip-off Britain'.

Ben Nunn, Caterham

I HAVE never seen the point of watch manufacturers boasting that their products work underwater. If you are underwater, then you're either on holiday or drowning in a canal somewhere. Either way, you wouldn't really give a flying fuck what the time was.

Morgan Flatbread, Derby

MUCH is said these days about the damage 'bullying' can do, but I think it's all nonsense. When I was at school, I would push Tubby Hawkins into the canal every day without fail and it never did me any harm. These hand-wringing do-gooders don't know what they are talking about.

Dr Trousers, Rickmansworth

I DON'T know why kidnappers always have to be so rude on the phone. Whenever they call to arrange getting the ransom money, they never say goodbye, but simply hang up. Kidnappers or not, a bit of civility and good manners costs nothing in my book.

Ada Bowelproblems, Luton

A DETAIL on the Bayeaux Tapestry shows what may be the earliest recorded instance of the classic school-yard fight technique of pulling the opponent's jumper over his head. No wonder we lost the battle with the Normans getting up to such dirty tricks.

John M, email

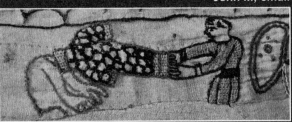

I DON'T know why outraged Transylvanian lynch mobs always carried those cumbersome flaming torches. Why didn't they simply ditch the torches and march to Dracula's castle during the day? The other advantage would be that he would almost certainly be having a kip, thereby giving them the element of surprise.

Bartram Stoker, email

BACK in the 1970s, chip pan fires were all the rage. These days everyone is so lazy that they don't even put their chips in boiling fat anymore, and these fires are a thing of the past. Come on people, help the fire service and enjoy a trip down memory lane by having a proper, good old-fashioned chip pan fire.

Iwan Carr, Upper Llandwrog

I'D be sorely embarrassed if my postcode was P155 OFF I can tell you. Thankfully, mine is completely different.

Egbert Henge, Penge

HOW come it's only doctors and scientists who get to go into space? It doesn't seem fair since they have good jobs already. Why not have a couple of welders or bin men go up there for a change? The welders would be well used to the heat in case it started burning up during re-entry and of course the bin-men are used to operating complicated machinery.

Edna Borgsdottir, Glossop

I ONCE did a shit at work that was so bad that they thought the drains had fractured and called out a plumber. Can any of your readers beat that?

Mike Rophone, Halifax

I DON'T know why "laughing hyenas" are so called. I was watching one on the telly the other night, and it sounded more like screaming to me than laughing. Mind you, it was being attacked and eaten by a bunch of lions, so maybe I just caught it on an off day.

Crawford Biscuits, Epping

WHILST on the job with my wife, in a moment of intense passion I inadvertently yelled out 'Oh Emilia!' as at the time, I may have been thinking about the lovely *Game of Thrones* actor Emilia Clarke. My wife seemed somewhat angry. I explained she should be flattered that I could look at her and still think of someone so attractive, yet this only seemed to make her even more irate. Was there something I did wrong, or should I just put this down to the mysterious workings of the female mind?

S Andrews, Bristol

TOP

TURN your gloss black car into a trendy matt black model by rubbing it all over with a brillo pad.

Hampton Dogood, Luton

HUSBANDS. Get yourselves into even more trouble by not knowing why you're in trouble in the first place.

James Wallace, Belper

KITCHEN roll makes an ideal toilet paper substitute if you have a big arse or shit a lot.

John Owens, Glasgow.

GENTS. Pouring vinegar onto a paper cut on your bell-end is the best way to get the upper hand when women are bragging about the pain of childbirth, like they do.

Steve Crouch, P'borough

DOG owners. Experience the feeling of being a priest by saying: "The body of Christ" every time you hand your mutt a dog biscuit.

Paul Doolan, London

THEY published a picture of a chubby cock and balls in the latest issue of *Classic Ford* magazine. I was so angry, I put my foot through the windscreen of my Escort and sent Ari Vatanen the bill.

Stuart, New Cross

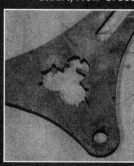

VERY well done for granting Sal Bundon's request for a picture of a Turbot on page 55. Your magazine truly does make dreams come true.

Gustaf Fish, Tooting

WHY don't footballers with large afro hairstyles shave the crown area, creating an 'egg cup' effect? They could then simply catch the ball in the 'hair cup' and run into the goal, depositing the ball in the old onion bag with a simple tilt of the head.

Vestan Pance, email

HOLIDAY makers. Recreate the experience of being in sunnier climes by walking round Asda in your swimming trunks and flip-flops and shouting: "Look, they've got McVities digestives" to your wife.

Ian Saxon, Hartlepool

SURGERY patients. Avoid the embarrassment of getting a raging hard-on while under anaesthetic by having a crafty wank on the trolley just before they give you the gas.

Hank, Staines

OVERCOME awkward silences on that first date by bringing an air horn with you.

Adam Lacey, Miltonton Keynes

ZOO owners. Convince your visitors that you have a dung beetle exhibit by painting a ladybird black and glueing it to a Happy Shopper Scotch egg.

Iain Devenney, Oxford

VIKINGS were using magnets to navigate a thousand years ago, and the things have hardly changed since, still sticking to metal and pointing north. Come on magnet manufacturers, lets have a bit of innovation. How about some magnets that stick to wood and glass, or point to other parts of the globe?

Mark Glover, Coventry

IT'S 2018 and we can put a car into space and safely re-land the rockets. We can genetically modify plants, animals and viruses, and we can lay carbon atoms in series to use as conductors with virtually no resistance. And yet I still have to wipe my own bottom. Come on, Silicon Valley, where's my bum-wiping droid?

Barry Williams, Northants

HOW come my wife's favourite gardening spade still has all concrete stuck to it eleven years after I used it to mix a load to mend a window sill, yet the repair itself fell off after two weeks?

Philip Berkin, London

INSTEAD of gritting the roads when it snows, why don't the government make the roads out of the grit so that the snow would instantly melt and everyone could get to work?

K Buck, Seaham

I RECENTLY went to Stuttgart on a plane that had propellers instead of jets. Just imagine if it had of crashed, everyone would laugh and say that I should of went on a plane with jets, not propellers.

C Pumpaloaf, email

IN their TV advert, one of those ambulance-chasing companies states that "when an accident happens, time stops." And they're right, too, because when I fell over outside my local after drinking 10 pints of strong ale, my watch broke and hasn't worked since. I also shit myself.

Greta Garbage, email

TO commemorate the anniversary of Andy Warhol's death, could you possibly show a picture of that bloke kissing that birds arse in the style of the iconic Andy Warhol Marilyn Monroe painting?

Handy Whorhol, Orkney

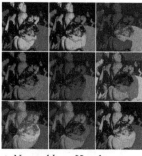

* *No problem, Handy.*

WHY don't you see paper-weights anymore? Is paper heavier these days, or has the average wind speed dropped in the last 30 years?

Peter Constantine, Merseyside

I RECENTLY saw on a nature program that the mosquito is the most dangerous creature in the animal world. Well I'd like to see someone take out a lion or an alligator with a rolled-up copy of *Gardeners' World*.

Foz, Neston

CGI OLLIE IS A HELLRAISER

DURING his lifetime, actor OLIVER REED earned a reputation as a hard-drinking, hard-living hellraiser. Tales of the star's notorious booze-fuelled benders, which often lasted several days, were the stuff of showbiz legend. It was sadly no surprise when he died aged 61, following an epic drinking match with sailors during production of the movie *Gladiator* in 1999.

Late actor still boozing it up in cyberspace

Reed: Virtual piss-up.

At the time of his death, Reed's scenes for the movie had yet to be completed, and director Ridley Scott was forced to complete filming using a computer-generated body double.

olly

But now, nearly 20 years after he hellrose himself to death, it seems that Reed's CGI avatar is back up to his old hellraising tricks, after it apparently went on a 72-hour drinks binge rampage during production of a special high definition 20th anniversary 'director's cut' version of *Gladiator*, set to be released next year.

"It was just like old times," said a spokesman

EXCLUSIVE!

for special effects company The Mill. "Following a bank holiday weekend, we were going to render a scene in the gladiator school, but when we looked in the hard drive for the virtual version of Ollie on the Tuesday morning, he was nowhere to be found."

"His cache hadn't even been slept in."

stan

Filming was called to a halt while SFX technicians scoured the internet for the missing 32 million pixel graphical embodiment.

"He must have got out of our computer system on the Friday night and somehow made his way into the drinks section of the Tesco website," said the spokesman.

bud

"Once in there, he had proceeded to booze his way through everything he could lay his virtual hands on over the whole long weekend."

"When we eventually found him, he was in a terrible state, completely drunk and slurring his words."

Later, the CGI Reed got into YouTube and

appeared completely drunk and slurring his words on several videos of chatshows where he hadn't already appeared completely drunk and slurring his words.

JIMBO JONES' ROBOT BEAUTY PAGEANT

Jimbo Jones was the luckiest boy in Barnton, for his Uncle Seth - an eccentric inventor who was on the Sex Offenders Register - had built him a fantastic remote control miniature beauty pageant of his very own...

One day...

...and our next contestant is Carmina Perez, who is Miss Venezuela.

Not too late for the swimsuit round, am I Jimbo?

No Uncle Seth, it's just starting.

Smashing. It's my favourite round, this. Much better than those long evening dresses...

...I mean, why would they want to cover themselves up...?

...there's nothing wrong with a pretty girl showing what she's got.

Carmina is 21 years old, and she is a student nurse in her home town of Caracas.

And I'm sure there are plenty of gentlemen in the audience who are "Caracas" about Carmen!

Phooar! She can give me a bed bath any time she likes!

And those all-important vital statistics are six and-a-half, three and a half, six-and-a-half.

Gwooar! Look at her!

What a little hottie!

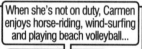

When she's not on duty, Carmen enjoys horse-riding, wind-surfing and playing beach volleyball...

I wouldn't mind seeing that... working up a sweat in the hot sun. A golden tan, in one of them skimpy bikinis

Eh, Jimbo? Gaaaaw!

I can just picture her, brushing the sand off her cleavage, pulling her knickers out of her crack.

...and her ambition is to work with children and animals, travel the world and meet interesting people.

Slaver!

...That's contestant number three... Miss Venzuela!

And now it's time to meet contestant number four, Inga Svenson who is Miss Finland.

Christ! Look at her, Jimbo! She's proper stacked! She must be eight inches up top at least!

Twenty-year-old Inga works in Helsinki where she is a dental receptionist.

Dental receptionist? She's got a cavity I wouldn't mind filling, eh Jimbo?!

If she wins today, she will use her title to raise awareness of world hunger and global warming. Her hobbies include badminton, cross country skii-ing and cake decorating. Her vital statistics are seven and three-quarters, three and a half...

Suddenly...

WE WILL NOT BE JUDGED

Oh no! It's a protest!...

...A load of bloody feminist lesbians!

Sexist pigs! Ban this filth! Feminism now!

STOP THIS MEAT MARKET!

It's that Millie from next door with her robot women's libbers!

WOMEN HATERS

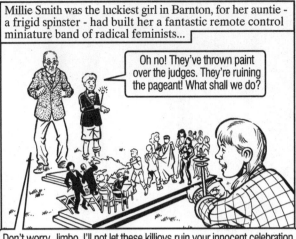

Millie Smith was the luckiest girl in Barnton, for her auntie - a frigid spinster - had built her a fantastic remote control miniature band of radical feminists...

Oh no! They've thrown paint over the judges. They're ruining the pageant! What shall we do?

Don't worry, Jimbo. I'll not let these killjoys ruin your innocent celebration of feminine beauty and elegance with their politically correct claptrap.

We are women! We are strong! Boo!

Hurry uncle! It's turning into a shambles and we haven't even had the national costumes round yet!

In his workshop, Uncle Seth worked feverishly...

Two minutes later...

Security's here!

Down with Men! Down with Men!

WOMEN HATERS

NO TO SEXISM

STOP THIS MEAT MARKET

Uncle Seth's squad of miniature burly backstage security guards quickly moved into action...

Go get 'em, lads!

Get your filthy hands off my miniature feminists, you sexist pigs!

ALL WOMEN ARE BEAUTIFUL

...and before long, order was restored...

The miniature police are here, Jimbo. You won't get any more trouble from this boot-faced rabble.

Right, time to get my pageant underway again.

POLICE

And shortly...

...the standard of beauty today has been incredibly high, and the judges have had a very difficult job...

...but the winner is...

CRY WALK UP DOWN

TWIRL KETTLE DRUM WANK OFF JUDGE

BRRRRRRR! RRR!

...Miss Trinidad and Tobago!

81

The End

JURASSIC MARC!

T-Rex set to walk the earth

SCIENTISTS at the University of Glamorgan have sparked excitement among glam-rock fans after announcing ambitious plans to clone late pop icon *Marc Bolan*, who has been extinct since 1977. Boffins say they have extracted intact DNA from a pair of the singer's flared loon pants found on an internet auction site. This genetic material will be introduced into a chicken egg, which they hope will hatch into the first living Marc Bolan to be seen on the planet for more than forty years.

21ST Century boy? Bolan's DNA could be used to produce a clone of the glam rocker.

"It's a really thrilling project for everyone here at Glamorgan," said Professor Tibor Szackacs, head of the Welsh University's Life Sciences department. "Most people only know T-Rex from the television or pictures in books, so they don't realise quite how big they were back in the seventies. If our experiment is successful, everyone will have the chance to actually see them in the flesh, and that's very exciting."

heyday

But Professor Szackacs's plans have met with widespread criticism. Many T-Rex fans were unimpressed at the prospect of their cloned heartthrob taking the stage four decades after his heyday. "For a start, Marc is going to be half chicken," said Barbara Drabness, life treasurer of the Glamorgan T-Rex fan club. "Chances are he won't look anything like he did on the posters I used to have on my bedroom wall."

"And secondly, it's not really the proper T-Rex if they don't also clone Mickey Finn or Steve Peregrin Took to play the bongos while Marc's warbling away about swans and wizards and stuff," she added.

According to Szackacs, the team has

T.REXCLUSIVE!

so far been unable to obtain any genetic material from Finn, who died from liver disease in 2003, or Took, who choked on a cocktail cherry in 1980. He told us: "If any groupies who had it off with them in the past happen to have saved their knickers as a souvenir, we'll happily scrape some off, stick it in an egg and see what hatches."

strawnight

Meanwhile, Archbishop of Canterbury Justin Welby claimed that it would be interfering with God's plan to clone the corkscrewed-haired pop minstrel. "The Lord clearly wanted Bolan to die, otherwise he wouldn't have made his car crash into that tree," he told Radio 4's Eddie Mair. "It is simply not for scientists to meddle in the wondrous ways of His creation."

And Dr Welby had this warning for Professor Szackacs and his team. "You bring Marc Bolan back to life if you want to, but don't come crying to me when you all get cast into the lake of fire for ever and ever. Amen," he said.

HOW IT'S DONE

THE SCIENCE OF CLONING WITH DR ADAM RUTHERFORD OF RADIO 4'S *INSIDE SCIENCE*

WE OFTEN read about cloning in the media, but how does this revolutionary gene-splicing technology actually work? How exactly will DNA be extracted from Marc Bolan's trousers and introduced into an ordinary chicken's egg? Here's a step-by-step layman's guide to this fascinating process.

1 The scientist searches for a pair of Marc Bolan's trousers on eBay and decides how much he's prepared to pay for them.

2 He waits until the very last few seconds of the auction, before placing his maximum bid.

3 Success! He waits for the page to refresh before clicking the Pay Now button that takes him straight to the PayPal log-in page.

4 The scientist shouts his wife and asks her if she can remember the PayPal password.

5 Once the payment has gone through, the loon pants are posted out to the scientist.

6 Back in the lab, he extracts the DNA from them, injects it into a chicken egg and sits back to wait for Marc Bolan to hatch.

NEXT WEEK: Using monoclonal antibodies to produce a vaccine against Dave Hill out of Slade.

THERE is a deep schism splitting the country in three from Land's End to Skegness and from St Bee's Head to John O'Groats. It's a violently raging war of words that shows no sign of abating any time soon, as Brits cross swords over the relative merits of 3 very different Danielses.

But just which one is the best? Is it Middlesbrough-born TV conjuror *PAUL Daniels*, who kept us spellbound with his wizardry in the 80s and 90s? Is it Tennessee bourbon magnate *JACK Daniels*, whose 70% proof firewater is still America's favourite tipple? Or is it glamorous US grumble star *STORMY Daniels*, whose films keep us constantly engrossed with one hand on the fast forward button?

It's time to pitch them one against the other, and the other, in a three-way battle to decide once and for all…

Paul, Jack or Stormy...
~Who's the Best Daniels?

ROUND 1:

MAGICIANS typically pick themselves glitzy showbiz names, such as The Great Soprendo, Dynamo, or Tony Slydini. The dull, workaday name 'Paul Daniels' clearly bucks this trend, so you might think that this was the appellation he was born with. But you would be wrong, for the Cleveland-based prestidigitator was originally christened 'Newton Edward Daniels'. His mother Ada named her son after her favourite biscuit, the Fig Newton, and her favourite variety of potato, the King Edward. As such, it's a low scoring opening round for the late conjuror.

THE WORLD of showbusiness was rocked to its foundation 1986, when Paul Daniels revealed he had been wearing a wig the past twenty years, tricking the entire planet into believing had a full, healthy head of lustrous hair. Pulling off this amaz illusion for two decades before pulling off his syrup earns h top marks in this round… *and that's magic!*

10

ROUND 3: ABILITY TO PU

ONE OF Paul's many tricks involved him being handcuffed and escaping from a lock crate suspended in water. To achieve this feat in such a confined space clearly requir him to contort his body into some quite extreme positions, and it is quite possi that at some point, the illusionist would have had his feet behind his ears and his li pressed against his chest. However, only Paul himself - and his fellow members of the Magic Circle - know how the trick was done and if this posture was indeed achieved. We can only speculate and award half marks.

ROUND 4:

EVERY Saturday evening, Paul would leave his prime tir TV show's viewers speechless with wonder as he opened his famous Bunco Booth and performed trick after stunni trick. And none was more amazing than when he seeming made small, red, sponge balls disappear from under one c and reappear under another while regaling the audien with his hilarious patter. To this day, nobody knows how the trick was done, and Paul has taken the secret to his grave.

10

FEW people are so honoured or feted in life that they are immortalised with a dri named after them, and Paul is no exception. At no point has anyone ever walked into bar and asked for a pint of Paul Daniels, or gone into a cockt lounge and ordered a Paul Daniels, shaken, not stirred. Th haven't even gone into a cafe and asked for a cup of Paul Danie with two sugars. It's the lowest score possible in this round for the Teesside wand-waver.

ANYONE who watched Paul's eponymous Saturday evening magic show will remember his hilarious catchphrase *"You'll like this… not a lot!"*. But the show only ran to a total of 120 episodes over 15 series between 1979 and 1994, with another 21 specials. And if we assume the magician delivered his catchphrase on average twice per show, viewers in fact only heard it a mere 282 times in his entire career.

2

PAUL

PAUL will like his score… *not a lot!* Although it was a magic performance from the late Cleveland conjuror which included two perfect rounds, at the end of the show he just couldn't pull the win out of the hat.

32

NEXT WEEK: IT'S THE BATTLE OF THE BOW

TLE OF THE DANIELSES!

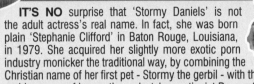

.....JACK.......... / .....STORMY..........

REALNESS OF NAME

BELIEVE it or not, the legendary 19th Century distiller was not christened with the same name that adorns bottles of his world-ous Tennessee bourbon to this day. Jack Daniels was actually 'Jasper Newton Daniels' in Lynchburg, Tennessee in 1849. mother, Dolly, named her son after her favourite Brummie edian, Jasper Carrott, and her favourite biscuit, the Fig Newton.

5

IT'S NO surprise that 'Stormy Daniels' is not the adult actress's real name. In fact, she was born plain 'Stephanie Clifford' in Baton Rouge, Louisiana, in 1979. She acquired her slightly more exotic porn industry monicker the traditional way, by combining the Christian name of her first pet - Stormy the gerbil - with the maiden name of her mother - dental receptionist Roxxxy Sugarpussy Daniels.

1

ROUND 2: BALDNESS

THE only photograph that seems to exist of the erstwhile bourbon-wer, Jack Daniels is sporting a wide-brimmed cowboy stetson . Under this ten gallon titfer, he could have been hiding thing; a Tito Jackson-style afro, a Bobby Charlton combover, even a shiny Kojak slaphead. It's a one-in-three shot that he's , giving him a score of just 3.333 recurring. Sadly, for hnical reasons, we've had this round this mark down to isappointing 3.

3

TO SEE the glamorous movie actress on TV, with her flowing blonde locks cascading over her shoulders, you might assume that she would be scoring zero in a round based on baldness. However, anyone who has seen one of her hardcore performances in films such as *Sex Door Neighbour*, *Dripping Wet Sex* or *Finally Legal 7* will attest that, like all today's porn stars, "down there", Stormy is as bald as a billiard ball. So it's half marks in this round for the collar-but-no-cuffs beauty.

5

HEIR FEET BEHIND THEIR EARS AND LICK THEIR NIPPLES

HIS biography *Blood and Whiskey: The Life and Times of Jack Daniels*, author er Krass makes no mention as to whether the American distiller and businessman s able to put his feet behind his ears and lick his nipples. As a rather stout man, most likely that he could not. But it is just possible that he could indeed perform party piece, but swore anyone who witnessed it to secrecy. We may never w, and consequently must once again award a median score.

5

THE MUCH-in-demand pornographic actress makes no bones about the fact that she can put her feet behind her ears and lick her own nipples. Indeed, by the boastful way she brings the subject up in interviews, and the number of times she insists on doing it in her films, you might almost believe that she is proud of this ability. But whether you look upon it as an enviable skill or a cause for shame, it ticks all the boxes to get Stormy full marks in this round.

10

RFORMING TRICKS WITH CUPS AND BALLS

DISTILLER Jack was the youngest of 10 children born to Calaway and Lucinda Daniels, and as such would have had plenty of playmates when he was growing up. It is almost certain that one of his siblings would have been in possession of an 'Ali Bongo Junior Magic Set' and would have performed simple tricks to amuse their youngest brother, one of which would have been the cup and balls trick. But from that fact we move into the realm of speculation, as it is impossible to say whether or not young Jack ever had a go at performing the trick himself.

5

LIKE HER namesake Paul, Stormy opens up her own Bunco Booth in every film she appears in, and she also performs an impressive variety of tricks with balls. But this is where the similarity ends as, unlike Paul, Ms Daniels makes no attempt to fool anyone about how she does it and we see exactly how everything is done - in extreme close up. However, after watching all 171 of her films performances, and then watching them all again in order to check, at no point do we recall her performing a trick using cups, except the ones off her bra.

5

ND 5: NAMESAKE DRINKS

TH over 150 million bottles of whiskey bearing his name sold each ar, you might expect this to be a top scoring round for the Tennessee rn businessman. But you'd be wrong. That's because, whilst each ttle clearly says 'Jack Daniel's' on the label, that is a misspelling, as man himself was actually christened Jack Daniel, without the final . It's a case of close, but no cigar, as this slip-up costs him a entially vital point.

9

WALK into *The Brighton* bar in Washington D.C. and ask for a 'Stormy Daniels', and you'll be given a delicious, cool beverage consisting of whiskey and ginger beer, which is described by its inventor as a 'real dirty cocktail'. The drink was named after the actress in recognition of her services to the film industry and her moving performances in movies such as *Pussy Sweat*, *When the Boyz are Away the Girlz Will Play* and *Toxxxic Cumloads 6*.

10

ROUND 6: CATCHPHRASES

VERY time anyone picks up one of the 150 million bottles of Jack Daniels Straight urbon sold each year, they'll see the words *"Old Time Old Number 7 Brand"* printed udly on the label. And with 40 single shots in a litre bottle, this means Jack's tagline picked up and read around 6 billion times each year - that's impressive exposure a catchphrase in anyone's books. However, these words are technically a gan rather than a catchphrase, so count for nothing in this round.

0

ANYONE who has watched one of Stormy's films will recall her famous catchphrase *"Fuck me! Fuck me! Oh, fuck! Oh, fuck! Oh, fuck, yes! That's it! Yes! Yes! Fuck me! Oh, fuck, yes!"* which she repeats endlessly while on camera. The adult star's snappy one-liner has found its way onto T-shirts, mugs, drinks coasters, lunchboxes, baseball hats and many other items of merchandise. And it's this omnipresence that sees Stormy take top marks in this round.

10

HOW DID THEY DO?

JACK

E MIGHT be the distiller of America's number 1 oak cask matured bourbon, but the Tennessee ooze magnate came bottom of the barrel in this ontest. A middling performance eventually saw ck Daniels on the rocks.

27

STORMY

OH GOD, she's coming... *first!* Stormy's hardcore army of short-sighted fans will be pumping their fists in celebration tonight as their favourite star is crowned top of the popshots in this three-way duel of the Danielses.

41

S! JIM vs JEREMY vs LAURENCE LLEWELYN

85

LUCKY FRANK

Big Day for UK's Oldest Man

THE bunting was out in a Chorley nursing home yesterday as Britain's oldest man celebrated his *THIRTY-SEVEN THOUSANDth* birthday.

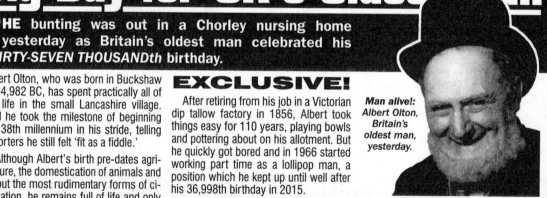

Man alive!: Albert Olton, Britain's oldest man, yesterday.

Albert Olton, who was born in Buckshaw in 34,982 BC, has spent practically all of his life in the small Lancashire village. And he took the milestone of beginning his 38th millennium in his stride, telling reporters he still felt 'fit as a fiddle.'

Although Albert's birth pre-dates agriculture, the domestication of animals and all but the most rudimentary forms of civilisation, he remains full of life and only entered the Quiet Sands nursing home at the age of 36,999 after suffering a fall last winter.

"I'm still in pretty good health," Albert told his local paper the *Chorley Prepuce*. "I get the odd twinge off an arrow wound I got at the Battle of Crécy, but that's about it."

old

Throughout his long life, Albert has had a variety of careers, including spells as a woolly mammoth hunter, cave painter, flint arrowhead maker, Neanderthal, spice merchant and tin miner. And it is only in the last couple of centuries that he has finally thought about taking retirement. "There was no such thing as the welfare state when I was a lad, or for thousands of years after," he said.

EXCLUSIVE!

After retiring from his job in a Victorian dip tallow factory in 1856, Albert took things easy for 110 years, playing bowls and pottering about on his allotment. But he quickly got bored and in 1966 started working part time as a lollipop man, a position which he kept up until well after his 36,998th birthday in 2015.

But the spritely tridecaseptokilogenarian didn't crack open open the champagne to mark his special day, because he has been practically teetotal all his life. "Alcohol wasn't invented until Neolithic times, when I was in my early twenty-eight thousands, so I never really got a taste for it," he told reporters. "I had a pint of rudimentary fermented ale at the opening ceremony for Stonehenge, but I didn't really like the taste. Apart from a small sherry to celebrate the Relief of Mafeking in 1900, that was about it."

man

Albert celebrated the big day with a few of his three-and-a-half million living descendants. He told the paper: "It's always nice to get together with my great times eighteen hundred-and-fifty grandkids and have a bit of a knees-up."

"I just hope they don't decide to give me the bumps," he quipped. "At a rate of one bump every two seconds, it would take more than twenty hours."

Also joining in the festivities was Albert's wife of 36,873 years, Ada. Mrs Olton still remembers the first time she set eyes on her husband like it was yesterday. "It was a village feast to celebrate the hunting of an auroch, a sort of Upper Palaeolithic wild bison," she said. "I saw Albert at the other side of the cave and that was it for me. It was love at first sight.

"Like all couples who've been together for more than thirty-six millennia, we've had our ups and downs, but I wouldn't change Albert for the world," said Ada, 36,996, who works three mornings a week at the Chorley branch of B&Q.

86

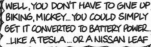

With the greatest respect, ma'am... IT'S TIME TO START

RECENTLY announced government figures revealed that the cost of maintaining the Queen has risen 13%, with taxpayers now forking out the thick end of £50 **MILLION** a year to pay for Her Majesty's upkeep. But with 92 years on the clock, is it now time for the country to think the unthinkable and start running our elderly and much-loved monarch on the cheap?

with Viz Money-Saving Expert Martin Lewys

old banger

Make no mistake, we've had our money's worth out of the Queen. The old girl's given us faultless and reliable service over the 66 years of her reign. But it's time to face facts; just as you wouldn't keep taking a rusty old banger that's been twice round the clock to a fancy main dealer for maintenance, isn't it now time to start entrusting Her Majesty's upkeep to the royal equivalent of a back lane garage?

Even well into her tenth decade, the Queen is still a good runner. She troops the colour, opens parliament and changes

EXCLUSIVE!

the guard first time without fail. But metaphorically speaking, next time she needs tyres, instead of going to ATS and forking out for a brand new set of top-of-the-range Michelins, we should fit her with a decent set of re-moulds.

We asked *Viz*'s Money-Saving Expert **MARTIN LEWYS** to take a close look at Her Majesty's budget and make suggestions as to where corners can be cut to save our cash-strapped country £££s as we run her into the ground.

Flush Royal? Simple everyday swaps might enable her majesty to be both frugal and regal.

GLASSES

AS WE get older, our eyesight inevitably deteriorates, and Her Majesty the Queen's vision is no exception.

As her prescription lenses get stronger, she changes her glasses every six months. And she doesn't just get her new lenses fitted in her old specs; she gets brand new top-of-the-range Bulgari or Versace frames each time, leaving the exchequer to pick up the eye-watering £15,000 annual bill.

But is the country getting proper value for money out of these right royal bins? Let's face it, she only uses them once a year, for reading her Christmas Message. A pair of £1 disposable readers from the pound shop would do the job just as well, and she could easily replace them 3 or 4 times a year, without

making a dint in the Civil List. When her prescription goes beyond the range available on the bargain homewares rack, she can simply do what generations of pensioners have done before her, and double up. The prospect of the monarch sitting down to make her annual address to the Commonwealth with two pairs of Poundland specs perched on her nose might not sound particularly regal, but in these times of austerity we all have to tighten our belts, and as head of state, ER should lead by example.

Saved £14,996

VOL-AU-VENTS

EACH year, the Queen munches her way through 1,825 Fortnum & Mason foie gras and caviar vol-au-vents.

At £10 a pop, these tasty indulgences cost the hard-working British taxpayer nearly £20,000, but whilst these gourmet treats are undoubtedly of superior quality, it's safe to say that the taste-buds of the nonagenarian monarch are probably not what

they once were. Would she really notice the difference if her butler served her up a plate of Iceland own-brand chicken in white sauce vol-au-vents, which come in at a much more economical cost of £2.99 for 50?

Saved £18,140.87

SLIPPERS

AFTER a hard day's reigning, the monarch likes to put her feet up in a pair of hand-made slippers made by the royal footwear warrant holders Lobbs of Piccadilly.

These luxury ermine-trimmed, chamois leather slip-ons don't come cheap; Joe and Josephine Taxpayer fork out a cool £5,000 for each pair. But next time they need replacing, why don't we say "Cobblers" to Bond Street and

get her some £9.99 mules from the bargain rack at TK Maxx? Sure, they may not last as long, but let's face an uncomfortable truth. With the greatest respect, shuffling around Buckingham Palace at the age of 92, Her Majesty is never going to wear out 500 pairs of slippers before the day we all dread when the Lord gathers her to his bosom, leaving the country quids in.

Saved £4,990.01

NNING YOU ON THE CHEAP

HORSE RACING

OVER the sticks or over the flat, the Queen is well known as a fan of racing, attending meetings at least once a week. But how much does her thoroughbred horse hobby cost the country? The answer is... *a lot*.

Entry to Ascot's Royal Enclosure costs at least £500 a ticket, and cucumber sandwiches, Pimms, and strawberries and cream add many hundreds more to that basic expense. In addition, when the monarch fancies a flutter on the favourite in the 3.15, many on-course bookies operate a minimum £10 stake policy, meaning that Her Majesty's day at the gee-gees can easily saddle her subjects

with a bill of £3,000 or more. A much cheaper alternative would surely be to send her off for a night at Romford Dogs. Entry is £7, which includes a pie and pea supper, and drinks in the Mick the Miller downstairs bar are just £2.50 a pint, with Tote bets starting at a mere 50p. For a no-nagenarian monarch with onset cataracts who is watching from the Senior Club stand through Poundland glasses, a dog will appear no different to a horse, and whilst greyhound racing may not exactly be the Sport of Kings, the going will be as good as it gets, with the savings romping home into the country's cash-strapped coffers.

Saved £154,960

OFFICIAL PORTRAITS

EACH year, the Queen sits for an official portrait. In the past, her image has been immortalised in oils by such eminent artists as Pietro Annigoni, Lucian Freud and Rolf Harris, and illustrious names like these don't come cheap. It's an undeniable fact that, with each commission costing at least £50,000 or more, royal portraiture is an area that is clearly ripe for cost-cutting.

For her next official likeness, Her Majesty should simply get her butler to snap her on his mobile phone and then use a free fun "app" to apply an oil-painting effect to the image. For a mere £15 or so, the finished portrait could then be printed out A2-size, with a matt or gloss finish, at the Mayfair branch of Snappy Snaps. For a few pounds extra, if it is going to be displayed at the National Gallery, the picture could even be applied to real canvas and then popped into a smart £10 frame from IKEA. Hold it, ma'am... Flash, bang, wallop! What a saving!

Saved £49,950

PET FOOD

NEXT to jewellery, ER's greatest love is her pack of pedigree corgis. These bad-tempered, short-legged pooches enjoy the sort of pampered palace lifestyle that many of her subjects can only dream of, tucking into tin after tin of Caesar Select - perhaps the most expensive petfood on the supermarket shelf at £1.25 for a small can.

But stop and think for a moment; whilst the Queen is royal and has therefore earned her luxurious, opulent lifestyle, her dozen-strong canine entourage have merely had the good fortune to be born in the right place and at the right time.

And with matching sets of dogs at her other residences in Windsor, Sandringham and Balmoral, there is no reason

why Buckingham Palace's outrageous yearly pet food bill of £43,860 cannot be brought to heel. Most supermarkets produce their own budget ranges of dog dinners, with prices starting at just 30p or less per tin. Or even better, butchers will often give customers a sheep's head or bag of guts for nothing.

Saved £43,860

EDITOR'S NOTE: *Her majesty the Queen was alive at the time of going to press, although she was suffering from a "summer cold". Should the unthinkable have happened by the time you are reading this, we offer our sincerest condolences to the royal family, and accept that this article was in extremely poor taste and, in retrospect, should never have been published.*

FOODIE BOLLOCKS

Hmm, what, exactly, is the fish in your fish and chips?

Cod or haddock.

And what's the provenance?

The what?

Where was it sourced?

The North Sea I expect.

Can you be more specific?

Not really, without calling my supplier.

So...

He says probably about a hundred mile off Whitby.

Probably...?

About...?

Do they know who caught it?

Er, who caught it?

No I ain't taking the piss. I wish...

He says be one of the big trawlers.

Tsk! Line-caught is far less tense.

It is fresh every day.

But fresh from where?...

...from whom?

Never mind... So, what's the story of your chips?

How'd you mean, story?

Well, what's the potato?

Oh right – King Edwards.

That's a shame.

Have you never considered using something traditional?

King Edwards are traditional.

Hardly! They were registered in 1902!

I mean a heritage variety, like Fortyfold.

Never heard of 'em.

Really?!? They were widely grown in the early 1800s.

Didn't you see the fascinating piece on Jez Rhodes in last week's Guardian Feast?

Who in what?

Surely you've heard of Jez Rhodes!

Nope.

He's turned over his Suffolk estate to produce dozens of crops not seen since the Civil War!

Jez is a downsized banker.

I bet.

Now, where are these *ahem* King Edwards from?

Lincolnshire.

Is there a name for the farm?

Manor Farm.

Can I get a postcode?

Oh no! Upwind of the River Witham!

Are you going to order any bloody food?

Only I've a bit of a queue on, if you hadn't noticed...

I expect to regret this, but I'll risk the fish and chips.

Coming up. Salt and vinegar?

Yes.

Himalayan pink salt and Normandy cider vinegar

There's always a Warm Welcome in Blackpool

...BUT NOT FOR PUTIN!

"I'm farting fire!" says Lord Mayor

I do KGB beside the seaside: If controversial Russian President Vladimir Putin tries to take a holiday in Blackpool he will receive a frosty welcome, says mayor.

THE LORD MAYOR of Blackpool yesterday expressed disgust at the Russian Secret Service's recent Salisbury nerve agent attack and announced that the Lancashire resort was planning a series of far-reaching sanctions against Vadimir Putin in response. "Everyone is guaranteed a warm welcome on the West Lancashire Riviera, except the Soviet President," Councillor Max Crabtree told the *Fylde Prepuce*. "The Prime Minister has already expelled some diplomats and frozen some of the Kremlin's financial assets, but we don't think those actions go far enough."

"I want to make it clear to the Russian dictator that Blackpool means business. I'm farting fire," he added.

secret

At a hastily convened meeting of the top secret BOBRA Blackpool Crisis Response committee, the mayor set out a series of punitive measures designed to hit the Russian President where it hurts. "Make no mistake, if Putin ever comes on holiday to Blackpool, he'll be left in no doubt what we think about his KGB assassination squads," he said.

The stiff sanctions against the USSR leader include:

in order to make clear to him that assassination attempts by foreign powers will not be tolerated on Blackpool soil.

- *He will not be allowed to purchase the popular Golden Rider 7-day unlimited travel tram pass. Instead, he will be required to pay full fare for each journey he takes*
- *Despite being 65, he will be refused a 'Cheapy Tuesday' pensioner's special meal deal at Taylor's Fish & Chips on St Anne's Road*
- *The number of tokens required to win a prize at all seafront Bingo halls will be doubled for Mr Putin*
- *On the North Pier Wild West Sharpshooter range, he will be given a rifle with the sights bent to the side even more than usual*
- *On the Hook-a-Duck stall, he will be given a stick with a loop on that is half the size of everyone else's*

The mayor also announced that he had summoned the Russian Ambassador Alexander Vladimirovich Yakovenko to the Town Hall

EXCLUSIVE!

"Mr Yavovenko's going to leave these council offices with more than a flea in his ear, believe me," said Councillor Crabtree. "I'm going to rip him a new arsehole."

"That's when he comes. I've left a message at the embassy but he hasn't got back to me yet," he added.

estate

Meanwhile, the town's bed & breakfast proprietors announced their own special measures against the Kremlin despot.

saloon

Chairwoman of the Fylde Coast Landladies' Association Mrs Edna Travis said: "We have a strict rule that all guests must vacate bed and breakfast premises during the day."

"However, we are quite lenient, and will occasionally let people back into the house for a few minutes, perhaps if they've forgotten their purse, they need the toilet or they have been taken seriously ill."

"But we won't show such kindness to Mr Putin," she continued. "He's out the door at eight sharp and he's not coming back in till five. No ifs, no buts."

gaol

"If he thinks he can waltz in here at half past ten to get his umbrella or do a number two after poisoning all them people, he's got another think coming," Mrs Travis added.

Tinker, Tailor, Soldier...STAR!

Guy Burgess, Kim Philby, Don Maclean, Sir Anthony Blunt... all household names who turned out to be Russian spies. Nobody suspected they were traitors because they were hiding in plain sight as upstanding members of the British Establishment. And it's a sobering thought that today, decades later, many of our favourite celebrities could also be KGB agents, working to undermine our society. We phoned up a selection of Britain's best-loved showbiz stars and put a simple question to them... *Are you a Russian spy?*

Sean Connery,
James Bond actor

"I played a British spy in seven Bond films, so I've certainly got plenty of experience in the world of subterfuge and espionage! Seriously, though, I am happy to confirm that I am definitely not a Russian spy. But of course, if I was a Russian spy, that's exactly what I would say, so I'm afraid you'll have to draw your own conclusions as to whether I actually am one or not."

Carol Vorderman,
Former celebrity

"I'm not a Russian spy as far as I know, but I did go to Cambridge University, so it's perfectly possible that I was recruited during my undergraduate days and brainwashed to become a 'sleeper' agent for the KGB. In fact, I may have unwittingly spent my entire time on *Countdown* passing 9-letter coded messages concerning the whereabouts of Britain's fleet of Trident nuclear submarines to the Kremlin. I certainly hope that wasn't the case, but now I've thought about it a bit, I'm quite concerned that I have betrayed my country."

Joe Swash,
King of the Jungle

"I'm not sure. Off the top of my head, I don't think I am, but don't quote me on that. You'd have to ask my agent, as she deals with all that stuff. If I'm not a Russian spy, I'd be quite happy to do it. I've eaten a kangaroo's cock and balls in the jungle, so obviously I'll try anything if the money's right."

Penelope Keith,
Snooty actress

"Certainly not. I would never spy for a foreign power and betray the country of my birth. Having said that, the life of a KGB secret agent does sound jolly exciting. All those clandestine meetings on park benches, using secret codewords and garrotting people with piano wire hidden up one's cuffs sound like a terrific wheeze."

Chris Kamara,
Red card-missing Sky Soccer pundit

"Funny you should ask, but yes, I am a Russian spy answering directly to President Putin, working under the codename "Red Card". But before you rush to call me a traitor, what my Kremlin paymasters don't know is that I am actually a double agent. I am feeding everything I know about Russian Intelligence directly to Whitehall, whilst the information I feed to Moscow is largely bogus but peppered with enough harmless true information to make it seem credible. But keep this under your hat."

DEAD MAN WALKING!

ADerbyshire man last night soiled his trousers with fear as he told how Soviet secret police assassins were hunting him down. "They done that bloke in Wiltshire and I am next on the Kremlin's list," said Cromford Hodthorpe, 62. "It's only a matter of time before Putin's KGB goons track me down and rub me out."

By our Russian Spy Correspondant Aleksandr Kolchinsky

"They want me dead because I know too much," the 16-stone bachelor told us. "I was innocently browsing the internet one day looking for some pictures of some things when I came across a pop-up advert illustrated with a picture of a cheerleader doing the splits."

moon

"When I clicked on it, it took me to a page with a link to a story about how the Russians had built a secret base on the moon. I read the headline in passing, but I didn't bother reading the whole article as I'd got another pop-up advert with a live webcam showing one of the things I'd originally been looking for."

"I didn't give the Russians on the moon thing another thought until the KGB turned up at the bus garage the very next day and tried to kill me."

starr

Hodthorpe explained: "I'd knocked off early to have my dinner. I don't go in the canteen any more following a misunderstanding regarding the works lottery syndicate a few years ago."

"I'd run that syndicate faultlessly for fifteen years, collecting a pound without fail off everyone in the depot each week. Then, would you believe it, the one time I forgot to buy the tickets, our numbers came up for an eight million quid jackpot win. Since that day, I usually eat alone in one of the buses," he said.

mitchell

"But on this particular day, as I opened the Tupperware box containing my packed lunch, I recoiled in horror and disgust. Kremlin goons had got there before me and put a dog dirt in with my corned beef sandwiches."

bonham

"They must have been hoping I'd just reach in and take a bite without looking, then die of dog dirt poisoning," said Hodthorpe.

"My blood ran cold as I realised just how close I had come to a horrible death."

KGB is out to get me, says Glossop bus depot cleaner

"I had to throw the top sandwich away, as the turd had been sat on it, and it could have become contaminated. As I ate the rest of my lunch, I looked across towards the canteen window to see my workmates pointing and laughing at me," he continued. "I went over to ask them if they'd seen anyone putting a dog dirt in my lunchbox, but they said they hadn't seen a thing."

"It was clear that the agents had put the frighteners on them. They were too scared to speak out in case they found themselves on Putin's assassination list too, for snitching."

It had been a brush with death that was too close for comfort, and Cromford knew that he was a marked man. He didn't have to wait long before the Russian death squad launched their next audacious attempt on his life.

"It was a couple of weeks after the dog mess incident, and I was in the sitting room, looking at some things on the internet when the hit men struck again," he told us.

watts

"Suddenly, without any warning, half a housebrick came flying through the window, missing my head by mere yards. There was broken glass everywhere as I ran to the front door to see who was responsible."

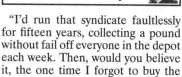

Kremlin goons had got there before me and put a dog dirt in with my corned beef sandwiches

"The assassins had clearly fled the scene seconds after their murder attempt. The only witness to the attack was my next door neighbour, who happened to be standing on my front lawn."

amperes

"Unfortunately, he wasn't speaking to me at the time following a misunderstanding that morning when I had been innocently looking through my binoculars at sparrows in his garden from behind my bedroom curtains, while his teenage daughter was sunbathing on the patio," said Hodthorpe. "He had spotted me and put two and two together to make five."

"As I turned to go back inside, I noticed that the KGB had sprayed the word 'Nonce' on my front door. I don't speak any foreign languages, so I can only assume it is a Russian word meaning 'Enemy of the State' or something like that. It certainly made my blood run cold when I saw it, I can tell you."

"At that moment, I cursed myself for clicking on that website about the Russians building a secret base on the Moon. Putin was clearly out to get me, and I was now a marked man," he added.

It occurred to Hodthorpe that he might be be safer off in a crowd. Out and about in public, he thought the Russian assassins would be more wary of launching a hit in front of witnesses, so right away he got in his car and headed to his local amusement arcade.

"I'm not exactly flavour of the month there, following a few misunderstandings over the years where I have accidentally put washers

Bus terminal: Cromford nearly died when packed lunch was contaminated with dog shite.

Woof justice: Heavily disguised hit squad made horrific murder attempt at dog track.

Putin on the hits: Russian President ordered audacious assassination attempts.

> ❝ **They were wearing rubber Mission Impossible-style masks, posing as two thugs who work for an unlicensed bookie to whom I had owed fifty quid for several months** ❞

in the fruities and fallen and bumped the tuppenny waterfalls, also by accident, on a number of occasions."

"In fact, last time I was there I was thrown out after trying to recover a jammed coin from the change machine using a coat-hanger with a bit of chewing gum on the end."

"I was told to get out and never come back, but nevertheless the arcade still felt safer than staying in my house. At home, it was only a matter of time before the Russians turned up again and succeeded where they had failed before."

"The boss clocked me as soon as I walked in. Picking up a Stanley knife that he keeps under the counter in his booth, he walked past me and out into the car park. A minute later, he came back in, threatened me with the knife, and told me to sling my hook," said Hodthorpe.

"I had been in the safe haven of the amusements for less than a minute. It clearly hadn't been enough time for me to have thrown the Kremlin agents off my scent, because when I went out to my car, I found that, acting on Vladimir Putin's direct orders, they had slashed all four of my tyres."

> ❝ **There was nothing wrong with that brake cable. I had fitted myself in 1986, so it had clearly been tampered with by the KGB hit squad** ❞

"They must have been planning on me driving off, spinning out of control, and perishing in a ball of flames. It would have looked like an accident; the perfect hit," he told us.

"The arcade boss had been out in the car park at the exact time it happened, so he must have seen everything. But as he stood there with his Stanley knife, grinning and sticking twos-up at me, he had clearly taken the decision not to get involved," said Hodthorpe.

"And who can blame him for not wanting to add himself to the KGB's sinister hit-list?"

talbot

But horrifyingly, Hodthorpe's ordeal was not yet over. As he gingerly set off for the pub at 4mph in his 1984 Talbot Solara, he suddenly felt the brakes give way. "As I rolled to a halt against the front of a shop, I realised what had happened," he told us. "The assassins had sawn through the brake cable too."

"I know for a fact that there was nothing wrong with that cable. It was a heavy-duty bus cable that I had fitted myself in 1986, so it had clearly been tampered with by the KGB hit squad," said Hodthorpe.

weller

"As I reversed out of the shopfront, my blood ran cold once again. I set off for the pub, this time using the handbrake, reflecting that, although I had dodged another Russian bullet, my luck couldn't hold forever."

Hodthorpe couln't have known how right his premonition was, because less than 24 hours later, the Russians made yet another attempt on his life. And although they didn't succeed in killing him, they did put him in hospital with serious, life-changing injuries.

"Once again thinking there might be safety in numbers, I'd gone to my local dog track for an evening meeting. Spending a few hours watching the greyhounds chase the hare round the track was a welcome relief from the stress of being pursued by the KGB. Even as I cheered on my dogs from the stand, I kept out a wary eye for Russian-looking heavies bent on doing me harm," he told us.

lee

"But I hadn't counted on the hit-men being masters of disguise as well as ruthless, trained killers. Suddenly, I felt a hand on my shoulder and turned to see them standing right behind me. They were wearing rubber *Mission Impossible*-style masks, posing as two thugs who work for an unlicensed bookie to whom I had owed fifty quid for several months."

"I knew it couldn't really be them, because just a few weeks before, the bookie had given me a bit of extra time to pay him off, and I was pretty sure I hadn't gone too far past the deadline yet," said Hodthorpe.

"They appeared very convincing in their disguises; they didn't have Russian accents. To hear them threatening me, you would have sworn they came from Glossop."

tommy

The heavy Politburo exterminators frogmarched the hapless bus cleaner round the back of the kennels, where they set about his lower legs with a crowbar. He told us: "I don't remember much about the assassination attempt itself. I suppose they must have left me for dead when I blacked out, because I woke up in the ambulance with two broken shins and badly bruised knees."

mini

Hodthorpe spent the next three weeks in hospital recovering from his injuries. And although the doctors have put him on the panel for six months, his bosses at the bus garage have told him they won't hold his job open that long. He told us: "I can only conclude that my line manager at *Go!Glossop* has been leant on by the Kremlin."

"Putin's going to get me one way or the other. I'm a dead man walking," he added.

We rang the Russian Embassy to ask if there was a KGB hit squad operating in the Glossop area, with orders from the Kremlin to assassinate Cromford Hodthorpe. A spokesman told us: "This is the Russian Embassy. Press one for visa enquiries, two for homeland affairs, three for general travel enquiries, and four for all other business."

THE RECENT attempted murder of Russian double agent Sergei Skripal in the middle of a genteel Wiltshire cathedral town has set alarm bells ringing from Land's End to John O'Groats. The thought that squads of ruthless Soviet assassins are operating with impunity on the British mainland means that we all have to be extra-vigilant when we're out and about or going to Zizzis. But would YOU know if the bloke next door was a member of one of Putin's sinister crack death squads? We ask the question...

Is YOUR Neighbour a KGB KILLER?

Answer the questions below a, b, or c and tot up your score to find out.

1 IT'S a nice hot day, and your neighbour is sitting out on his front lawn in a deckchair. What is he wearing?

a. Bermuda shorts, a vest, and a knotted hankie on his head

b. Socks, sandals and a pair of extremely high-waisted 1970s bathing trunks

c. A floor-length dark grey great-coat, leather gloves and a black bear-fur cossack hat

2 WHILE out walking your dog in the local park, you see your neighbour sitting on a bench, holding a briefcase. You sit down next to him for a breather. What does he say to you?

a. "Turned out nice again, hasn't it?"

b. "Out walking the dog, are you?"

c. "The geese are flying south because Spring comes early in Berlin."

3 IT'S a windy day and your neighbour's wheelie bin has blown over, spilling some of its contents onto your shared drive. What does it contain?

a. Empty bean tins, plastic milk cartons and used nappies

b. Empty fish finger boxes, carrot peelings and an unopened packet of out-of-date mince

c. A hazmat suit, a gasmask and a copy of last week's Pravda

4 YOU pop round next door to deliver a leaflet about stopping a local wind farm and your neighbour invites you in for a cuppa. What does he put in the teapot?

a. Two tea bags

b. Three heaped teaspoons of loose tea

c. Two tea bags and a glowing phial of Polonium 210

5 YOUR neighbour is doing DIY late in the evening, making a lot of noise when you have to be up for work in the morning. You go round to remonstrate. How does he respond?

a. He apologises, saying he didn't realise it was so late and he will finish putting up his shelves in the morning

b. He mumbles a rather unconvincing apology and says he'll be finished in five minutes, if that's alright with you

c. He drags you up to the top floor of his house, pins a typed suicide note to the front of your pyjamas, and pushes you out of the window

How did you do?

MOSTLY A: Relax, chances are your neighbour is not a KGB killer. He probably makes his living doing something completely innocent, such as driving a bus, selling Venetian blinds or working at a key-cutting and footwear repair franchise, such as Timpsons or Shoe Doctor UK.

MOSTLY B: On the surface, your neighbour doesn't seem to be a Russian spy, but he may be a "sleeper" or working for the Soviets under deep cover. Keep your suspicions to yourself; if he suspects you are about to unmask him to the authorities, he may decide to eliminate you. To be on the safe side, wear a bulletproof vest at all times and keep some anti-radiation pills in your top pocket.

MOSTLY C: Oh dear, your neighbour is almost certainly spying for the Russkies. It's no use going to the police, as you will be under 24-hour surveillance. Nonchalantly leave your house and make your way to London via a circuitous route, changing your clothing and mode of transport several times. Once in London, go to the MI6 building, ask to speak to M, and report your neighbour. If M's not in, ask if you can speak to Q instead or leave a message with Miss Moneypenny.

The Russians are Coming!

RUSSIAN MEN on average can only manage two or three pushes before climaxing during intercourse. That's according to a new report put together by a leading sex expert.

Oxford professor **Rex Strepsils** claims that the vast majority of Soviet males lack staying power. "Believe you me, those poor Russkies are up and over like a pan of milk," he told us. "It's pitiful to see."

Professor Strepsils, who is not affiliated with the town's University in any way, based his study on a DVD entitled *1001 Moneyshots*, a compilation featuring heavily edited ejaculation footage from Russian porn films that he found under a hedge at the top of the Banbury Road.

telly

"I couldn't believe it when I got back to my bedist and put it on the telly," he continued. "When you think all these blokes are adult movie professionals, it just beggars belief how quickly they were chucking their muck, time after time after time."

Russian dolls: Some Soviet crumpet yesterday.

"Not one of them lasted longer than about five seconds before he went off. Then the next one would come on and it was the same story all over again," he said. "No wonder all them beautiful Russian women are desperate to come over here and get banged by us British blokes who are famous for our stamina between the sheets."

Reds all on hair trigger, says top sexologist

Rushin' roulette: Reds shoot bolt too quickly, says prof.

And Professpr Strepsils says he knows what he's talking about. He told us: "My own girlfriend, Tatyana or Svetlana or something, is a beautiful Russian woman and she's sick of having it off with these two-push Ivans. I haven't met her yet, because she's in Minsk, but she can't wait to come over here and get properly seen to by a real man who can keep it up for a reasonable length of time."

"Certainly long enough to hopefully bring her off anyway," he continued.

yul

"I've sent her the plane fare over via Western Union. Three times actually, because the first two lots got lost in the post, but once she arrives she's going to get a taste of what she's been missing, believe you me."

"Ooh yes, she's going to get it alright. Right up her, and more than two pushes, and all. You just see if she doesn't, the dirty bitch," Professor Strepsils added.

mr. LOGIC hmm...

HE'S AN ACUTE LOCALISED BODILY SMART IN THE RECTAL AREA.

...AND FOR MY NEXT TRICK... COULD I HAVE A VOLUNTEER FROM THE AUDIENCE, PLEASE..?

YOU THERE, SIR... YES, YOU... COME UP HERE. BIG HAND, PLEASE, LADIES AND GENTLEMEN, FOR OUR MEMBER OF THE AUDIENCE!

...AND YOUR NAME IS..? LAWRENCE LOGIC.

NICE TO MEET YOU, LAWRENCE.

NOW FIRSTLY, WE HAVE *NEVER* MET BEFORE, HAVE WE?

hmmm...

YES. WE HAVE DEFINITELY MET BEFORE.

ERM... HAVE WE?! WHEN..?

SIX SECONDS AGO, WHEN YOU INVITED ME ONTO THE STAGE AND SHOOK MY HAND.

THAT DEFINITELY HAPPENED BEFORE YOU ASKED ME TO CONFIRM THAT WE HADN'T MET BEFORE.

YES, BUT I MEANT BEFORE THAT...!

OH, I SEE.

hmm... LET ME SEE... AS OF TODAY, I AM 37 YEARS, 6 MONTHS, 12 DAYS, 8 HOURS, 16 MINUTES AND 43 SECONDS OLD...

...44 SECONDS...45 SECONDS...

ASSUMING THAT I ENCOUNTER, ON AVERAGE, SAY, 8 DIFFERENT PERSONS EACH DAY, THAT WOULD MEAN THAT I HAVE MET OVER THE COURSE OF MY LIFE TO DATE, AT LEAST 109,896 PEOPLE...

THE CURRENT UK POPULATION IS 65.64 MILLION MEANING THAT THERE IS A 0.167422% CHANCE THAT I HAVE MET A PARTICULAR RANDOMLY SELECTED INDIVIDUAL...

THUS, IN ANSWER TO YOUR ORIGINAL QUERY, I CAN NOT -WITH ABSOLUTE CERTAINTY- CONFIRM THAT WE HAVE NEVER MET BEFORE. HOWEVER, THERE IS A PROBABILITY OF 99.832578% THAT THIS IS THE CASE.

WELL... THAT'S GOOD ENOUGH FOR ME, LADIES AND GENTLEMEN...HEHE.

BOO!

FIX!

NOW LAWRENCE, I'D LIKE YOU TO PICK A CARD... ANY CARD YOU LIKE... DON'T LET ME SEE IT...

NOW SHOW IT TO THE AUDIENCE... MAKE SURE THEY CAN SEE IT...

PUT IT BACK INTO THE PACK... ANYWHERE YOU LIKE...

NOW LAWRENCE, BE HONEST, THERE'S NO WAY I COULD KNOW WHAT YOUR CARD WAS, IS THERE..?

hmm...

THERE ARE, IN FACT, A VERY LARGE NUMBER OF MEANS BY WHICH YOU COULD KNOW THE IDENTITY OF MY CARD... FOR INSTANCE, YOU MAY BE USING A MARKED DECK OR AN AUDIENCE STOOGE...

...YOU COULD HAVE UTILISED ANY ONE OF SEVERAL WELL-KNOWN 'SLEIGHT-OF-HAND' TECHNIQUES TO GET ME TO PICK A PARTICULAR CARD, FOR EXAMPLE THE ELIMINATION FORCE, THE RIFFLE FORCE, THE STOP FORCE...

...IN FACT, SINCE YOU ARE A PROFESSIONAL CONJUROR, I WOULD BE VERY SURPRISED INDEED IF YOU HADN'T PRACTISED SOME FORM OF FURTIVE SUBTERFUGE IN ORDER TO ASCERTAIN EXACTLY THE IDENTITY OF THE CARD I PICKED...

OKAY THEN, LAWRENCE. LET'S FORGET THE CARD TRICK, SHALL WE..? I'VE GOT SOMETHING MUCH MORE SPECTACULAR IN MIND...

SHORTLY...

NOW, CAN YOU CONFIRM TO THE LADIES AND GENTLEMEN THAT THERE IS NO WAY YOU CAN UNDO THOSE IRON MANACLES AND ESCAPE FROM THIS CHINESE WATER CELL OF DEATH BEFORE YOU RUN OUT OF OXYGEN IN EXACTLY 60 SECONDS..?

hmm-ubble-blubble...

RICKY GERVAIS
versus GOD

HELLO READERS, I'VE JUST RECEIVED YET ANOTHER TRUCKLOAD OF **ROYALTY CHEQUES** FOR THE OFFICE! I'M FUCKING **MINTED**, ME!

SOLID GOLD BATH

SORRY TO INTERRUPT, SIR, BUT IT'S **GOD** ON THE PHONE. HE'S LOOKING FOR COMPLIMENTARY TICKETS FOR YOUR NEXT STAND-UP SHOW.

OH, NOT **HIM** AGAIN!

HELLO, RICKY, I'M A HUGE FAN! **LOVED** YOU IN THE OFFICE. ESPECIALLY THAT **FUNNY DANCE.** I WAS JUST WONDERING IF YOU HAD SOME SPARE TICKETS...

WELL, GOD, OBVIOUSLY I'D **LOVE** TO HELP OUT, BUT...

YOU DON'T EXIST. SO... **GET KNOTTED!!**

YOU **NOTIONAL NON-ENTITY!**

IDEA FOR SHOW... **KARL PILKINGTON** IS REPEATEDLY FIRED OUT OF A **CIRCUS CANNON,** WHILE **STEPHEN MERCHANT** AND I FLING SHIT AT HIM AND CACKLE.

SHORTLY...

IDEA FOR JOKE FOR GOLDEN GLOBES AWARDS... I LIKE A NICE STEAK AS MUCH AS THE NEXT MAN, UNLESS THE NEXT MAN IS **JEREMY CLARKSON!**

DING DONG!

SOLID GOLD THRONE

JEEVES! THE DOOR!

SORRY TO INTERRUPT AGAIN, SIR, BUT **GOD** IS HERE. HE WAS WONDERING IF YOU COULD POSSIBLY SIGN HIS **EXTRAS** DVD COVER.

OH, FOR FU-

YOU WERE BRILLIANT IN EXTRAS, RICKY!

BRILLIANT? YEP! GUILTY AS CHARGED! BUT, UNFORTUNATELY...

I'M NOT SIGNING ANY DVD COVERS FOR AN **IMAGINARY CONSTRUCT.**

BOOT!

SO GET LOST, YOU **FICTITIOUS FREELOADER!**

YEAH! COME BACK WHEN YOU'VE GOT YOUR OWN STAND-UP SHOW, YOU **APOCRYPHAL ALSO-RAN!**

IDEA FOR SERIES... **FAKE DOCUMENTARY** OF ME, BEHIND THE SCENES, PLAYING **MYSELF,** PLAYING **DAVID BRENT**... IT'S **THE OFFICE** MEETS **EXTRAS.**

CLICK!

BRILLIANT, SIR!

I KNOW, BUT SHUT IT, JEEVES I'M BUSY WRITING AN ARTICLE ABOUT WHY ATHEISTS ARE SIMPLY **BETTER PEOPLE.**

OF COURSE, SIR. QUITE RIGHT TOO.

RING! RING!

PHONE FOR YOU, SIR!

IT'S NOT THAT **GOD** AGAIN IS IT?

NO, SIR, IT'S **NETFLIX!**

HMMM... YES...OK... WELL, THAT SOUNDS FINE. FINE. OK... RIGHT... SURE... OK...THANKS FOR CALLING.

YEEESSSSSS! 14 MILLION DOLLARS FOR TWO STAND-UP SPECIALS! GET IN!!

AT LAST, I'LL BE ABLE TO COVER MY ENTIRE HOUSE IN SOLID GOLD!!

THAT EVENING...

JOKE FOR STAND-UP SPECIAL... I LIKE **KANYE WEST** AS MUCH AS THE NEXT MAN... UNLESS THE NEXT MAN IS **KANYE WE-**

RING! RING!

I'LL GET THE PHONE FOR YOU, SIR...

WHAT THE--?! NO WAY!! YOU CAN'T DO THAT TO ME!!

THOSE BASTARDS! THEY'VE JUST **CANCELLED** MY NETFLIX SPECIAL!

THEY'VE HAD TO CLOSE THE THEATRE BECAUSE A PLAGUE OF LOCUSTS AND FROGS GOT IN... AND THEY'VE FOUND **ANOTHER** STAND-UP SHOW THEY'RE GOING TO BROADCAST INSTEAD.

I LIKE MONEY AS MUCH AS THE NEXT MAN.

GOD ON NETFLIX

UNLESS THE NEXT MAN IS **RICKY GERVAIS!!**

97

LETTERbOCKS

Viz Comic, P.O. Box 841 Whitley Bay, NE26 9EQ : letters@viz.co.uk

I WONDER if Trappist monks who take a vow of silence are allowed to text each other, or go on Facebook and Twitter. I suppose it depends on whether it's talking or communicating that God doesn't like them to do.

Torbjorn Elstree, Goole

AS a joke I bought my wife some sourdough bread, yet it turned out to be fresh and she enjoyed it. I was forced to put a brick through the bakery window for being mis-sold this product. Yet it's me up in court next week whilst the baker gets off scot-free.

David Craik, Hull

IT is a sad reflection on the state of our overcrowded and unreliable rail service that spies can no longer fight on trains. In the old days, this Sergei Skripal business would have been sorted out with a prolonged bout of dramatic hand to hand combat on the 11.30 from London to Salisbury and nothing more would have been said about the whole affair.

Dan, Deal

LOOKS like the local beautification parlour does a bit more than just buff toenails.

Lord S, Hastings

I DON'T know why people complain about there being fewer police on the streets to deal with crime these days. I watched an episode of *Police, Camera, Action* the other night and about eight police cars turned up to arrest a man caught pissing in a shop doorway in Newcastle.

Bartram Golightly, Derby

STAR LETTER

I'LL never understand Americans' obsession with tickertape parades for their so-called heroes. Surely the poor devils who have to pick up all the paper the next day are the real heroes. In fact, I think they should have a tickertape parade for those people the day after that.

Terrence Nutball, Deal

WHO do these farmers think they are, driving their tractors and heavy machinery around on the public roads? No doubt they'd be the first to complain if we all decided to drive our cars through their crops and across their fields. Yet again, it's one rule for the farmer and another for the ordinary motorist.

Milton Ramsbottom, Hexham

I SEE a lot of moaning in the press about online bullying. When I was a kid I used to get the shit kicked out of me by a gang of boys on my walk home from school, and I'd have loved it if they'd all just called me a twat on Facebook instead. Bullying victims these days don't know how good they've got it.

J Kenny, Thrapston

I WALKED past my local Poundland and was astonished to see Pot Noodles on sale for 50p. How this retailer has the audacity to call itself 'Poundland' when it clearly has no intention of sticking to its own pricing policy is beyond me. I have no desire to be hoodwinked, thank-you very much, so in future I shall purchase my Pot Noodles in PoundStretcher where they are two for a pound.

Joley Green-Giant, Truro

ON page 76, there is a letter from Egbert Henge of Penge, expressing potential embarrassment in the event that his postcode was P155 OFF. Well rest assured Mr Henge, because the first two characters of UK postcodes are always two letters, never a letter and a number, so this would never happen. You might have a cause of concern however, if your postcode was PI55 0FF. Perhaps this might be a good time to re-introduce "Pedants' Corner." You could even call it "Pedant's Corner" to encourage responses.

Pete Ring, Lancing

I FOR one am right behind the women's movement against sexual harassment in the workplace. It has gone on long enough. Just because a woman has got a nice, smackable arse is no excuse for this kind of behaviour.

Frank Cardboard, Luton

I WAS very surprised to hear that the Pope has declared that Hell doesn't actually exist. He's obviously never been shopping in Morrison's supermarket in Droitwich on a fucking Saturday morning.

Stu Mandry, Droitwich Spa

I DON'T see why blind people have to be registered. Lord knows they have problems enough without having to suffer the stigma and shame of being put on some kind of register.

Toblerone Chocmonocly, Leeds

THE other day I brought home a cup of coffee from the local cafe. My wife observed that the cafe was now using black cups, where they used to serve their coffee in brown cups. I countered that the cafe had been using black cups for quite a while and she admitted that it had been some time since she had bought coffee there. I'd be interested to learn how other readers keep the spark alive in their marriages.

Bill Harrington, Letchworth

ACCORDING to today's news, there are 502 public statues of historical figures in the country, but only 80 of these commemorate women. I can't help but think that the ladies haven't been pulling their weight over the past few hundred years. Come on girls, time to raise your game.

Cole Trickle, B'ham

ToP TiPs

OWLS. Fool people into believing you are wise by simply keeping very still and looking as though you are thinking hard. Even if you are actually only thinking about how stuffed you still are after that water vole you scoffed half an hour ago.

Jane Hoole Garner, St Ives

LIBRARIANS. Save time shushing people by simply releasing air from a bicycle tyre each time a patron makes too much noise.

SCREENWRITERS. Always ensure that it's pissing down at any funeral. It's a handy tool for dramatic effect, and I don't think anyone else has thought of it before.

Albert Speilberg, Hull

SEA farers. Don't put your life jacket on until after you've fallen in the water, otherwise you won't feel the benefit.

Nick Lyon, Truro

BILLY Grayson, Bundaberg QUORN pieces make an ideal chicken substitute for people who have never tasted chicken before.

T. O'Neill, Glasgow

toptips@viz.co.uk

ON page 76, you printed a scene from The Bayeux Tapestry showing the underhand behaviour of the French. This reminded me of my own viewing of the tapestry, which was ruined for me by unnecessary foul language stitched in it, as bold as brass. Well I for one do not welcome its arrival to these shores, and I would discourage your readers from going to see it.

Gary Price, email

CLIFF Richard says the BBC caused him "profound and lasting damage" in covering the police raid on his house. That's as may be, but after 30 years of *Mistletoe and Wine* every Christmas, I have very limited sympathy.

Steve Crouch, P'borough

IF Olly Murs thinks he can just appear on my telly and not get turned over, he's very much mistaken.

Jerry Lecherous, Stockton

APPARENTLY giraffes only sleep for two hours a day. Isn't it about time that these wildlife film makers left them the fuck alone and let them get some decent shut-eye?

Egbert Crowsfoot, Tring

IT'S all very well this move to get rid of glass and plastic bottles from the oceans, but what hope does that leave stranded castaways, as they'll have nothing to send their messages in? I don't think these so-called ecological boffins have properly thought this through.

Ian Smith, Livingston

IF there is such a thing as Insect School, then I reckon wasps would be the bullies, ants would be the swots and slugs would be ones that brought notes in for PE. And you might find a few flies smoking behind the bike sheds.

Desulphdaz, M'brough

I'M not particularly interested in the Royal family, but I think the BBC coverage has become a bit unsympathetic to Ms Markle recently.

Mike Tatham, St Andrews

15:47 Fri, 4 May

BBC News 14:25
Royal wedding: Meghan Markle's fat...
Top News

I KEEP having this nightmare that Cilla Black came to Holyhead when I was about 7 years old and made us sing a song called *'Hooray for Holyhead!'* while dancing along the main high street with the local councillor. I went to a psychiatrist and she said it was the most stupid thing she'd ever heard. Yet when I checked up on YouTube it was actually true. Have any of your other readers had nightmares about Cilla Black that turned out to be true?

Keith Queef, Llanllyfhi

WHENEVER you see vets on telly, they always wear shirts with the sleeves rolled up as more than likely at some point in the programme they will be elbow deep in a cow's hoop. Why don't these people simply wear short-sleeved shirts in the first place?

Gus, Paisley

I THINK people from the olden days were more clever than us because they would all go to a Shakespeare play every Saturday. I've only been once in my life, and even then I was forced to go by the school. All I remember is that there was some bloke in a crown and some seriously fucking ugly women. And it was about as understandable as a Glaswegian hen party.

Tonka, Pontardawe

"THREE -and-a-half billion women on the planet, and no two are the same, so why would their pads be?"** says the Always advert, before presenting us with a grand total of four types of pad.

Christina Martin, Bexhill

WHY is it that Londoners have their phone boxes decorated with all pictures of nude women when up here in Newcastle, and indeed everywhere else in the country for that matter, our phone boxes are plain? We pay our tax too.

Hampton Crumbhorn, Newcastle

WHY do scientists call the event that created the universe 'The BIG Bang'? It was the first thing that ever happened in space and time, so they wouldn't have had anything to compare it to. Consequently, they wouldn't have known whether it was a big bang, a small bang, or something in between. Surely 'The Bang' would be a more suitable name? If we can't get the basics right, we're never going to get to the stars.

Dave Gibbs, Mowbray

Oh Heavenly Father

Dear Justin,

I READ in the Bible recently that we are all the Lord's children. Does this mean that every human being on Earth should send God a card on Father's Day?

Barnaby Buddha-Monk, Hull

Justin says: The Good Book does indeed state that God is the Father - but it also clearly adds that He is the Son and the Holy Spirit, too. Therefore, since God is both your father AND your son, you should technically be sending each other Father's Day cards. But don't worry, that's only metaphorical. As his biological offspring, Jesus is the only person that needs to make the effort for the Almighty on the third Sunday in June. He probably sends Him a nice card and perhaps takes Him for a day out at the footy or a Dads 'n' Lads Tank Driving Experience.

Dear Justin,

OVER the past few weeks, I have been hearing rather severe prophetic voices in my head, instructing me to take my firstborn son to the top of a hill and sacrifice him to the Lord God's glory. However, Father's Day is fast approaching and my firstborn son tends to get me very good gifts - last year, for instance, he bought me a subscription to *Top Gear* magazine, and the year before that he gave me a six-disc Boz Scaggs box set. I was wondering, therefore, if God would mind if I waited until after June 17th to slaughter my son, just in case he's got something equally good up his sleeve this year?

Nigel Killah-Priest, Herts

Justin says: God works in mysterious ways, Nigel, and if He is instructing you to kill your son up a hill then there must be a decent reason for it. However, between me, you and the gatepost, given His past form I've got a feeling that God might be just testing you and he'll tell you to stop just before you put the knife in. I wouldn't be at all surprised if your firstborn is still around on Father's day and you'll be in for another fab pressie off him.

Dear Justin,

FORTY YEARS ago, I gave my father a 'World's Best Dad' mug for Father's Day. Six weeks later, he ran off with his secretary, taking all my mother's money, and even stealing the £3.45 I had in my piggy bank. I haven't seen him since. I realise the Ten Commandments condemn bearing false witness as a deadly sin, but I honestly believed my father was the World's Best Dad at the time of purchasing the mug. Do you think God is likely to punish me for this ultimately fraudulent and blasphemous drink container?

Dorothy Theodore-Unit, Scholes

Justin says: God does indeed take rather a dim view of lying, Dorothy, so I'm afraid that whilst your mug purchase was made in good faith, it still means that you are bound for the flames of Hell. On the bright side, it sounds like your father may be heading there, too, and so you will have all eternity to get back in touch with him and try to rebuild your relationship whilst you are both having your skin flayed ceaselessly from your bodies by Beelzebub's despicable legions.

HAVE YOU got a question about Father's Day that also relates some way or other to the Church of England? Why not write into Justin Welby's 'Oh, Heavenly Father', letters@viz.co.uk

I NOTICED recently that when I'm using a vegetable peeler to peel a carrot, I push the instrument away from me. However, when using the very same instrument to peel a potato, I draw it towards me. How about that?

Gary, West Brom

MAJOR MISUNDERSTANDING

QUEEN BEE-FY EGGO

UK & US in diplomatic stink over dropped gut

Queen: Guff.

One who smelt it, dealt it: McQuaid III and Queen, yesterday

AN international row has broken out between Great Britain and the United States after a high-level US diplomat accused the Queen of audibly passing wind during a formal banquet.

American consul **CYRUS MCQUAID III** told reporters that the 91-year-old monarch broke cover during the hot appetizer portion of a five-course sit-down meal at Windsor Castle yesterday.

"Her Majesty's butt sneeze sounded like a '65 Ford Mustang with a busted tailpipe," McQuaid told the *International Herald Tribune*. "I said to her: 'Your Majesty, I'll name that tune in one.'"

"The hum off that guff just about made my nose hairs curl," said McQuaid. "It was like pea soup that had been left on the stove top for about two and a half weeks, and I ain't even joshin'," he added.

issue

Other guests were quick to take issue with the American plenipotentiary's characterisation of the royal dinner table Exchange & Mart, variously describing its smell as

EXCLUSIVE!

like a dead badger whose innards had been exposed to the hot afternoon sun, a laundry hamper filled with nothing but John McCririck's used jockstraps and a dog's tongue.

British businessman Sir Lawrence Caviar-Bone, who was also present at the meal, acknowledged that her Majesty did indeed strike up the colliery band.

"We all heard the Queen step on a duck and it wasn't half minging," he told *The Times*. "But the stench was more like a soiled nappy mixed with Camembert."

"And it was a wet one," added Sir Lawrence anonymously. "Her majesty definitely dropped a bit of shopping in there."

brother

Meanwhile, etiquette experts criticised McQuaid's decision to make light of the situation with a

witty riposte. "One should never address a jocular comment to a member of the nobility following an arse bark," said Ingrid Pointless, Good Manners editor of *Debrett's Peerage*. "The correct response is to change the subject while discreetly wafting one's hand under the nose to disperse the tripey ronk."

mac

Unfortunately, it is feared that McQuaid's actions may have soured the already delicately poised state of transatlantic diplomatic relations.

The Prime Minister is understood to have sent an urgent letter to President Trump, requesting clarification on the matter, saying, in part, that the British Sovereign's anal announcements are not a matter on which US citizens, even those with diplomatic immunity, should make public comment.

Downing Street is not expecting an immediate reply from the Oval Office as the communiqué is said to be in excess of four paragraphs long with no pictures.

john holmes

But it is feared that, if the notoriously thin-skinned POTUS does eventually read the strongly worded letter, he may infer a veiled insult, as he is especially sensitive to issues relating to English flatulence after being made aware that his surname means 'fart' in Great Britain.

This is not the first international incident Mr McQuaid has precipitated. Franco-American relations were strained only last month when, as part of a trade delegation in Paris, the US emissary pointed out a dark pee spot on President **EMMANUEL MACRON'S** tan slacks after the French premier visited the toilet, commenting: "Wet penny in your pocket, eh Manny?"

101

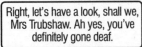

That's it! The nap! That's the missing piece of the jigsaw!

Aunt Meg, you're a genius!

Next day...

Come on, everyone. Eat up your Margherita pizzas with extra Edam.

Tsk.

Now, PC Brown! Arrest Mrs Churchill! And arrest her husband too!

What the...?

Eeeh!

Fancy.

Well I can arrest Mrs Churchill, Jack. But Mr Churchill isn't here.

That's right. He left about half an hour ago after he fitted Mr Wrigley's hearing aid.

It's a bobby dazzler, is this little gizmo. I can hear a pin drop now.

This is no hearing aid, you senile old idiot. It's a bent paperclip with a sugar puff stuck on the end.

My God, it is too.

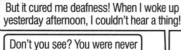

But it cured me deafness! When I woke up yesterday afternoon, I couldn't hear a thing!

Don't you see? You were never deaf! And I'll show you why...!

Gasp! Mr Churchill!

I... I think you'd better explain, Jack.

Bollocks.

Mr and Mrs Churchill have been in cahoots all along to con your residents into buying fake hearing aids. First of all, they bought a job lot of Edam cheeses from a local cash & carry...

CASH & CARRY

MEALS ON WHEE[L]

...The meals Mrs Churchill made for the residents were cheese-heavy, because her husband needed the wax for the next part of his sneaky plan, which began with him concealing himself in the bottom of the trolley...

...When the residents were full of cheese and dozing, Churchill snook out and pushed little balls of Edam wax into his victims' ears, rendering them deaf as a post when they woke up. Then he would re-conceal himself and wait for his wife to collect the trolley...

...The next morning, after being called in by Aunt Meg, he would pretend to examine the patient using a specially modified otoscope fitted with a small hook to pull out the wax plug...

...before fitting a dummy hearing aid.

Well well well. I've investigated some sick crimes in my time, but this takes the biscuit.

Mr and Mrs Churchill, I am arresting you for the excessive feeding of cheese to pensioners, the malicious pushing of wax into their ears, and the defraudulent purveying of sugar puff hearing aids.

I hope the judge throws the book at them.

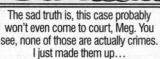
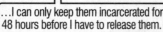

The sad truth is, this case probably won't even come to court, Meg. You see, none of those are actually crimes. I just made them up...

...I can only keep them incarcerated for 48 hours before I have to release them.

But don't worry. The steps down to the cells can be very slippy at this time of year. You'd be surprised how many miscreants end up taking a tumble.

Come on everyone, let's have a cup of tea and some cake to celebrate!

As long as it's not cheesecake!

Ho! Ho! Ho!

The End

the BROWN BOTTLE

8.30AM, AND BARRY BROWN IS ON HIS WAY TO WORK...

...WHEN SUDDENLY, A TERRIBLE COMMOTION GOES UP!

LEAVE US ALONE!

WHAA!

SCREAM!

WHAT'S THIS? I'D BETTER INVESTIGATE...

BARRY RUNS TOWARD A COACH STATION...

GASP! IT'S THE CASTLEMAINE XXXX-MEN!

THEY'RE BLOCKING THESE INNOCENT PASSENGERS FROM TRAVELLING... IF I'M NOT QUICK THE COACH WILL LEAVE WITHOUT THEM!

THIS SOUNDS LIKE A JOB FOR...

...THE BROWN BOTTLE!

QUICK AS A FLASH, BARRY HEADS FOR THE NEAREST CONVENIENCE TO CHANGE, NOT A MOMENT TO LOSE...

30p? HANG ON, LET ME CHECK...

NO, I'VE ONLY GOT TWENTY. WAIT THERE, I'LL GET SOME CHANGE FROM THE SHOP...

A TEN MINUTE QUEUE LATER...

SORRY LUV. WE DON'T GIVE CHANGE. YOU'LL HAVE TO BUY SUMMIT

B-B-BUT...!

GO ON. I'VE GOT CUSTOMERS WAITING...

---

15 MINUTES LATER...

FINALLY! I ONLY HOPE I'M NOT TOO LATE!

WHEN BARRY DRINKS A BOTTLE OF NEWCASTLE BROWN ALE, A REMARKABLE TRANSFORMATION OCCURS...

Click CLACK CLACK!

KA-BROON!

...FOR BARRY IS THE BROWN BOTTLE!

YAAAAH!

GAH! YAH... FUKKAAHH!

C'MAHN! I'LL FUCKINN TEK YAAHS!

SMACK!

GAAHYAH! Y' DIRTY BASTAAH!

RIIIP!!

AAH... THAT'S FUCKINN BERRAHH

AW, HAD ON... AH NEED A FUCKINN PISS...

GAH!

PUSH!

HEAVE!

LERRUS IN! LERRUS IN THIS FUCKINN BOGS!

YOU NEED THIRTY PENCE MATE

THORTY FUCKINN PEE? THEY CANN FUCKK OFF! F-FUCKIN' ROBBIN CUNTS!

AAH! F-FUCKIN' NECTAH

WHAA! STOP THIS!

LEAVE US ALONE!

WASSATT?

WITH HIS INSTINCTIVE BOTTLE SENSE TINGLING, THE BROWN BOTTLE GOES TO INVESTIGATE...

THE XXXX-MEN! F-F-FUCKINN HELL!

PLEASE, JUST LET US GO ON!

CALL THE POLICE, GERALD!

THE BROWN BOTTLE KNOWS WHAT TO DO! HE'LL USE HIS SUPER BOTTLE-BREATH TO BLOW THE BAD GUYS AWAY!

HURRRP!

BOOOOARGHHH!

GAAH! Y' FUCKKAHS! GO GO F-FUCKIN' BOTTLE LASER RAY!

OH DEAR!

URGHH! Y' F-FUCKIN' DIRTY BASTAAAD, BOTTLE!

LET'S GERROUT OF 'ERE!

RETREAT DOON THE FUCKIN TRAIN STATION!

EXCUSE ME, I'VE CALLED THE POLICE, THEY'RE ON THEIR WAY RIGHT NOW.

AYE, FF-FUCK YAAHS!

GERRIN! I'VE FF-F-FUCKIN' SAVED THE DAY AGEN!

QUICKLY DOROTHY, GET ON BEFORE THIS ONE STARTS TO GET HIS SPITTLE ON YOU

YAH BASSTAAAHS!

AND SO, THANKS TO THE VALIANT WORK OF THE BROWN BOTTLE, THE PASSENGERS WERE SAFE TO CONTINUE THEIR JOURNEY, WITHOUT FEAR FROM PISSED UP TROUBLEMAKERS...

RIGHT, IT'S NINE HOURS TO LONDON. LETS CRACK THESE TINS OPEN!

WAHAAAY!

PSS-TCHH! PSS-TCHHH! PSS-TCHHH!

DON'T MISS NEXT WEEK'S THRILLING ADVENTURE WHEN THE BROWN BOTTLE TAKES ON CIDERMAN

SEX, TIES AND VIDEOTAPE!

WE all love celebrity sex tapes. Whether we're sat alone squinting at grainy footage of Rob Lowe's buttocks or ogling Kim Kardashian's gyrating breasts on a friend's laptop, watching shoddily-filmed A-List skin flicks is a raunchy rite of passage for every red blooded male. And there isn't one among us who hasn't dreamed of making the transition from viewer to participant by bedding a famous Hollywood star on camera.

But for one man, that dream is very much a reality. Chingford bachelor **FRANK TESTES** has spent the past two decades working as a travelling necktie and cravat salesman in Essex and its surrounding counties. And in that time the randy 64-year-old has filmed himself enjoying **FULL SEXUAL INTERCOURSE** with some of Tinseltown's hottest babes!

"I know it sounds far-fetched, but it's absolutely true," chuckles 15-stone Frank. "I got into the tie-selling business because I love providing high quality neckwear at low, low prices. But I had no idea that one of the many perks of the job would be getting to have on-camera rumpy-pumpy with the planet's most iconic females."

Now Frank is set to tell his barely-believable story in an explosive autobiography, *Sex, Ties and Videotape!* In these exclusive extracts, the tie-selling lothario spills the beans about what happened when he hit the 'record' button after encountering some of Hollywood's sexiest stunners.

LIGHTS, PAMELA, ACTION!

Frank's foray into the celebrity sex tape world all started one day back in the mid-nineties when Frank had done a good bit of business in Chelmsford, selling two dozen 100% polyester twin packs on the Tattersall Way industrial park. And believe it or not, his first co-star was none other than sex tape queen **PAMELA ANDERSON**.

❝ It was a sunny day, and I was celebrating my sales with a few tins of Kestrel and a stroll along the Essex Waterway when I noticed a gigantic white superyacht moored in among all the houseboats at the end of the Heybridge Basin.

Thinking the owner must have

EXCLUSIVE!

a few quid to spare, I clambered aboard with my sample case and rapped on the cabin door. Well, you could have knocked me down with a feather when I saw who opened it. Standing there in front of me, wearing nothing but her famous red bathing suit, all pulled up into her crack, was blonde *Baywatch* bombshell Pamela Anderson herself!

tie

Pamela explained that she and her then-husband, rock wild man Tommy Lee, were enjoying a brief tour of the East Anglian canalways. Tommy had nipped out to fetch them some chips, so I took the opportunity to ask her if she or her hubby were in the market for high-quality neckwear at low, low prices.

The buxom siren nodded enthusiastically, claiming that Tommy was always on the lookout for ties on account of his regular court appearances for drug possession and/

Wham! Bam! Thank you Pam: Anderson got Frank to film sex.

"I've filmed scud flicks with Hollywood's hottest stars," says cravat salesman Frank

or assault. Sniffing an easy sale, I informed her that a simple black or dark blue tie will usually impress judges and juries alike, and offered to come in and show her my wares.

I opened my case and showed her some of the twin pack ties that had sold so well earlier in the day. I explained to her that they were the same quality as you'd get in Tie Rack, but without their overheads, and that's why I was able to offer them at a third the price.

But Pam seemed more interested in the portable camcorder that was nestled alongside my samples. I told her that I used it to practise my sales pitches by recording them and watching them back later. She then shot me a saucy wink that sent the blood rushing straight to my nether regions.

'I've got an idea for something else you can record and watch back later,' she purred, peeling off her iconic bathing suit to reveal her mountainous, golden-brown breasts.

down

Well, I won't go into detail about what happened after I pressed the 'record' button, but let's put it this way: the quality of my ties was quickly forgotten. Only after I'd done her in literally every position in the book, and I'd brought her to no less than **FIFTEEN** earth-shattering climaxes,

Frank confession: Testes' tie business saw him hobnobbing with Hollywood's hottest women.

did we pause to get our breath back.

I got up for a quick pipecleaner, leaving the chesty *Barb Wire* vixen lying on the bed, still reeling from all her multiple orgasms. But when I turned round, my heart almost stopped. Her hubby Tommy Lee was stood in the doorway with two bags of chips, and he'd seen everything.

Now the Mötley Crüe drummer was a big bloke with biceps like sandbags, and I was certain I was all set to be on the wrong end of a good thumping off him. So I could of fell through the floor when he simply smiled and asked me if I'd like to have a chip butty with him and Pam.

It turned out that Tommy and Pam had one of these open relationships you hear about, which I thought was refreshingly modern. After I'd had

CONTINUED OVER...

my chips I packed the video camera back in my case, but not before the wild man of rock had bought two of my 60:40% rayon/polyester ties, which, at £5 the pair, was a deal that the shops found hard to beat.

When I got back to the Premier Inn that night, I could hardly wait to rewatch my nautical A-List tryst in all its high-definition glory. However, when I hooked the camera up to the telly, I got a nasty surprise. *I'd only gone and left the ruddy lens cap on!* There was no record whatsoever of my four-hour bonkathon with one of the planet's hottest women.

I had to laugh to myself when, a few weeks later, Pam and Tommy released their very own sex tape, filmed on that same superyacht. As I watched the saucy footage on the internet, I couldn't help feeling a twinge of regret that it wasn't me up there on the laptop screen enjoying my own no-holes-barred romp with Pam.

I consoled myself with the thought that nothing could take away my memories of that afternoon of full sex I'd had with her. Even though I had absolutely no way of proving it, no-one could say for definite that it hadn't happened. 99

NIGHT'S WATCH WAS DISAPPOINTING

A few years passed, and Frank assumed his on-camera A-List sexploit with Pamela Anderson had been nothing more than a magical one-off. But he got the shock of his life one day in the early noughties when, over in Witham, he came face to face with none other than Game of Thrones star EMELIA CLARKE!

66 I was peddling my wares in the Holiday Inn just off the A12, which is usually quite busy with reps and commercial travellers who always need ties. Canvassing on the premises is strictly forbidden and I'd been warned off a few times by the reception staff. However, I managed to sneak back in through the kitchens while the chef was having a fag.

It's best to start from the top floor of a hotel and work your way down. That way, if you get caught and thrown out, you can make your way to the exit knocking on the room doors as you go. This day, I'd made a few sales, including six nylon floral patterned ties to a powdered egg salesman from Crewe, before a cleaner asked me to leave.

As I did so, I knocked on a door on the ground floor and was amazed when it was answered by Daenerys Targarian herself. It turned out that they had been shooting some *Game of Thrones* battle scenes with dragons in nearby Hatfield Peverel, and she had popped back to the hotel to relax between takes. I enquired as

to whether she might be on the look-out for any high quality neckwear at low, low prices, and her eyes quite literally lit up.

sport

The luscious-lipped Stormborn queen explained that it was her boyfriend's birthday in a couple of weeks, and a tie or two would be just the job. She ushered me into her room with a cheeky grin, and something told me that my sample case wasn't the only thing she was interested in.

Throne a bone: Star Clarke showed Testes saucy use for his neckwear.

I asked her if it was okay to videotape my sales patter so I could use it for training purposes, and she agreed. I put my camera on the dressing table and set it running, starting my pitch by showing her some of the 60:40% nylon-polyester mix ties that were my best sellers. The price tag said £2.39, but I told the 'breaker of chains' that she could have them for two quid a pop. She pouted her famous lips and raised her equally famous eyebrows: 'Can I see them in action?' she cooed. I unravelled one and slipped it round my collar to demonstrate the quality.

'They're not for my boyfriend's neck,' she purred. 'They're for my ankles and wrists.'

Before I knew what was happening, Daenerys had stripped naked and tied herself to the bed using four of the ties. You could see everything, tits, arse, fanny - the whole kit and caboodle. My jaw was quite literally hanging open. I went to turn the video camera off, but the 'Mother of Dragons' stopped me. 'Why don't you leave it running,' she saucily suggested.

chopper

Well, I'm too much of a gentleman to divulge exactly what happened next, but I will say this: we had frenzied, no-holds-barred *Fifty Shades*-style intercourse for at least five hours, and afterwards she told me I was easily the best lover she'd ever had. I wiped my battered chopper on the curtains and went to turn my video camera off.

Our bondage sex session had left the four ties horribly crumpled, but I assured the fireproof queen that because of the high polyester content, the creases would iron out beautifully. I gave her an extra discount and she bought them for six quid the lot.

I thanked her and half an hour later I was back at my own hotel with my camera hooked up to the telly, ready to spend the evening watching myself going at it hammer and tongs up one of the world's sexiest women.

However, when I put the tape into the machine, I had never been more disappointed. *I must have had forgotten to charge the battery, so it had recorded nothing.* As the blank screen flickered before me, I cursed my bad luck, realising that once again there was no hard evidence for my hardcore celebrity sex session. My friends, family and colleagues would simply have to take my word for it that it had actually happened. Which it had, and they couldn't prove for definite that it hadn't. 99

MY RED-HOT TRUMPY-PUMPY WITH MELANIA

Frank was naturally devastated, but little did he realise that he would be granted many, many more opportunities for on-camera A-List intercourse. But it was his XXX-rated romp with the USA's First Lady MELANIA TRUMP that sticks most in his mind.

66 Literally every sales call I made somehow ended up with me bedding a Tinseltown stunner in front of my trusty camcorder. SCARLETT JOHANSSON, BEYONCE, MEGAN FOX, CAROL KIRKWOOD to name but a few.

Infuriatingly, however, every single scrap of this priceless triple-X footage was lost due to my own cack-handed carelessness when it came to inserting the tape properly, setting up the tripod or remembering to switch the camera on. Finally, I decided it was high time I joined the 21st Century and bought myself a smartphone. And I didn't have to wait long for an opportunity to christen its camera.

tomahawk

I was doing the rounds in the Horndon Industrial Park just outside Brentwood, trying to shift a load of polyester seven fold neckties. These are made from a square yard of material folded seven times, so they don't need a lining. This makes them quite pricey, but I was doing them for the unbelievable price of four pound a pop.

I knocked at the door of one of the lock-ups and nearly jumped out of my skin when it was answered by

none other than the US first lady herself!

The large-breasted president's wife informed me that her hubby was meeting with high-level UK business dignitaries in the warehouse next door, and she had come along to keep him company. I asked if either of them had any interest in high-quality neckwear at low, low prices, and after checking the coast was clear, she ushered me straight inside, locking the door behind me.

'My husband's birthday is coming up,' purred Melania in her broken English. 'I want to buy him some nice ties as a surprise.' I told her she'd come to the right bloke, and opened my case.

When I looked up, I saw that Melania was starting to undress. 'That's not all I'm interested in,' she cooed as she unzipped her trouser suit top. 'But we have to be very quiet. My husband, who doesn't satisfy me, is just next door.' As she yanked down my trousers, my brand new smartphone tumbled out of the pocket. She flashed me a cheeky grin and pressed it into my palm.

burner

'Why don't you film our sex session?' she suggested with a wink. I didn't need asking twice, I can tell you. I hit the 'record' button, and the FLOTUS and me got down to it. I won't go into detail about what happened, for fear of inciting an executive order for my assassination, but I will say that by the time we were finished, the *first* lady had enjoyed her *fifth* orgasm.

Un-presidented sex-cess: First lady Melania had film fun with Frank.

After several hours of passionate, unbridled love-making, Melania bought a couple of great value ties which she said she was going to get sewn together to make one long one for her racist hubby. I did my trousers back up and staggered back out onto the industrial estate. Back in my Vectra, I flicked straight to the 'videos' section of my phone to watch the saucy action back, only to experience that familiar sting of disappointment. *I had failed to switch the camera to 'selfie' mode.* As a result, instead of capturing what could have been the most explosive celebrity sex tape of all time, I had simply recorded four hours of footage of the ruddy cabin wall.

Cursing my technical incompetence yet again, I realised I had no absolutely no way of proving that I had just had loads of full sex with the US president's wife. But believe me, it's not fake news, I definitely did have. And people will just have to take my word for it. **"**

PARIS IN THE THE SPRING

*By now, Frank took making Hollywood sex tapes in his stride, and it was an unusual day at the office if he didn't get close up and personal with a Tinseltown A-lister. So last March, when he came face to face with **PARIS HILTON** in a call centre in Great Notley on the outskirts of Braintree, what happened next came as no surprise.*

" Call centres are always good business, and in this particular one I can usually shift about a dozen units before the manager spots me and throws me out.

spokey-dokeys

On this day, I was furtively going from cubicle to cubicle selling my stuff when I spotted a familiar face. It was Paris Hilton! The glamorous hotel chain heiress was apparently filming one of her reality shows where she does a normal job, which this week was working in a call centre. She was cold calling people about them being in an accident that wasn't their fault, and to be frank she looked pretty bored. So when I turned up with my case, she was eager to look inside.

She was immediately attracted to some nylon scarves which were just like ones that Dolce and Gabbana do, but a fraction of the price. She bought two, one for herself and one for her bff Nicole Richie. What's more, she was so pleased with the quality and price of her purchases that she insisted on saying thank-you 'in her own special way.'

Well, I don't need to tell you what that way was. And being an experienced sex tape maker, she insisted that we record the action to put on the internet. She propped my phone up by the leg of a desk to get a good view, set it recording and we got down to action.

Hilton heat: Paris insisted Testes film their erotic encounter.

Now believe me, she may have spent the day cold-calling, but she was definitely hot to trot. And our tryst was made all the more exciting because we could have been interrupted at any moment by her line manager, a bald-headed bloke who the week before had threatened to call the police if he saw me on the premises again.

travelodge

Unfortunately, that is just what happened. Paris's moans of pleasure were so intense as I did her that they alerted the baldy bastard who called security. I was dragged out into the foyer and held for forty minutes until I was handed over to the cops.

As it wasn't my first offence, I was given an exclusion order that forbade me from entering the call centre again, which was a shame as it had been one of the more profitable establishments on my tie-selling rounds. In spite of that, I contented myself with the fact that at least I had had it off with Paris Hilton, and I had my own 100% genuine sex tape to prove it.

But when I got back to my Travelodge room that night and settled down to watch the footage back, my heart sank. One of Paris's teacup dogs must of stood right in front of the camera throughout the entire length of our X-rated tryst. Instead of seeing mine and Paris's red-hot sex session, there was just a twenty-minute close up of a chihuahua's arse. **"**

Frank's book, *Sex, Ties and Videotape!* is in the shops next week, and he expects sales are to dwarf those of the recent best-selling *Fire and Fury* White House exposé.

"It might be a little delayed, because the printer has said that I can't have the books until I've paid his bill, and I'm a bit short at the minute because January and February are always slow months for selling ties," he told us. "So I might have to delay publication until March or April when things usually pick up a bit."

ROGER'S PROFANISAURUS

A Partytime Selection from Britain's Favourite Lexicon of Filth and Profanity

profanisaurus@viz.co.uk

alkytraz *1. n.* The police station drunk tank. *2. n.* Any Saturday night spent incarcerated on the salubrious Welsh island of Barry.

alkie seltzer *n.* An effervescent drink taken to settle the stomach following a night *on the lash*. The hair of the dog. *'Christ, my guts are fucking rotten this morning, but I'll be right as rain after a few cans of alkie seltzer. You seen my pilot's cap anywhere, love?'*

banjoed *adj.* *Pissed-up, wankered, arseholed, shitfaced, rat-arsed.* Nearly drunk enough to appear on *This Week*.

bear claw *n.* Late night, drunken, clumsy pawing at a ladyfriend's *honey pot*, possibly resulting in torn garments.

beer compass *n.* A homing device that ensures your inexplicably safe arrival home after a night *on the pop.*

beer callipers *n.* Miraculous leg splints which enable *wankered* stragglers to make their way home at closing time.

beer cones *n.* Invisible contraflow system surrounding a drunkard meandering up the road, allowing traffic to move freely around him.

beeriod *n.* Twice-weekly malady suffered by men after a night *on the lash*. Symptoms include headache, mood swings and a bloated stomach. *'Leave me alone, woman, me beeriod started this morning.'*

binjuries *n.* Ailments acquired while in a drunken stupor, *eg.* Griddle burns on the *arse* cheeks caused by falling onto an electric fire on Anglesey, to pick an example entirely at random.

Black Eye Friday *n. NI.* The Friday immediately preceeding Christmas, on which Ulsterfolk of all sexes, ages and mental capabilities descend upon drinking establishments to celebrate with each other the anniversary of the birth of Our Lord Jesus Christ. The traditional end result of this festive gathering incorporates (in no particular order of preference) violence, molestation, vomiting, crying, marital breakdown and pregnancy. Also known as *amateur night*.

bland job *n.* Being *tossed off* by a lass while so *pissed* that one can hardly feel it. See *no job*.

blitzed *adj.* See *wankered*.

Blofeld's kiss *n.* The tell-tale facial pillow scar left by a shaken but un-stirred, drunken night's sleep. *'"And for God's sake wash your face, 007," added M. "You can't meet the Swedish Ambassador sporting a Blofeld's kiss."'* (from *James Bond and the Blustery Day* by Ian Fleming).

blotty *n. coll.* *Pissed-up tussage, soused mackerel.* From blotto + totty. *'There's a nice bit of blotty at the bar, Sid.'*

blottopilot *n.* Inbuilt male homing device which secures a safe return to one's house after a night *on the sauce*, whatever one's level of inebriation. Often fitted to one's *beer scooter*.

booze tardis *n.* A four-dimensional *beer scooter* that can transport a *wankered* person through both space and time.

cheggered *adj.* *Pissed* as an *Exchange & Mart*. Derivation unknown.

cherubimical *adj.* *Wankered*; an expression noted by Enlightenment polymath Benjamin Franklin in a treatise of 1737. *'Leave him, Mifflin. He's cherubimical as a fucking newt.'*

chocnose *v.* A traditional end of party trick whereby a guest drops his trousers and rubs his *arse* on the nose of a comatose friend for the amusement of the other guests. *'August 3rd. Opening night party for Cavalcade at The Savoy. Kit [Hassall], Gerty [Lawrence] and Fanny [Brice] were all in attendance. Ivor [Novello] passed out on the chaise longue after drinking far too much Bolly, and Jimmy [Clitheroe] chocnosed him, poor dear. How we laughed!'* (from *The Diary of Noel Coward*).

chuff mountain *n.* A surfeit of *cabbage* at a party.

cuntlashed *adj.* Twice as drunk as *shitfaced*.

dog beers *n.* Any ale quaffed by one who is unable to handle their drink. Downing one *dog beer* leaves the average *two-pot screamer* feeling and looking like he has drunk seven.

Dutch tilt *1. n.* In photography, a composition whereby the camera is set at an angle so that the vertical lines are out of kilter with the side of the frame. *2. n.* A *pissed up* gait whereby an individual who has recently been drinking Continental lager is set at an angle such that his vertical axis is out of kilter with the walls of nearby buildings.

festive perineum *n.* The famously nondescript bit between Christmas and New Year. *'What are you doing over the festive perineum?'*

finger food *n.* Something small and delightful you pick up at a party, but which leaves your hands smelling of fish.

ghost sighting *euph.* The nominal cause of soiled nether apparel amongst thoroughly *wankered* gentlemen making their way home from country locals. *'Looks like you've had another ghost sighting in the churchyard, vicar.' 'Yes officer. It was very frightening, as you can see.'*

hen don't *n.* The sight which, when a chap walks into a bar in which are ensconced 15 *pissed-up* orange women wearing pink cowboy hats, causes him to turn on his heel and immediately walk straight back out again.

Hitler piss *n.* A braced, inadvertent nazi salute position from which to have a drunken *piss* at the pub toilet trough.

incapability brown *n.* A *shit* in the garden, left by a passing drunkard.

jarred *adj.* *Pissed, sloshed, wankered.*

kebab compass *1. n.* Drunken navigation system which allows a chap to retrace his steps by following the trail of dropped salad along his "walk of shame". *2. n.* The hand-held device which late night revellers can be observed waving around on street corners in an attempt to get a bearing on their front door. See also *midnight mouth organ*.

kebabble *n.* The incoherent mumblings and inept attempts at ordering food endured by the staff of greasy takeaway outlets after the pubs have closed.

knobstacle course *n.* Attempting sex while in a drunken stupor. See *labiarinth, Hampton Maze*.

lagerlepsy *n. medic.* Falling asleep suddenly when you have had one beer too many. *'My client would contend, your honour, that he was not drunk while in charge of his vehicle. Tragically, he suffers from a rare medical condition which is exacerbated by sitting down between the hours of 11.00pm and 5.00am, and had merely sunk into a lagerleptic coma while driving home from the pub.'*

lay a cuckoo's egg *1. v.* A party trick where a foreign *bogie* is introduced into an unconscious reveller's nostril for the amusement of the other guests. *2. v.* To get someone else's missus *up the duff*.

Marlboro maracas *n.* The act of shaking random fag packets at a party in search of one that has one or two left in it.

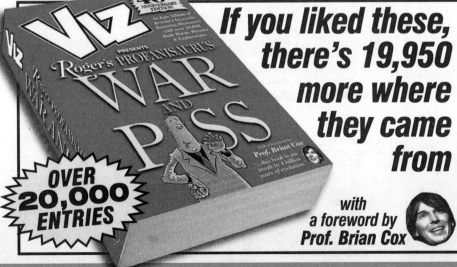

merryneum n. *Twixtmas*, that period between Christmas day and New Year, a term coined by potty-mouthed *Countdown* lexicographer Susie Dent.

misanthropissed adj. Drunk to a state of curmudgeonliness, like one of those blokes you see in your local Wetherspoon boozer, drinking heavily in silence.

moth boy n. The member of a drinking party who, upon entering a pub, proceeds directly to the bandits, attracted by the flashing lights. *Fruit fly.*

nan's mattress sim. To be in an extreme state of *refreshment*. '*Ladies and gentlemen, welcome aboard flight BA103 from Oslo. We would advise you to keep your safety belts fastened throughout the flight as it looks like it could be quite a bumpy ride. We're not expecting any turbulence, it's just that the captain is as pissed as your nan's mattress.*'

no job n. Being *sucked off* by a lady while so *pissed* one can hardly feel it. See also *bland job*.

party willy n. The special form of blunderbuss-style penis wielded by houseguests. A *dick* that liberally distributes *wazz* on the seat and cistern, and also the floor, wall, and occasionally the ceiling, of your smallest room.

ploughing the sand 1. *euph*. A seemingly never ending and unrewarding job, *eg*. Painting the Forth Rail Bridge, checking Jeffrey Archer's novel manuscripts for spelling errors and grammar mistakes. 2. *euph*. Being *on the job* while far too *wankered* to *shoot one's stack*.

pressed ham n. The effect achieved by pushing one's naked *buttocks* onto the photocopier at the works Christmas party. In addition to *getting the sack*.

printercourse n. *Having it off* on an item of office equipment. Hopefully not the shredder or an upturned stapler.

rat-arsed adj. Merry. '*And a rat-arsed Christmas to you, reverend.*'

pisticuffs n. A comical, drunken attempt at combat, perhaps initiated outside a chip shop.

pistorectomy n. *medic*. The act of vomiting up one's own internal organs while life-threateningly *merry*.

shedded adj. Trousered, cattled, wankered. Nearly drunk enough to go on *This Week*.

taint week n. The pointless period that falls between December 25th and January 1st. Because "it taint Christmas, it taint New Year and it taint worth going back to work." See also *the perineum, the festive perineum, merryneum, twixtmas*. '*Hello. Is that the police? There's a masked man with an axe trying to smash the front door down.*' '*Sorry love. I can't send anybody out till a week Tuesday at the latest, only it's taint week and there's no fucker here.*'

tomfuckery n. Light-hearted dealings with a *lady of the night*. '*I don't know what you're getting so cross about, darling. It was just a spot of drunken tomfuckery on a lads' trip to Amsterdam.*'

Tommy's out n. A light-hearted party game where one of the guests secretly *lays a cable* in the house and shouts "Tommy's Out", whereupon everyone else tries to find it. '*To Aldeborough for the weekend, guest of Benjamin [Britten]. What a hoot. Simply everyone was there including Larry [Olivier], Ivor [Novello], Terrence [Rattigan] and Alfie [Bass]. Charades in the orangery, then after supper we played a game of Tommy's Out which ended at three in the morning when Kit [Hassall] found a dead otter in the piano stool, courtesy of Johnny [Gielgud].*' (From *The Diary of Noel Coward*).

train horn n. A lady's party trick in which she firstly *drops a gut*, and then *drops her hat forwards* in quick succession, creating a tuneless, two-toned blast. Also known as a *Robson and Jerome*.

trunking n. An amusing gentleman's party trick whereby he pushes his *dobber* up his own *nipsy*, in a style that is charmingly reminiscent of the way an elephant pushes a bun into its mouth.

turpsichord n. A public house pianoforte, as played by rubber-fingered drunks.

twiglet tips 1. n. The brown stains left on the fingertips after consuming the nation's favourite marmite-flavoured, timber-based party snack. 2. n. Of similar appearance, but as a consequence of an inadvertent *hull breach*. Also *taxi driver's tan*.

Urinarnia n. *prop*. A *pisstical* destination at which you arrive during a drunken sleepwalk. A dream fantasy toilet that is in reality the back of the wardrobe.

wobbly landing n. Trying, when drunk, to manoeuvre your under-inflated *zipper Zeppelin* safely through your wife's *hangar doors*.

wankered adj. *Shit-faced* as a newt.

zuffle coat n. The topmost item of clothing in the pile on a bed at a party. Used by a male guest to clean the *sloom* off his *three card trick* after a furtive *poke*.

PARTYTIME PROFANISAURUS WORDSEARCH

HIDDEN in the grid below are all of the entries in this Festive Partytime Profanisaurus. They may read up, down or diagonally, backwards or forwards. If you can find them all, you can win a free Viz Cheap Pen. Simply send a **LARGE LETTER STAMP** to: *Festive Partytime Profanisaurus Wordsearch, Viz Comic, PO Box 841, Whitley Bay, NE26 9EQ* stating that you have honestly completed the wordsearch and found all of the entries.

```
H M D B U K N I D W I X B L O F E L D S K I S S M Y L J M L U M D A U B C Y L
Z A A B M L J P V I K N X C P L L A Y A C U C K O O S E G G L P F E R X G M L
S R C Y H B S S A P M O C B A B E K I V U K D T S N R M L B Z V R D T E E H K
A L O B K M Y G R R A B I A E K L N B W Z P O V Y R P K X B E F N W L J T C P
E B P Y E S B H U J T M L T P E R Y E P M U G T Y E B Y L S N Y I O L O U R G
R O A Z T E N I J E G Y T H I A C Y A I L K B N C T G K L S T G T B J N O H H
S R C Y H G R X B M I G W R N Y B L R W C Y E L M U K E A I L O H B T O F T O
A O S V Y D V C G K L T E I E S Y I C J I U E L N A X E T E L J U L M U B G S
K M S B U E R L O T O B R J L A D K L O M G R L H T D W T M L D A Y M L G T T
G A B I J S B I K M L U V Y D L A K A I M U S I M F A T L M I S T L P G E U S L
T R C M U S H F M I P K L I R G Y U W N T D J U T L I N Y K H S E A C K R U I U N
P A P I H I A Y N U E A R M O L F E S A I Y L P Y P L I B E X R U N Z P L O G D I
Q C M O P P S L L R Y F S M P L Y S G L L O B T S X Y A D L M L T D S O K U H M I
L A K G B O F Y K R E K O S B Y L N E K M L R R C Y E T M P O W A I L P K U T M I
S S J I U R A N Y Y M L H X R G P T S I O J Y Y O M L Z G U R T C N P O C T I O L
H Y O T X H P L E X T N P L S T E F T E G I T M W A C Y I P H T G F H M Y N M P
Z D C L W T T K S Y H R M P D Z F A B S R T D M U T N M S Z O M I O U X C T G R K
M S J D Y N C C L R T D A C I U C N P E O M O W B P L G X R B Y P F P P K A C T L
C O L A H A C Q F L T L R Z C M L X T L W I O Z H T G E D V T Y F A I I L N R Z R
C O T E L S W L X Y K V I I N S C I B T O M F U C K E R Y K L M S W Z U L L Y N R
A R R B T I M U C R L J T T N P J S V Z M I R L Z T D M H P O W T P C U D O M L P
H N A N S M A T T R E S S K H L I G J E O P E L P E T B O U L P F R E M I F T O H
C O I M P G B L D C I T H B O C M Z T R L P G X Z M V Y N G T A O C E L F F U Z K
B F N N L C R E L P D Z D L A T T M F V Y H N T B P Y T P B T D E L K N R L K P T
M O H A C T R T E L N R S E G O P U M Z Y J I L F W A L M S J U X Y R N P E P O D
A C O W I R I K B R M U C R S M L S D O F L F L P I T H E N D O N T I C B B G M T
R A R X A J G W L T I M P J Y R T N L L B Y S I N B Y Z L T M O F E S A M D T A P
B A N J O E D L A B J O M Z Y O A L P F R T S M O I C R A H K Y G T B M L C T R L
M X Y H E L P G N M O F D T D S E T L U D T V H P G N T B W K P D B M L S X T E P
S F M O T G R S D M L Z R T E N U T A X O P T D E C T U G E D J L L B T D G I O H
S W E M F Y D C J L U N R H G P K T E R O U L T F D Q Z T E E E Z R V U J S I P H
A C Y S E S R U O C R E T N I R P X E E Z U C P U H D L R B T R P L D N P Z B R T
S B Y T T M O F B L X G P M F C E C M P Z H H C S P J E L Z T E C M M P B T S G N
B M N L G I M P H T N C I J K S T C T G E L O M B Y K D D L M L F A A L Y V I M P
I B K L G R V H U I N I S C O O L R H R M P C E R N K V H N K P G H L M L P D N U
N N L V R S F E H M K C R E M L N F U J L C N R A M J T D Z F G I D B L S R R X L
J X Z B O K D G P V H V R Y N A V B Y N L G O W M P F E E N P T G E L P I Y A A H
U L P Y M C U C I E A M L C Y O I K I R K T S M X T L K R L P S S D H U P T L P
R A V I T O C L D O R Z P N E M C N O S T I E V O E Z R U E M P S S B O S T E K P
I S Y H L F T A V U T I V Y Y I K W R H I Z T N Y G L P T R M L T G E P Y M L Z R J
E W C P U D E H M L V T N C O K U T E M T H V G M O G P L P R D W R Q X U T O U S
S P Q H Y D K Y B P B Y A E L M Z F E E R T E A Y F I L M U X P T P A I D P O P U
P B Y A L T F K U O X L M I U L O X Y T B H Y P Z S L V T S H I T H E L P C B L H
M L C T S H U R D W Y L O G R M L O C R C L P E S R U O C E L C A T S B O N K T E
```

profanisaurus@viz.co.uk

THIS CHRISTMAS PARTY IS THE LOWEST POINT... BASTARDS ARE GOING TO HAVE ME IN A FAT SANTA SUIT WITH THE BEARD AND EVERYTHING, HANDING OUT PRESSIES TO COMPANY BIGWIGS WHO'VE PROBABLY ALL SEEN THE PICS...

FUCKING HUMILIATING!..

...AND I'LL NOT GET A FUCKING BEAN FOR IT!

CHRISTMAS EVE...

IT'S A SHAME ROGER ISN'T HERE, TOM... I'VE GOT A NEW GAME SHOW IN DEVELOPMENT THAT I'D HAVE LIKED TO TALK TO HIM ABOUT.

YES...WELL...I THINK HE'S DOING A...ER...CHARITY THING IN LONDON

MERRY CHRISTMAS, TOM

ROGER!?... I THOUGHT YOU WERE...ER...ELSE-WHERE!

WELL, I WAS SUPPOSED TO BE, TOM, BUT THEY DON'T NEED ME...SO THEY CANCELLED AT THE LAST MINUTE.

OH?..BUT...

THEY'VE GOT JEREMY PAXMAN TO BE SANTA CLAUS THIS YEAR...

...HE'S JUST HAD AN ENSUITE PUT IN HIS BEDROOM AND HE USED THE SAME BUILDERS AS ME

HE'S GOING TO FRONT THE TITS BINGO AS WELL

BUT I'VE FLOWN ALL THE WAY FROM THE NORTH POLE ON MY MAGIC SLEIGH TO...

WELL YOU CAN JUST FUCK OFF BACK THERE, CUNTY-CHOPS, BECAUSE YOU AIN'T GETTIN' IN 'ERE...END OF.

NOW FUCKIN' DO ONE WHILE I'M STILL IN A GOOD MOOD. Y'DON'T WANT TO PROVOKE ME, SON, BELIEVE ME...

I MOST CERTAINLY WILL NOT. MY ELVES HAVE BEEN WORKING ALL YEAR TO...

HEY, SEE THIS FUCKER 'ERE? THIS SAYS I'M LICENSED TO USE REASONABLE FORCE TO PUNCH YOUR FUCKIN' FAIRY LIGHTS OUT, TINKERBELL.

I JOLLY WELL DON'T CARE!

THESE CHILDREN HAVE BEEN VERY GOOD, AND I'M GOING TO DELIVER THEIR PRESENTS WHAT-EVER YOU HAVE TO SAY ON THE MATTER!

OOH, PROVOCATION..! JUST WHAT I WANTED. THANK-YOU.!

SHORTLY, BACK AT THE NORTH POLE...

YOU'RE HOME EARLY THIS YEAR, DEAR. EVERYTHING ALRIGHT..?

≥GROAN≤

WOOOOOOSH!

WOOOAH!

JA!..ZIS IS ZE BIGGEST NUSSKNACKER IN ZE VORLD! ZE JAWS CAN EXERT EIN PRESSURE OF 40,000LB PER SQUARE INCH... ENOUGH TO SHATTER DIAMONTS

HOW DOES IT WORK?

I THINK I KNOW WHAT'S GOING TO HAPPEN!

READER'S VOICE

VELL...YOU JUST LIFT ZE HANDLE...LIKE ZO...

...UND PUSH IT DOWN TO CRRRRRACK ZE NUSS INTO EIN MILLION PIECES!

SMACK!

CRUNCH!

POP! POP!

≥GAAAAAA!≤

PLORT!

RP!

PUSTULENT FESTERING BOILS ARE BREAKING OUT ALL OVER MY BODY!

AT THE DOCTOR'S

YOU HAVE A RARE ALLERGIC REACTION TO RAFFLE TICKETS WHICH HAVE THE NUMBER SIX ON THEM.

YOWP!

IT IS A FATAL CONDITION, AND YOU WILL SHORTLY DIE.

AND SO

≥CROAK≤

SO LONG, READERS! LOOKS LIKE MY CHARACTERISTIC GOOD LUCK RAN OUT WHEN I BOUGHT THIS RAFFLE TICKET!

FRANK, WAIT!

YOU'VE BEEN HOLDING THE RAFFLE TICKET UPSIDE DOWN, YOU SILLY SAUSAGE!

IT'S NOT A NUMBER SIX—IT'S A NUMBER NINE!

WHICH MEANS THAT YOU'RE NOT DYING AFTER ALL, AND HAVE ALSO WON A CHRISTMAS PUD IN THE CHURCH RAFFLE!

CLEAN BILL OF HEALTH

YOINKS!

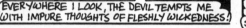

AH..! THAT TAKES ME BACK TO MY OWN BOATING DAYS, MRS SAUNDERS.

I NEVER KNEW YOU WERE A ROWER, MR GUMLET.

OH YES, I WAS IN THE OXFORD EIGHT, YOU KNOW, AS A YOUNG MAN.

GOSH!

WE HAD TO BE UP AT DAWN EVERY MORNING TO PRACTISE IN OUR BOAT, UP AND DOWN THE RIVER WITH OUR COACH RIDING HIS BIKE ALONG THE TOWPATH, SHOUTING "PULL! PULL! PULL!"

IT MUST HAVE BEEN EXHAUSTING!

IT WAS, MRS SAUNDERS. MANY'S THE TIME AS A STUDENT THAT I PULLED MYSELF DIZZY SEVERAL TIMES BEFORE BREAKFAST.

FNARR! FNARR!

CHOPE! CHOPE!

SNUT! SNUT!

YIK! YIK!

WOOT! WOOT!

OF COURSE, IT WAS ALL LEADING UP TO THE BIG DAY OF THE ANNUAL UNIVERSITY BOAT RACE...

I'LL NEVER FORGET THE EXCITEMENT AS WE BOBBED BY PUTNEY BRIDGE... OUR HANDS POISED ON THE OARS AS WE WAITED FOR THE STARTER'S GUN...

THE RACE ITSELF PASSED IN A BLUR, AS WE ROWED FOR ALL WE WERE WORTH, FINALLY SNATCHING VICTORY FROM CAMBRIDGE AS WE CROSSED THE FINISH LINE...!

...BUT DO YOU KNOW WHAT MY FAVOURITE MEMORY IS OF THAT MARVELLOUS DAY, MRS SAUNDERS.? WHEN THE WHOLE CREW STOOD ON THE LANDING STAGE AT CHISWICK AND WE TOSSED OUR COX INTO THE WATER.

♪...JOLLY BOATING WEATHER AND A HAY HARVEST BREEZE! BLADE ON THE FEATHER...!♪

NONK! NONK!

FWIB! FWIB!

K-YUK! KYUK!

UGH! UCH-UGH!

SPUMP! SPUMP!

UGH! UCH! UCH!

PORN star Stormy Daniels recently hinted that she may be in possession of intimate photographs featuring President Donald Trump exposing his manhood. If such pictures do exist and become public, many believe they could spark a scandal that could rock the White House to its foundations.

But what if Trump is hung like a carthorse? Could the revelation of an impressive Trump Tower in the POTUS's pants boost his flagging reputation and see the Donald swagger back into the Oval Office for a second term? It's certainly an intriguing possibility, but until we actually see the snap we won't know for sure.

We took a stroll down Hollywood's star-studded Sunset Strip and asked a selection of Tinseltown celebrities...

Copper's Torch *or* Bookie's Pencil? What's the President Packing?

Ted Nugent, musician and killing enthusiast

"What sort of a goddam faggot question is that, you cocksucking Limey piece of shit? I don't think about other men's cocks, but if I had to answer, I'd say Mr Trump is undoubtedly packing some serious goddam weaponry down there. I reckon his dick must be at least eight inches on the slack, and probably ten or more when it's on the bonk. I for one can't wait to see the pictures, and that's why he's gonna make America great again."

Neil de Grasse Tyson, astrophysicist

"We scientists don't make statements of fact without first examining and carefully evaluating all the evidence available to us. But just from looking at him, I reckon the President's probably got a knob like a cashew nut - one of them really little ones that gets left in the bottom of the bag."

Meryl Streep, Oscar-winning actress

"This is a fat, 74-year-old man with a risible combover, who seems nevertheless to attract a succession of beautiful young women to his boudoir. It's got to be either his money or his manhood that they're after, and since he's filed for bankruptcy four times, it must be his Charlie. I take no pleasure in saying this, but the POTUS must have a chopper like a dead German hanging out a window."

Jim Bakker, televangelist

"The Lord chose to give the President of the United States of America very small hands, but He works in mysterious ways, and I am certain that He will have compensated for that in other ways by giving him an absolutely massive bellender. Oh,

and by the way, the End of Days is near, and also the Devil is a many horn'd beast. Send me your credit card details now to ensure eternal salvation. Remember, places by God's right hand in the hereafter are strictly limited, and the more you donate, the greater your chances of not being thrown into the pit of eternal fire."

John Voigt, Midnight Cowboy actor

"All this fevered online talk about the size of the President's manhood is completely hypocritical. None of these people are speculating about the size of Stormy Daniels's mingepiece. Mind you, that's probably because you can see it in close-up, Technicolor detail in thousands of grumble vids on the internet. Let me tell you, I've seen my fair share of them and it's like a fucking welly top."

 Derek Cheesecock... **ALIEN HUNTER**

114

Scum mothers who'd have 'em

Take It

THE GUINNESS BOOK OF RECORDS is as much a part of the traditional British Christmas as roast turkey with all the trimmings, singing carols round the tree and breaking your children's iPads to teach them a lesson. But glossy hardback books don't come cheap, and many cash-strapped families can't afford to pay out the thick end of £20 for this perennial yuletide favourite (not my family, obviously, as my dad's a duke or something). But don't worry, because I'm going to show you how to make your very own Guinness Book of Records from things you already have lying around the house!

1 **TO MAKE** your own Guinness Book of Records, first you're going to need to construct a basic printing machine. Blow up some leftover party balloons and twist them together, forming them into the shape of a simple platen press.

2 **MIX UP** a thick paste using flour and water. Take some old newspapers, telephone directories and first class in-flight magazines, and tear them into small strips. Soak these in the paste to form a papier mache mixture.

3 **COVER** the balloon printing press former with the papier mache strips, applying several layers. This is great, messy fun for all the family, so get the kids to muck in too! If they refuse, break some more of their things until they do.

5 **TO GIVE** your home made machine a more professional finish, paint it dark red and silver and fasten springs to the mechanism. Don't forget the ink roller, which can be made from a hot dog sausage or a condom filled with chestnut stuffing.

6 **OIL-BASED** printing ink is expensive, but you can easily make your own from black treacle or molasses. Use the organic type from Fortnum & Mason, as it has a smaller carbon footprint than the mass-produced sort.

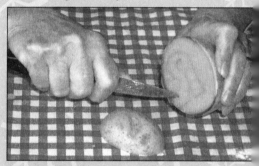

7 **CARVE** your type into potatoes using a kitchen knife. You'll need more of some letters (eg. E's and S's) than others (eg. Q's and Z's). Top Tip - Make the letters backwards so they come out the right way round on the paper.

9 **PAPER** is expensive (not for me because I'm loaded and my husband probably runs a hedge fund), but if you go to a shop that sells it, they'll often give you some for free. You'll need 300 A4 sheets plus 2 bits of card for the covers.

10 **THEN**, simply print the 600 pages of your book onto both sides of the paper. Hey presto! You've got a beautiful copy of the Guinness Book of Records for a mere fraction of the price of the shop-bought version!

SAVE £20!

Make It
with Kirstie Allsopp
How to Make...
a GUINNESS book of RECORDS

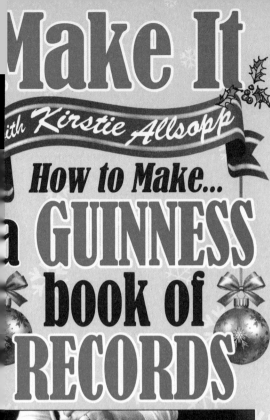

4 ONCE the flour and water paste has dried, use a pin to pop the balloons, before pulling them out through a small gap which I forgot to mention in the previous instruction. You will be left with a papier mache printing press.

3 NEXT, set the 600 pages of type you'll need to print your Book of Records. Fit them into the papier mache forme of your press, and use the sausage or stuffing-filled rubber Johnny to coat your potato type with treacle ink.

Next year:
Spend Christmas on the Moon with your own SATURN V rocket made from discarded wrapping paper, unwanted clippers and an old Quality Street tin!

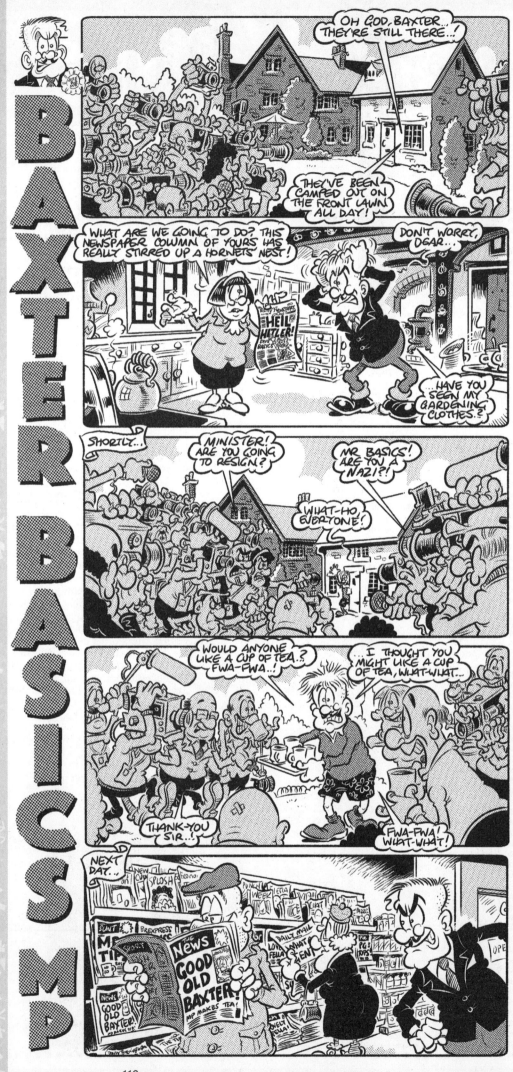

Letterbocks

Viz Comic, P.O. Box 841 Whitley Bay, NE26 9EQ : letters@viz.co.uk

ST★R LETTER

APPARENTLY the word dinosaur means 'terrible lizard'. That seems rather harsh as it looks to me like they were pretty fucking amazing lizards. They are certainly better than the crap little ones we get these days.

James Thompson, London

DO hunky outdoors types like Bear Grylls have magic breath? When they blow on kindling, they get a roaring fire, but when I blow on a candle, it goes out.

P Wee, St. Helens

IF you kill a wasp, can you get stang off of its ghost, or do they wait until you're a ghost to sting you? That would be a terrible welcome to the afterlife, to be stang off of the ghosts of all the wasps you've ever killed. It's the main reason why I've very little interest in being a ghost. The one reason why I would be a ghost is to watch ladies get undressed.

Greg Jones, Wakefield

I HAVE just seen a charity advert on TV that said, what

with the polar ice caps melting due to global warming, polar bears are running out of things to feed their young. Well I happen to know that bears don't even eat ice. Just another scam.

Tony, Oxford

THE sight of a majestic polar bear stranded on a single floating piece of ice, unable to hunt because of the melting sea ice, is truly heartbreaking. But then, when they cut to a shot of it from the back and you can see shit all over its fur, it's not quite so appealing, is it? Come on environmentalists - clean those polar bears' arses up a bit.

Mick Halibut, Halifax

"IF a tree falls in a forest and there's nothing there to hear it, does it make a sound?" is a question many philosophers pose. Well of course it doesn't. It vibrates air molecules, yes, but unless these vibrations are picked up by an ear and transformed into electrical impulses in a brain, they are not sound. There, that's *that* fucker cleared up. Next!

Prof. Stanley Jordan, University of Oxford

I NOTICE that on *Question Time*, people in the audience have their hands up for ages whilst waiting for Fiona Bruce to come to them, but she often never does. Surely keeping your hand down, giggling, chewing gum and talking to the person next to you would get her attention? I guarantee that he'll come to you and ask you for your opinion on the discussion in hand. It always used to happen to me in school anyway.

Bartrum Golightly, Derby

I THINK my wife was abducted by aliens last night as she got ready for bed, and I have photographic proof.

Billy Tinfoilhat, Tring

WE all know that the wireless technology Bluetooth was named after Harold 'Bluetooth' Gormsson' an olden time king of Denmark and Norway who famously loved blueberries so much that his teeth were stained blue. Having consumed 1.5kg of the tasty fruit yesterday, I can confidently state that we could just as easily be pinging data to each other using something called PurpleSquits.

Ross Pure, Shittlehampton

I RECENTLY took out a subscription to *Your Dog* magazine. However, when the latest issue arrived through the post, I found that it had someone else's dog on the front cover and nothing about my dog anywhere inside. Have any other readers been caught out by this scam?

Brett, Stalybridge

I'D just like to inform any husbands reading this that if your wife asks you how much do you love her on a scale of 1-10, the answer is 10, and not 7 as I had originally assumed.

Stephen, Birmingham

IF I was walking through an abandoned town in a post-apocalyptic world and I happened across a fancy dress shop I would, for a few reasons, put on one of those costumes that makes it look like you're riding an ostrich. Firstly, the ostrich would give me some company on my lonely journey. Secondly, were I to be spotted by zombies, during the chase they may find my disjointed attempt to run away whilst frantically clinging to the ostrich so funny they wouldn't be able to run for laughing. And thirdly, the costume would provide an ideal ice-breaker when I eventually came across other marauding groups of survivors.

Johnny T, Kirkcaldy

I KNOW the internet is amazing and everyone loves it and everything, but it been around a good few years now. Isn't it about time someone came up with something better? Whatever happened to onwards and upwards?

Stench Peters, Corb

I WAS wondering if any of your twitcher readers could help me identify a bird at the bottom of my garden. It goes 'w-wurrr-woo, w-wurr-woo'.

David Smallbone, email

✱ *That's an interesting one, David. Can any Viz readers put a name to this species of garden bird? There's a Viz pen for anyone who identifies it correctly.*

"I BEFORE E except after C," I can still hear my teacher say. His name was Mr Mamdani, and after fleeing persecution in his home country he was teaching in a rough inner-city comprehensive, determined to give something back to the country that had offered him asylum. His passion and enthusiasm were infectious and I often bump into old school mates who still talk about how 'Mr M' changed their lives. It wasn't until years later that I noticed several words have an 'ie' after a 'c', such as species, science and sufficient. Now I don't trust anything anyone says, especially foreigners.

Ian Yates, Garstor

COCKS? Tits? Boobies? Shags? Birdwatchers' puerile obsession with naming these wonderful animals after smutty obscenities really disgusts me. If they discover another bird, what's the betting they'll call it a "lesser-spotted knob-crested fanny" or a "golden-showered eagle". Quite honestly, you couldn't make it up. If they'd put down their binoculars once in a while, and go out and meet a real woman, they wouldn't need to inflict their frustrations on the rest of us with their filthy innuendos.

Phil Kitching, Isle of Jura

ToP TIPs

GENTLEMEN. Need to know if you can re-use yesterday's grundies? Use an old mining industry test and drape them over a canary's cage. If the bird doesn't fall off its perch, you're good for another couple of days.

Graham, email

UNFIT and need to stop jogging after just 5 minutes? Pretend you have reached your goal by slapping a nearby lamp post whilst looking at your watch with a satisfied nod of the head.

Tam Robb, East Kilbride

SAVE hot water when taking a bath by filling the empty spaces around you and between your legs with bricks.

Jamie Cuffe, Ashby de la Launde

ALWAYS keep the centre of gravity in the middle of an egg box by buying the larger 15 (5×3) egg boxes. Remove the eggs 2 at a time from diametrically opposite points in the box, leaving the final egg in the middle of the centre row.

Albert, Zurich

GO into KFC and tell them you're allergic to Thyme and keep a note of whether they say you are safe to eat their food or not. Repeating this with other herbs and spices and you will eventually be able to work out all 11 in the Colonel's secret blend.

Joel Robinson, Manchester

toptips@viz.co.uk

MY eagle-eyed children gleefully pointed out this cock spurting spunk in the illuminated wall art at our local "Grill'd" restaurant today. I put my foot through my burger and paid the bill.

Joshu Turier, Brisbane

FIRST I catch one pigeon watching me have a wank, then his mate lands next to him on the windowsill and looks my way as well. Dirty fuckers.

Eddie Tipton, Bilston

I RECKON about 5% of my gaseous anal emissions smell of popcorn, but I never eat the stuff. Maybe the boffins at CERN could look into that puzzle, if they stopped fannying about with Higgs Bosons for five fucking minutes.

Dr Andrew Turner, Barrow-in-Furness

MY wife just did a loud fart whilst the Prince Harry and Meghan Markle were saying their wedding vows. Could that be classed as treason?

R Clarke, Preston

* We contacted monarchy and constitutional expert Dr David Starkey on your behalf, Mr Clarke. He said that treason constitutes a crime of disloyalty to the crown, including plotting to murder the monarch, committing adultery with the consort or wife of the heir to the throne, and aiding and giving comfort to enemies of the crown. Your wife breaking wind during the recent royal marriage ceremony hardly describes any of these offences. She could be said, however, to be guilty of sedition, the crime of bringing contempt, or exciting disaffection against the person of Her Majesty, her heirs or successors. However, it is unlikely that a successful prosecution would be brought unless the Crown could prove beyond reasonable doubt that it was your wife who had dealt it.

"FLY me to the moon, let me play among the stars. Let me see what spring is like on Jupiter and Mars", sang Frank Sinatra. With such a poor grasp of astrophysics, it's hardly surprising that so many people think the Americans faked the moon landing.

Steve Crouch, P'borough

CAN anyone tell me where I can buy those sticking plasters that adorn the bums of your comic characters? You know, the cross-shaped ones that appear on the mudflaps of the likes of San, Tray, and Baz. I need an answer quickly as I've got a big spot on my right cheek and I'm in imminent expectation of some bedroom shenanigans.

Bob Pitt, Kendal

IT'S all very well The Drifters singing "Saturday night at the movies, who cares what picture we see." If one of those *Police Academy* films was on, or anything with Steven Seagal in it, they would be singing a different fucking tune, believe you me.

Frank Micropub, Leeds

I DON'T suppose you're going to publish it, but I spotted a mistake in my last submitted letter. I should have written: "…he would perhaps HAVE wing mirrors instead of ears" etc.

Mike Hatchard, St Leonards-on-Sea

* You were absolutely correct, Mike, we're not going to publish it.

WHY are Old English Sheepdogs so called? The fat, hairy bastards never chase a single sheep. All they do is sit around al day advertising paint. Border Collies do all the graft and get none of the lucrative TV work. Perhaps John fucking Craven can do a *Countryfile* item about this.

Nesta Tables, Truro

BACK in the seventies, whenever Kate Bush was on the radio at work I always used to get a laugh by saying, "I love a bit of Bush, me." Of course, those were different times, and you couldn't say it now because it would be totally inappropriate. But back then women never used to shave their fannies.

T Crumbhorn, Goole

I DON'T know why environmentalists are so pissed off about plastic being harmful to marine life. I reckon that rubber is just as bad. I was checking out the live lobsters in a restaurant the other night, and the poor little bastards had got elastic bands all tangled around their claws. Come on postmen, your reputation is bad enough already.

Niels Boredom, Luton

MY friend Andy was in court for petty fraud. When he was convicted, the judge told him that his crime was 'as good as' stealing the money straight from his victims' pockets. I think he was quite surprised that the judge seemed so impressed with his skills. He still got a 12 month suspended sentence and 200 hours of community service though.

Phil Kitching, Isle of Jura

THINGS that are absolutely shite in this country are referred to as "ten a penny," which is equivalent to 0.10 pence each. In the USA, however, they are said to be "a dime a dozen" which is 2.08 cents each. Why is it that America's worthless things are worth more

I THINK my fireplace looks like Skeletor.

He-Man, Portstewart

than ours? If that's the special post-Brexit deal we have to look forward to with America, then heaven help us.

Jim Corncrake, Tooting

THE combined weight of the anchors on the RMS Titanic was 31 tons, I understand. Now I'm no marine engineer, but *thirty one tons?* It's no wonder the bloody thing sank.

Barry Cheeseboard, Scarborough

IT'S NATIONAL FUCKING SOMETHING DAY

YOU might not be aware, but today is *National Fucking Something Day*, which means that some fucking thing is happening, or continuing to happen that somebody has arbitrarily decided is important enough to be given a whole day to its fucking self.

And we can look forward to 24 hours of people glibly saying 'did you know it's National Fucking Something Day?' before we can ignore whatever the fuck it is for the next 364 days.

busy

And it's a busy time, as while yesterday was *National*

EXCLUSIVE!

Something Fucking Else Day, tomorrow will be *National Some Other Fucking Thing Day*. And next Monday sees the start of *International Some Fucking Thing Or Other Week*, with hundreds of events planned across the

Day to remember: Fucking Something Day.

country and people wearing fucking badges for it.

awareness

Next month is *Stop Fucking Doing That Month*, which aims to raise awareness of why you should stop fucking doing that, especially among schoolchildren.

SPOILER ALERT!

A CACHE of *Game of Thrones*'s most closely guarded secrets has sensationally been LEAKED by a West Midlands pub landlord in a dramatic security breach that has rocked the blockbuster HBO fantasy show to its foundations. Plots from the epic series's hotly anticipated eighth and final season were apparently left on a pub table in Tettenhall, Wolverhampton by the show's creator, George RR Martin.

The barely legible storylines, scribbled on the back of a beermat, were found by Eddie Spoiler, manager of the Albion Pub on the town's Davehill estate.

quiz

Spoiler, 62, told local paper the *Wrottlesby & Smestowside Argus:* "We'd had one of our popular strip show, quiz and meat raffle nights, and me and big San were clearing up the empties in the main bar. It'd been quite busy, so there was a lot of rubbish left on the tables; crisp bags, answer papers and what-have-you."

"I was just scooping a load into my bin-bag when I noticed the names 'Daenerys Targaryen' and 'Tyrion Lannister' scrawled on the back of a beermat," continued Mr Spoiler. "That puzzled me a bit. I knew there'd been no Game of Thrones questions in the quiz, so I read on to see what it was all about."

grub

He told the paper: "When I realised what I had in my hand, my hat flew about a foot in the air off the top of my head. It was the plots for the whole next series of the biggest show on TV!"

"Suddenly it all made sense. The fat little bearded man who had been sat nursing his pint at the table by the fruity all afternoon must've been George RR Martin, the author of the Song of Fire and Ice books on which Game of Thrones is based," said Mr Spoiler.

phillips

"In between the topless floorshow, the meat draw and the quiz, he had clearly been sat there quietly thinking up plots for his top-rated sword and sorcery show."

Storylines for the top-rated series, which follows the fortunes of the rival

Landlord Eddie leaks GoT Secrets

EXCLUSIVE!

Leaked: Game of Thrones cast yesterday.

houses of Lannister and Stark in the mythical realm of Westeros, are closely guarded secrets. *Game of Thrones* fans regularly throng internet message boards in search of leaked snippets, and even the actors and crew are kept in the dark about forthcoming twists and turns in the plot.

"I knew the soggy beermat in my hand was dynamite," said Mr Spoiler. "All the storylines for the final season of the world's biggest telly programme were there laid out in front of me."

spencer

According to Spoiler, these are just a few of the explosive surprises that the new series, set to air in 2019, has in store for viewers:

● *In episode one, Tyrion Lannister pretends to forget his wedding anniversary while secretly planning a surprise party for his wife Sansa Stark. However, when the evening of the party arrives and all the guests are hiding behind a curtain at Winterfell,*

Plots thicken: (Clockwise from top left) Jora Mormont has embarrassing dinner with boss Daenerys Targaryen, Jon Snow loses brother's best sword and Tyrion Lannister forgets wedding anniversary.

Lannister finds a note from his wife telling him that she has gone to stay with her sister Arya

● *In episode three, hoping to secure a promotion, exiled knight Sir Jorah Mormont invites his boss Daenerys Targaryen round for a meal. Unfortunately, he forgets to tell his wife that Targeryen is the Mother of Dragons and she inadvertently decides to cook a dragon lasagne for dinner*

● *In episode four, Ned Stark's bastard son Jon Snow borrows his half-brother Bran's Valerian Steel sword to cut his hedge. Bran says he wants it back by Saturday morning as he needs it to slay Roose Bolton for forcing his sister into a bigamous and abusive marriage with his son Ramsey. However, on his way home, Ned leaves the magical weapon on the bus to King's Landing*

Plotty time: Tettenhall publican Eddie Spoiler found cache of top secret Game of Thrones storylines scribbled on beermat following quiz night and meat raffle.

Mr Spoiler said: "Obviously, I'm not going to divulge how these sensational plots develop. Rest assured the beermat went into much greater detail, revealing a series of fantastic twists and turns that will have viewers clinging to the edge of their seats in suspense."

ferguson

But he did reveal that *Game of Thrones* fans could expect plenty of the explicit eroticism and nudity that has become one of the hit show's trademarks throughout the final, climactic season. According to Spoiler, shocked viewers will see:

● *Brienne of Tarth stood in stockings and suspenders when her armour is ripped off after it gets trapped in a car door*

● *Eunuch spymaster Lord Varys climbing into bed with naked Dothraki King Khal Drogo after the number 9 on his bedroom door drops round to look like a number 6*

● *Cersei Lannister's bra flying off as she's doing her morning exercises in the Garden of Betrayal*

And season eight is set to leave fans reeling as a tranche of beloved characters are killed off in one fell swoop. "I don't want to reveal too much about the scene in question," said Mr Spoiler. "But I will say that this massacre will make the Red Wedding look like a picnic in the park."

An HBO spokesman told us that he could neither confirm nor deny that a scene was planned in which a meeting of the Council of the King's Hand takes place in Winterfell, wth the members of the council, including Lord Varys, Sir Jaime Lannister and Sandor 'The Hound' Clegane, unaware that Sam Tarley, his brother Rodney and his Uncle Albert are in the room above, unbolting a big chandelier off the roof joist to take it down and clean it.

Albion: Eddie's pub, scene of the GoT leaks.

GoT-CHA!

OVER SEVEN SEASONS of the top-rated fantasy drama *Game of Thrones*, viewers have enjoyed a gripping white-knuckle ride as the Lannisters, Starks, Targaryens and Greyjoys have fought tooth and nail to secure their place on the Iron Throne of the Seven Kingdoms of Westeros. The show's bewitching cocktail of political intrigue, sex, and violent death keeps millions glued to their screens week after week.

GoT is famous for having more on-screen deaths than any other TV drama, and this grim statistic could easily take its toll on the show's stars. It would be quite understandable if the endless acts of violence and murder featured in episode after episode were to send the actors spiralling into a bottomless pit of depression.

Luckily, help is close at hand, in the form of **TERRY MCGUIGAN**. Terry, 46, runs the Titanic Laffs joke shop, situated just a stone's throw from the Belfast studios where the HBO epic is filmed. He told us: "My shop is a treasure trove of light-hearted novelties that are guaranteed to tickle anyone's funny bones. And believe it or not, when they need cheering up after a hard day's filming, the Game of Thrones stars are my best customers."

Terry was reluctant to talk about his *GoT* patrons, claiming that to speak out publicly would breach joke shop owner/client privilege, and possibly even damage his business. But after we gave him £300 cash, he agreed to lift the lid and sensationally spill the beans about his A-list regulars.

Stark raving bonkers

Sansa: Put Krapalot sugar into Ramsey Bolton's tea with desired effect.

66 It was while they were making the first series of *Game of Thrones* that Sansa Stark came through the door of my shop. I recognised her immediately because she was still in costume, complete with her trademark long plaits and flowing gown. She looked pretty glum, so I asked what was wrong.

peel

She explained that it had been a particularly harrowing day on the set. Ramsey Bolton had just filmed a scene where he was required to peel the skin off an old couple while they were still alive in order to extract information from them. Not surprisingly, the gory episode, complete with lashings of blood, had taken its toll on the actor who, she told me, had retired to his dressing room looking visibly distressed as soon as shooting ended.

Sansa said she was looking for a practical joke or novelty to cheer him up. I asked her what her budget was, and she said about £2. Luckily, I had just the thing in stock - Krapalot Sugar. Now some Krapalot sugar that other joke shops stock is just normal sugar with a bit of liquorice mixed in. Frankly, that's not going to get anybody's bowels moving. The stuff I stock comes from China, where the health and safety rules are frankly a lot more lax - a bit like they are with their fireworks.

'Stick a couple of lumps in his next cuppa, and he'll be too busy running backwards and forwards to the toilet to worry about skinning pensioners!' I chuckled.

ramsey

Stark was back in the shop the very next day to update me on how her leg-pull had gone. She told me that day's filming had promised to be, if anything, even more harrowing than the day before, as Ramsey Bolton had had to cut off Theon Greyjoy's manhood with a dagger. She had slipped the sugar into Ramsey's tea ten minutes before filming started.

"The Game of Thrones cast are some of my best customers" says chuckle merchant

Between girlish giggles, she explained: 'What should have been one of the goriest on-set moments of the show turned into an absolute hoot. Every time Ramsey pulled out his dagger to sever Greyjoy's old fella, he suddenly found himself grabbing his arse and sprinting off to the bogs as fast as his legs would carry him.'

douglas

'Over and over again, every time the director shouted 'Action!', the same thing happened,' she said, wiping the tears of mirth from her eyes. 'The poor sod was shitting over nine hedges and everybody, himself included, 99 was in fits of laughter.'

The black eyes have it

One of the show's most iconic scenes features Cersei Lannister doing the 'Walk of Shame', where she is humiliatingly forced to parade naked through the streets of King's Landing as a punishment for her sins. The day before filming, Cersei came into Terry's shop and confessed that she was feeling nervous about having to get her whole kit and caboodle out in front of so many people on the set. But the veteran jokemonger knew exactly what to do.

66 I told her not to worry, and took a tin of Black Eye Paint off the shelf. 'Just rub some of this round the camera eyepiece when no-one's looking,' I said. 'Then stand back and watch the fun.'

A lot of joke shops will just sell you boot polish and tell you it's Black Eye

Cersei: Black paint made sure all eyes were on the director.

Paint, but the stuff I stock is much better quality. It doesn't have tha distinctive smell that can easily giv the game away, and it won't come of except with turps.

castletown

Apparently, the prank worked treat. I later found out that the directo couldn't understand why everyone wa pointing and laughing at him after he' squinted down the camera to line up hi shot. In fact, all the members of the cas the extras and the crew were so bus making fun of the poor bloke's black ringed eye that they completely forgo about the scene, and Cersei was able t complete the whole ten-minute Walk o Shame without anyone looking 99 at her tits, arse or fanny.

Coronation treat

The Coronation of Prince Joffrey i Season 2 was to be the most ambitiou episode of Game of Thrones filmed u

MR. S. HITS KRAPALOT SUGAR

PUT SUGAR INTO A HOT DRINK & RETIRE TO A SAFE DISTANCE

MR. S. HITS KRAPALOT SUGAR

PUT SUGAR INTO HOT DRINK RETIRE TO A SAFE DISTA

Ingredients: Sugar, Magnesium Sulphate
NOT SUITABLE FOR CHILDREN
UNDER 9 YEARS OF AGE
Made in England for Funn

J45 A "FUNNYMAN" ©TM GAG FOR "JARROY OF LONDON"

BLACK EYE PAINT

Jokee dokee: A rollcall of Game of Thrones stars that reads like a Who's Who of Westeros A-listers thronged to Terry's Belfast shop (right) to buy Krapalot sugar (left), black eye paint (bottom, slightly to the left), Whoopee cushions (bottom, slightly to the right of the black eye paint), and them arrow-through-the-head things (bottom right).

TITANIC LAFFS

Shaft of inspiration: Simple joke shop trick saved the day for SFX crew.

o that time. But it went badly wrong, thanks to one of Terry's best selling lines.

The shooting script called for a grand procession through King's Landing to the Great Hall, featuring a cast of thousands, to be hot as one continuous take. The scene culminated in the boy king offrey mounting the steps and ceremoniously taking his place on he iconic Iron Throne.

Joffrey: Uncle Tyrion put the wind up the boy king.

Filming went without a hitch, as offrey strode up the steps to fulfil his destiny as monarch of the Seven Kingdoms of Westeros. But what nobody in the studio realised was that earlier that morning, yet another member of the cast had called into Titanic Laffs.

Peter Dinklage, who plays Joffrey's uncle Tyrion Lannister, told me he wanted to play a practical joke on his nephew in the show. 'I want to really bring the house down,' he grinned.

trick

I knew exactly the novelty that would do the trick - a genuine Whoopee Cushion! They're one of my best-selling lines and I've always got plenty in stock. As I told Tyrion: 'You won't get a better laugh in East Belfast this morning for £1.99.'

Back to the filming, and as Joffrey sat down, a proper, ear-splitting Bronx cheer echoed round the Great Hall! There are many inferior quality Whoopee cushions on the market these days, but the ones I sell in my shop are the real McCoy.

johnson

Not a single person in that room had any doubt that King Joffrey had just dropped his guts and possibly even followed through. Everybody was falling about laughing… except the director. He was absolutely furious that the whole meticulously planned scene had been ruined and would have to be shot again at a cost of $2 million.

'Arrowing' shot

Terry's novelties may have been responsible for ruining a few Game of Thrones scenes, but there was one time when they saved the show's bacon. The episode in question once again

Bolton: Gruesome scene went ahead thanks to Terry's special effect.

featured the sadistic Ramsey Bolton, the Lord of Dreadfort's bastard son, played by Iwan Rhion. The script called for Ramsey to shoot a peasant through the head with a bow and arrow at point blank range.

The Special Effects team were at a loss as to how to achieve the effect. They had tried everything: CGI, animatronic models, green screen… nothing was working. Then Emilia Clarke, who stars as Daenerys Targaryan, remembered something she'd seen on the shelf in my shop when she'd been in the previous day to buy a Naughty Fido fake dog turd.

yeltsin

It was two halves of an arrow, joined together with a flexible plastic band that gives the impression that the

shaft has passed all the way through the wearer's head.

The ones I stock are really good quality, too, not like the cheap ones that other joke shops sell. When you put them on, the two halves of the arrow line up more or less properly.

becker

Minutes later, the bell tinkled on my shop door, and I looked up to see who had come in. It was the giant simpleton Hodor, carrying Bran Stark on his back. They bought a Through-the-Head Arrow and rushed back to the studio, where shooting on the gruesome scene had already been stalled for half an hour.

Bolton pulled back his bow, the camera stopped and everyone stood still while the arrow was clipped onto his victim's head, and then the camera was started again. The harrowing scene was in the can!

karloff

That night, George RR Martin came into my local on the Shankhill Road and bought me a drink. 'Cheers Terry, you saved our bacon today,' he laughed.

● Terry's shop Titanic Laffs is currently having a closing-down sale, with up to 80% off all stock. He told us: "If you'd like to own a piece of real *Game of Thrones* memorabilia, pop in and I'll do you a deal."

"All prices are negotiable. If you see anything you like, make me an offer. I'm fecking desperate," he added.

GILBERT RATCHET

...AND THAT'S WHY, AS EDUCATION MINISTER, I HAVE DECIDED TO BRING IN WEEKLY TESTING OF PUPILS ON THEIR TIMES TABLES FROM THE AGE OF THREE...

...THIS WAY, WE CAN SEE WHICH PUPILS ARE FALLING BEHIND AND IDENTIFY THEM AS FAILURES, SO THAT LATER IN THEIR EDUCATION THEY CAN BE STREAMED TOWARDS LESS ACADEMIC SUBJECTS, SUCH AS WOODWORK AND REMEDIAL STUDIES.

MINISTER... WHAT ARE EIGHT NINES?

I BEG YOUR PARDON...

YOU JUST SAID THAT TESTING ON TIMES TABLES IS IMPORTANT, SO WHAT ARE EIGHT NINES..?

HO, HO, HO..! OH NO...

NO, NO, NO..!

YOU'RE NOT GOING TO AMBUSH ME LIKE THAT... HO, HO...

COME ON... EIGHT TIMES NINE.

NO, NO...

WHAT YOU'RE TRYING TO DO IS SIDETRACK ME FROM TALKING ABOUT THE REAL QUESTION, WHICH IS...

YOU DON'T KNOW, DO YOU, MINISTER..?

YES, OF COURSE I KNOW... OF COURSE I KNOW!

WELL, WHAT'S THE ANSWER, THEN? EIGHT NINES.

THE ANSWER IS NOT THE POINT AT ISSUE...

OKAY THEN... LET'S TRY A MORE SIMPLE ONE... FIVE FIVES.

NO, NO.. I'VE SEEN THIS HAPPEN BEFORE. IT'S A CHILDISH RUSE THAT YOU EMPLOY...

TWO SIXES..?

...THAT YOU EMPLOY TO TRY TO DISTRACT ME FROM GETTING MY MESSAGE ACROSS THAT CONSTANT TESTING...

TWO TWOS..?

...CONSTANT TESTING IS THE ONLY WAY TO DRIVE UP..., TO...ERM... TWO TWOS, DID YOU SAY..?

YES, TWO TIMES TWO.

OKAY...

ERM...

ER....

NO... THAT'S ENOUGH. I REFUSE TO PLAY THIS SILLY GAME OF YOURS ANY MORE...

MR BASICS...

IN FACT, THIS INTERVIEW IS AT AN END. I'M LEAVING.

GOOD DAY TO YOU.

WELL, THANK-YOU, MINISTER.

TV STUDIOS

QUIDWORLD

CALCULATORS £1!

QUIDWORLD

CALCULATORS £1!

...SO WHAT GAVE YOU THE IDEA TO WRITE A BOOK ABOUT JOHN CRAVEN..?

WELL, I'VE ALWAYS BEEN A BIG FAN OF HIS SINCE NEWSROUND...

...BUT WHEN I WENT INTO THE BOOKSHOPS TO FIND OUT MORE, I DISCOVERED THAT THERE WERE NO BOOKS ABOUT HIM.

SO YOU DECIDED TO WRITE ONE YOURSELF.

THAT'S RIGHT, YES, I DID, YES...

...AND DID YOU HAVE TO DO LOTS OF RESEARCH BEFORE YOU...

IT'S FOUR!

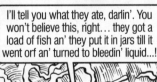

Well I don't know about that, but it sounds fackin' disgustin' to me, gel.

Fack me, look at this fackin' idiot.

Cam on! Get a bleedin' move on, you fackin' mappet! I've got another 600 years to go yet!

I tell you wot, I 'ate drivin' in the Middle Ages. It's gettin' worse, an' all.

Roll on the bleedin' peasants' revolt, I say...

...I've got a lot of time for that Wat Tyler, ah 'ave. I don't agree wiv everyfink 'e says, mind, don't get me wrong...

...But 'e's dead right about Richard the bleedin' first. 'E's let far too many of these immigrants in, see, if you arsk me. Far too many.

I've got naffink against 'em. There's jast too many of the barstads. Rahnd 'ere, you'd be lacky to 'ear an Olde English bleedin' voice these days. It's all yer Carpathians an' yer Saxons an' yer bladdy Frieslanders.

They cam over 'ere an' they're straight t' the top of the rude wattle an' daub dwelling list...

Hang on. This isn't Roman times...this is Neolithic Times!

Are you taking me round the houses to rack the fare up?

No, no, darlin'... I 'ad to do a detour rahnd the fourteenth century on account of they've got the Black Deff, see.

Scouts 'onour, via the Stone Age is the quickest way, gel. On my free kids, I ain't no robdog. Just along the Bronze Age bypass an' we'll be there. Two minutes.

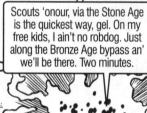
Half an hour later...

Struth! I tell yer, that was the busiest I've ever seen the Palaeolithic. Anyway, 'ere you go, darlin'...You want me t'keep the meter rannin'?

No thanks. I'll be quite a while. How much is that?

Twenty-six fifty to you, darlin'.

Here you go, keep the change.

Gaw. You're a darmond, mar gal.

Be lacky darlin'!

Salve. Ut ducas unumquodque ad Pontem Londoniarum in MDCCLXI, quaeso? Ego got esse in horam..

Bleedin' stroll on. No offence, but can't you speak fackin' English, mate?

Your lot conquered us two 'undred years ago, pal. Yer should've learned the bleedin' language by now.

NEXT WEEK: *Nobby picks up a Roundhead soldier who does a runner when he drops him off at a pub in 1902. And a young Protestant man escaping the persecution of Queen Mary in 1555 is charged a £100 valeting fee after he is sick in the back of the cab.*

THE END

WHETHER YOU WANT to get from Dover to Calais, from Newcastle to Amsterdam, or from Stanraer to Belfast, there's only one way to do it in style... *on a ferry*. A journey aboard one of these mighty leviathans of the sea is like taking a trip back in time to the golden age of cruising - a sumptuous experience that would be instantly familiar to stylish travellers of the past such as Noel Coward, Agatha Christie or the Great Gatsby. But whilst today's ships retain all the romance and opulence of former years, progress doesn't stand still, and they now boast every state-of-the-art luxury and convenience that a modern passenger could demand, including superfast wireless internet, contactless credit-card shopping and fruit machines. So let's pipe ourselves aboard MS Ocean Duchess to find out...

The **CAPTAIN (1)** spent his boyhood engrossed in tales of maritime adventure. As a child, his heroes were romantic adventurerers such as Horatio Hornblower, Francis Drake and Christopher Columbus, and he dreamt of a life criss-crossing the world's oceans, calling in at such exotic destinations as the Spice Islands, the pirate haven of St Marys in Madagascar, or rounding Cape Horn in a Force 10 gale to dock safely in El Quique. He now spends his days dreaming about taking up early retirement while reversing his ferry up to a jetty in North Shields so that 50 articulated lorries full of Nissan car parts and Dutch cucumbers can get on and off in less than 15 minutes.

The **DUTY-FREE SHOP (2)** is one of the busiest parts of the ship, providing everything a passenger could need. From small items such as Toblerones, tins of salted peanuts and Danielle Steele novels, to high-end items like designer clothing, exclusive perfumes and really big Toblerones, it can be bought here, and all for an improper fraction of the price you'd pay on the high street.

The **QUARTERMASTER (3)** is in charge of all the ferry's supplies. It's a big responsibility, because once the ship leaves port it is on its own; it must carry all the fuel it needs to make the crossing and enough food to feed 1500 hungry passengers and crew. Not only that, the Quartermaster has to ensure that the onboard shop doesn't run out of Toblerones, tins of salted peanuts or Danielle fucking Steele novels.

Welcome to the onboard **CINEMA (4)** where movie buffs can settle back in one of the ten seats available and enjoy the very latest blockbusters two months after they came out on a screen slightly less than twice the size you can buy in Currys. A state-of-the-art surround sound system competes and loses against the thrum of the engines hammering their way through 5 tons of heavy oil every hour on the deck below.

Once the ship has left British coastal waters, high-rollers head straight for the Ocean Duchess's 'Monte Vegas' **CASINO (5)** to play blackjack, shoot craps, or to wager a stack of chips on the spin of the roulette wheel. Thanks to the vagaries of maritime law, the casino is able to operate its own "ship's rules", which will be explained to you by an attractive croupier each time you think you've won but you haven't.

Gamblers who don't want to lose all their holiday money in the casino may like to check out the onboard **AMUSEMENT ARCADE (6)**, where they can lose all their holiday money in a range of one-armed bandits instead.

A modern ferry is equipped with all the modern amenities you would expect in a 5-star hotel, including a **SWIMMING POOL (7)**. It may look tempting on the ferry company website as it reflects the photoshopped azure blue of the sky, but only the most brave or foolhardy passenger would ever dare to risk taking a dip and being instantly dashed to unconsciousness in its 5˚c water as it mimics the pitching and rolling movement of the north sea.

Just like an army, a modern ferry sails on its stomach, and the 1500 hungry passengers and crew on board MS Ocean Duchess will all need feeding during their voyage. Here in the ship's **RESTAURANT (8)**, they can tuck into the sort of haute cuisine they might expect to be served in a 2-star restaurant, all at the sort [of] prices they might expect to pay in a 5-star one.

Hidden from view in the bowels of the ferry are the **VEHICL[E] DECKS (9)** - vast, steel-floored hangars that can accommodat[e] mind-boggling numbers of cars, trucks and coaches. Believe it or not, at any one time there could be as many as 15[0] articulated lorries, 50 buses and 1000 cars packed into th[e] vehicle decks, all with their alarms going off.

Just like back in the golden age of cruising, **PASSENGER CABIN[S] (10)** are available to suit every need. The budget-conscious ca[n] opt for a basic internal room with no windows, where they ca[n] doze off to the relaxing throb of the ship's 22,000 HP heav[y] diesel engines. For a few pounds more, a sea view cabin offer[s] the chance to peer through a rust- and salt-encrusted portho[le] for a few seconds before trying to doze off to the soothin[g] throb of the ship's 22,000 HP heavy diesel engines. And we [...]

ON BOARD THE FERRY

heeled passengers may wish to splash out on first class accommodation. This is the very definition of travelling in style, as they enjoy a wallet-emptying drink from the mini-bar while peering at the ocean through two rust- and salt-encrusted portholes for a few seconds, before trying to doze off to the soporific throb of the ship's 22,000 HP heavy diesel engines.

Roll-on, roll-off ferries are important arteries for international trade, and HGV drivers are regular customers. These knights of the road are provided with their very own area - the **TRUCKERS' LOUNGE (11)** - where they can relax away from holidaymakers. Here they can swap stories of life behind the wheel and chat about things that interest them, such as the latest developments in CB radio, how to piss into a Tizer bottle without spilling it, and how best to roll up a shop dummy in a carpet.

What time does the bingo start? Is that proper or foreign time? Is there anywhere on board where I can buy a Toblerone? The **PASSENGER INFORMATION DESK (12)** is the buzzing hub of the vessel, where travellers can find the answers to all these questions and more. Helpfully, the staff on duty also regularly pipe loud customer announcements - which can't be turned off - into every cabin and public space on the ferry, then repeat them in four languages.

Can You Spot...?

● **PASSENGERS** who have popped outside to the smoking area, all fruitlessly trying to strike a match in the teeth a Force 10 gale.

● **BIG TELEVISIONS** showing Sky News and Sky Sports with the sound off.

● **A COUPLE** who have dressed up in the hope that they will be asked to dine at the Captain's table.

● **PEOPLE** who haven't booked cabins, who are now in their ninth hour of nursing a single warm cola in the bar.

● **A CABARET** covers band starring somebody who was in a late, touring version of Showaddywaddy for a couple of weeks in the mid-eighties.

● **SOMEONE** emptying their father's ashes off the windward bow of the ship, realising that, with hindsight, it might have been better to have done it off the leeward bow.

● **HALF A DOZEN** families pleading to be let back to their car because they all think they might have left their lights on.

● **A MAN** who, having elected to wait until he was onboard before purchasing his holiday money, is being defibrilated after checking the rates on offer at the Bureau de Change.

● **A KIDS'** play area that is exactly the same as the one you would find in a wacky warehouse fun pub, plastered with badly drawn dolphins, octopii and seahorses, none of which you typically spot while travelling from Stranraer to Belfast.

● **A FAMILY** on their seventh full circuit of the ferry, as they can't remember what deck or side of the ship their cabin is.

● **A QUEUE** of couples waiting to do that thing from Titanic at the prow.

● **A MAN** staring intently at a spot in the sea where he thinks he might have just seen a dolphin out of the corner of his eye, but it wasn't. And anyway, it's not there now, whatever it was.

133

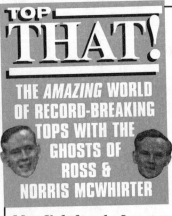

TOP THAT!

THE *AMAZING* WORLD OF RECORD-BREAKING TOPS WITH THE GHOSTS OF ROSS & NORRIS MCWHIRTER

Most Xs before the L on top sizing label

The size label on a top worn by darts player Andy "The Viking" Fordham (UK) during his semi-final match against Raymond van Barneveld (NL) at the 2004 BDO World Darts Championships, had 27 Xs before the L. Fordham later explained that although he usually took a 25XL in tops, this particular shirt had been made a couple of sizes bigger so as not to restrict his throwing arm. During a demonstration of the top on the BBC TV *Record Breakers* programme, it comfortably contained all 4 members of the pop group *Bucks Fizz*, with Therese Bazar and David Van Day out of *Dollar* simultaneously occupying the arms.

Most number of buttons on a top

A shirt belonging to Mr Ernest Dowdeswell (UK) was assessed in August 1978 to have 51 buttons. Having bought an ordinary shirt from his local branch of Marks & Spencers in Granby Street, Leicester, he proceeded to sew 4 extra buttons in the gaps between the 7 original buttons up the front, and added a further 9 buttons to each cuff. Mr Dowdeswell spent several years touring Britain and Europe as part of a travelling fun-fair, where he was billed as 'The Shirt Button Man of Leicester'.

Cappest sleeves

A black Fruit-of-the-Loom T-shirt worn by Mr Hymen Prepuce III of Minnesota (US) has the cappest sleeves ever recorded, measuring a whopping 10.8 on the International Cap Sleeve Scale. By comparison, the sleeves on the black T-shirt worn by the actor John Travolta in the film *Grease* measured 9.288 on the same scale, meaning they were nearly 15% less capped.

Remotest top

Terrestrial: The top that was furthest from the next nearest top on the earth's surface was a Damart PTA thermal vest worn by polar explorer Sir Ranulph Twistleton Whickham-Fiennes (UK) at 11.14am on 6th April 1991, when he reached a latitude of -87°34'26" during a single-handed traverse of Antarctica. At this moment, the next nearest top to Sir Ranulph's was a track suit jacket worn by Mr Boco Perez, who was standing on the corner of Calle Via Quatro in the Chilean town of Cabo de Hornos, 2241m (3607km) away.

Space: During a pass behind the Moon during the Apollo 11 mission on July 20th 1969, a T-shirt bearing the legend 'Keep On Truckin" and a drawing by Robert Crumb (US) of a man with a big foot, worn by Command Module pilot Michael Collins (US), was momentarily 247,368 m (398,100.207 km) from the next nearest top, a yak-hair jerkin worn by Sherpa Tensing Norgay (Tib), who was stood on the summit of Mount Everest. Collins' fellow astronauts, Neil Armstrong (US) and Dr Edwin "Buzz" Aldrin (US), were not wearing tops at the time, as they had elected to go 'top commando' under their spacesuits during their descent to the lunar surface in order to save weight.

Mrs Brady Old Lady

Panel 1: IS THERE ANY NEWS ABOUT YOUR BROTHER TODAY, ADA...? / THERE'S NO CHANGE, DOLLY.

Panel 2: STILL DEAD, THEN, IS HE..? / THAT'S RIGHT. SINCE 1987.

Panel 3: EEH, IT WERE A TERRIBLE BUSINESS. 'E BATTLED IT, YOU KNOW, BUT IT GOT 'IM IN THE END. / WERE IT, ADA, IF Y'DON'T MIND ME ASKIN'..? WERE IT... / WHAT

Panel 4: ...A-HEM...

OOH NO. IT WEREN'T... / ...A-HEM...

IT WERE A KANGAROO...'E'D SOMEHOW GOT IN ITS ENCLOSURE AT AN UNLICENSED SAFARI PARK IN BARROW...

THEY REAR UP, KANGAROOS, ON THEIR TAILS, Y'KNOW DOLLY, AND THEY EVISCERATE YOU WITH THEIR BACK LEGS...LIKE THAT..! / EEH... FANCY.

STILL, IT'S A NICE DAY OUT, IN'T IT, TRIP TO A SAFARI PARK..? / OOH YES, DOLLY. OTHER THAN THAT, WE 'AD A LOVELY TIME.

Millie Tant AND HER RADICAL CONSCIENCE

EVERYONE APOLOGISES

THERE were angry calls last night for everyone to apologise to everyone else after they said something in a series of tweets and Facebook posts. Everybody was unavailable for comment yesterday, but a spokesman for them said: "Everyone is extremely sorry if anything they have said on social media has caused offence to everyone else."

"It was never everyone's intention to upset anyone, but with hindsight everybody now realises that what they said was an error of judgement that they now deeply regret," he continued.

Everybody: Yesterday.

"Everyone on social media would now like to put all these unhappy episodes behind them, draw a line under everything and get on with all their lives," the spokesman added.

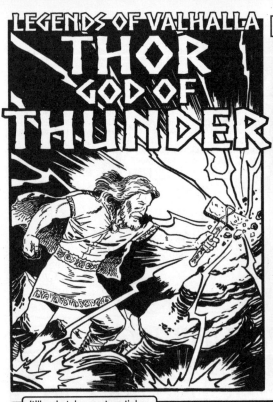

LEGENDS OF VALHALLA
THOR GOD OF THUNDER

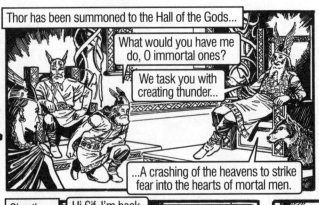

Thor has been summoned to the Hall of the Gods...

What would you have me do, O immortal ones?

We task you with creating thunder...

...A crashing of the heavens to strike fear into the hearts of mortal men.

I shall strike my anvil with my mighty hammer Mjolnir, and the terrible sound shall make the people tremble throughout the Earth!

Excellent! So shall our will be wrought!

Shortly...

Hi Sif. I'm back.

That was quick. What did they want?

They just want me to make some thunder to shit everyone up again.

Tsk.

It'll only take me two ticks. They just want a few claps.

Okay love.

Eh? Where the bloody hell is it?

Aw, bloody hell.

Sif, have you seen Mjolnir?

It's in the shed.

I've just been in the shed and it's not there.

It is. You've not looked properly. Go and have another look.

Where the bloody hell..?

It's definitely not there.

Well I haven't had it. And if I had, I would have hung it up back in the shed.

Well where is it, then?

Hold on... You lent it Baldyr last week, didn't you...?

Did I...?

I did, you're right! He was putting some trellis up at Ragnarok.

You see... blaming me!

Sorry.

I'd best go get the bugger back.

As if I've had the bloody thing.

I *said* sorry.

137

THE END

138

HE THINKS IT'S ALL OVER

MARK LAWRENSON's Premier League predictions have long been a weekend highlight for footy fans, allowing *Match of the Day* viewers to flex their punditry chops against the sharp-shirted soccer authority's expertise.

However Lawrenson, who goes by the nickname 'Lawro', sparked confusion at BBC headquarters this week when, instead of predicting the weekend's scorelines, he prophesied the end of the world!

BBC Sport intern Delwin Arbuckle told reporters: "Yesterday, when I got my notepad out and asked Lawro what he thought would happen when Swansea faced Huddersfield, his eyes clouded over, and he spoke with a deep, booming timbre that was very different to his usual watery Scouse whine."

antichrist

"'I see the fire falling', he intoned darkly. 'The seas will swell and the Antichrist shall rise once more to walk the Earth'."

Arbuckle revealed he was slightly taken aback by the ex-Liverpool man's forecast.

"He usually just rattles through the scorelines for the forthcoming Premier League games robotically and then nips off for a shit," he said. "But I jotted down what he had told me nevertheless."

anarchist

"I figured Lawro had just had a late one last night," Arbuckle continued. "So I moved on and asked what he reckoned to Burnley v Leicester for the late kick-off. But he just kept staring intently into the middle distance, chanting: 'I see the rivers running red with blood; I see plagues of locusts swarming from a blackened sky; I see aeons upon aeons of ceaseless night. Repent, O ye sinners, repent, for the end is coming'."

Arbuckle promptly posted Lawrenson's predictions on the *Match of the Day* website, sparking chaos and panic-buying

Lawro-stradamus: Pundit's predictions caused panic amongst footy fans.

Footy fave Lawro foretells of global apocalypse

of tinned goods, bread and toilet paper up and down the country.

island

Both the BBC and Lawrenson have since issued apologies for the apocalyptic outburst, with the veteran pundit claiming it must have been something he ate. However, telly medium DEREK ACORAH believes there could more to it.

iams cat

The silver-haired *Most Haunted* fave told reporters: "As the 21st Century's most high profile prognosticator, Lawro was most likely being used as a corporeal vessel to channel the visions of long-deceased mystics such as Mother Shipton, Emmanuel Swedenborg or Ali Bongo."

This is not the first time a BBC broadcaster has publicly predicted Armageddon. In 2014, weatherman Tomasz Schafernaker warned viewers of "angelic trumpeters sweeping in over the North East, and a lamb with seven eyes and seven horns to follow as we move through towards the middle of the weekend."

STRONG AND STABLE GROVELMENT

ONCE AGAIN, gangly PM *Theresa May*'s bizarre style of curtseying has curled the nation's toes. Meeting Prince William at a recent ceremony to commemorate the Battle of Amiens, the mantis-like premier abased herself with an awkward bodily contortion that some cruel observers likened to a pissing giraffe. Indeed, the second-in-line to the throne showed admirably steely resolve in stopping himself from laughing in her face, an act that could easily have led to a constitutional crisis.

And this isn't the first time that May's maladroit style of showing regal deference has turned Britain's cringe-o-meter all the way up to 11. At previous meetings with the Queen and other members of the royal family, the spindle-shanked PM has thrown a whole series of ludicrously graceless shapes as she struggles to genuflect in front of her betters.

But before we rush to judgement, we should ask ourselves a simpl question; *Would WE do any better*? If we suddenly found ourselv face to face with the magnificence of a genuine, blue-blooded roy could we demonstrate our abject obeisance and submission withou coming off like Bambi on a frozen lake?

Don't worry, because we're here to guide our readers through thi tricky, and potentially embarrassing, etiquette minefield. Here's ou handy reference guide to curtseying, bowing and scraping. It is your to cut out and keep.

The Bow

1 Place your left hand behind your back. If you are wearing a cape, use this hand to flick it backwards like a Phantom of the Opera.

2 Move your right foot backwards approximately 18" (457.2mm). Under no circumstances should you move your left foot forwards by the same distance.

3 Bend your right elbow 90° and place your right hand on your stomach, level with your cummerbund. If you are not wearing a cummerbund, they can be purchased at any gentlemen's outfitters

4 Keeping your head facing downwards out of respect and deference, bend from your waist at an angle of 85° while bending your right knee at an angle of 22°.

5 Use your right hand to perform a series of slack-wristed, open-palmed rolling twirls towards the royal personage, as if wafting away a fart.

6 To complete the manoeuvre, simply perform steps 1-5 in reverse order. Congratulations, you have sucessfully carried out the perfect royal bow.

The Curtsey

1 Daintily take hold of the side pleats of your frock with the forefinger and thumb of each hand.

4 Place your right tippy-6" (152.4m behind you left heel.

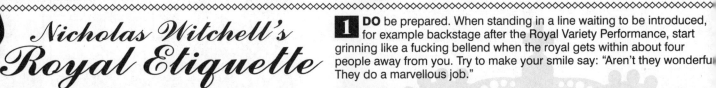

Nicholas Witchell's *Royal Etiquette*

A handy cut out 'n' keep guide to the DOS and DON'TS of meeting Royalty.

MEETING a member of the royal family can be an overwhelming experience. And amidst all the fluster and excitement, it can be very easy to "get it wrong" and cause offence to someone we should be showing cringing obeisance to. But fear not, help is at hand. Here former journalist Nicholas Witchell, now the BBC's chief royal fartsucker, sets out ten DOs and DON'Ts to observe when being introduced to your blue-blooded betters.

1 **DO** be prepared. When standing in a line waiting to be introduced, for example backstage after the Royal Variety Performance, start grinning like a fucking bellend when the royal gets within about four people away from you. Try to make your smile say: "Aren't they wonderfu They do a marvellous job."

2 **DON'T** allow a royal to see the soles of your feet. This is the worst insult that any subject can deal to their monarch.

3 **DO** look the royal family in the eye. There is a misconception that you should never look a royal in the eye, but in reality they like to maintain ey contact while asking what you do for a living, how long you have been doing that, and whether you have come far today.

4 **DON'T** ever move towards a royal. They are easily startled and could bolt.

5 **DO** shake their hand, but only if they offer you theirs first. If it's a female member of the royal family, kiss their hand even if they are wearing a glove.

Have Your Say

THE PRIME MINISTER'S Pink Floyd-teacher-puppet-style curtsey may have embarrassed the UK, but at least it has sparked an important national debate: *"In the 21st century, should we still be expected to show deference to members of the royal family?"* We went out on the street to find out what *YOU*, the plebs, thought.

"**...WHETHER** you choose to believe it or not, it is a fact that Her Majesty was appointed to her lofty station by the Lord God. That being the case, it is only right that the rest of us show her cringing deference by bowing and curtseying as low as possible if she deigns to allow us into her gracious presence."

Nobby O'Toole, binman

"**...BOWING** and curtseying are outdated practices that should be consigned to the dustbin of history. When meeting a modern monarch, we should show respect by doing a high five, a fist bump, or perhaps doing that thing basketball players do where they run towards each other, jump, turn in mid-air, and bang their arses together."

Mrs Audrey Frobisher, housewife

"**...RATHER** than me bowing to the Queen, it should be the Queen bowing to me, as it's me that pays her ruddy wages. Well, it would be if I didn't do all my jobs for cash, but the principle still stands."

Sid Churchill, builder and odd-job man

"**...IN MY** book, anyone who doesn't bow or curtsey when in the presence of a royal is guilty of High Treason, and should be hung, drawn and quartered by being tied to four horses, and then the horses would be whipped to make them all run off in different directions. And what's more, I'd crack the whip."

Rev J Timmins, curate

"**...IT BREAKS** my heart to think that the Queen might meet someone who refuses to bow and scrape before her. It's a simple act that costs us nothing and must make Her Majesty's day."

Iris Chlorine, doctor's receptionist

"**...I THINK** it is ridiculous that British people are expected to bow or curtsey to the Queen. It should be just foreigners and immigrants who have to do this. And if they refuse, we should send them back where they came from, and further."

Nigel Farage, MEP

"**...I AGREE** in principle with Mr Farage's proposal, but what if the immigrants he was sending back came from Portobello in New Zealand? In this case, sending them further - as he suggests - would actually mean that they were actually getting closer to Britain again. Perhaps we should simply send them back where they came from, and leave it at that."

B de Witt, groundsman

"**...BOWING** and curtseying to the royals is so old-fashioned and outdated. Surely these days we could show respect using a smartphone app."

Elon Lisk, tech entrepreneur

"**...WHAT** about people who have bad backs? When they meet the Queen, they are already bowing without putting in any effort in, so they get all the credit without actually showing any respect. These slackers should put the work in, and stand up straight when they meet the Queen."

Ron Bollinger, slaughterman

"**...EVERYONE** should be compelled to bow or curtsey when they are in the royal presence, unless they have a valid medical reason why they can't. On meeting the Queen, such people should present her with their exemption certificate that has been signed by their GP, and countersigned by another doctor and an independent healthcare professional."

Frank Gripe, pond cleaner

"**...ABSOLUTELY** we should bow and curtsey to the Queen. Not only that, it should be made part of the National Curriculum and taught in schools."

Anthony Regents-Park, MP

2 Curl the other three fingers daintily out of the way as if drinking a cup of posh tea (eg Earl Grey) in Fortnum and Masons.

3 Raise both hands to chest height while keeping your elbows bent at 90°.

5 Bend both knees so that your body drops while remaining perfectly vertical, until the hem of your dress is 7½" from the ground.

6 Perform the steps in reverse order to complete the manoeuvre. Congratulations. You've just done a proper curtsey

6 **DON'T** be offended if they wash their hands immediately after. It is one of their charming idiosyncrasies that they are terrified of catching lower class germs off their inferiors.

7 **DO** walk backwards when leaving the Queen's presence. Once you have taken six steps backwards, you are deemed to be out of the royal orbit and can turn round without igniting her rage.

8 **DON'T** leave the bag in the cup if you're making the Queen a cup of tea. Let it brew for a couple of minutes and squeeze it twice against the side of the cup, before taking it out and putting it on the saucer.

9 **DO** remember to not mention the monarch's future death. This is a treasonous act that is still on the statute books, and is punishable by at least 3 years in prison and a £50,000 fine.

10 **DON'T** kick a member of the royal family up the arse. Although it might be tempting, such a disrespectful act is not the done thing and could land you in hot water, quite literally. The punishment for such an act, introduced by Henry VIII, is to be boiled alive.

LetterbOcks

Viz Comic, P.O. Box 841 Whitley Bay, NE26 9EQ : letters@viz.co.uk

ST★R LETTER

POLITICAL correctness has changed our world in so many ways. Thirty years ago I used to work in a factory that made industrial copper wire, and one of our workmates had a massive cock. For a laugh we would regularly strip him naked and gaffer tape him onto the side of one of the massive wooden drums the copper wire was wound on. Then we would roll the drum through the factory to where the windows of the offices were, and we'd roll it backwards and forwards so all the women in the office could see his cock flopping about. You couldn't do that these days.

Bartram Golightly, London

MY wife just asked me who I think does all the cooking, cleaning and housework. To be honest, I think it's her as she doesn't exactly make it a big secret about it. But it seems so obvious that I'm beginning to wonder if it's a trick question. Could any of your readers help me out?

Steve Fowler, Manchester

I HAVE no idea why people use the phrase 'motherfucker' as an insult. I once had sexual relations with an attractive mother-of-two, and it was perfectly pleasant.

Iwan Carr, Upper Llandwrog

I WISH we had an England player on the left wing named Dutchie, just so we could all sing when the ball was passed to him.

Rick Pistol, St Albans

DURING a TV ad break recently, there was an advert for Tena Lady, immediately followed by one for vaginal dryness. I'm no expert on these matters, but come on ladies, which one is it?

Graham, email

IF any readers have lost a moth, it's in my house if you want to come and collect it.

Magenta Cartridge, West Kanyeville

I LOVE it when weather forecasters inform us that it's hotter where we are than it is in places like Miami or Barbados. As I walk down my local high street in 30 degree heat, trying to avoid seeing hairy, sweaty blokes with no top on, I think of those people on their golden beaches, sipping pina coladas while watching bikini-clad women stroll past, and I pity them with their paltry 29.5 degrees.

Steve Crouch, P'borough

I AM allergic to peaches, so imagine my delight when Coca Cola announced the launch of their new Zero Peach drink. Finally, a Coca Cola I can enjoy, I thought. However, it actually tasted peachier than any of their other products.

Marc Griffiths, Liverpool

PEOPLE always complain about plastic not being biodegradable, but they'd be pretty annoyed if they got home and their fridge had disintegrated.

Joel Robinson, M'chester

OUR towns and cities have been practically buried in litter and discarded plastic for decades and nothing is done. But one whale chokes on a carrier bag on the other side of the Atlantic and all of a sudden, I can't have a straw in my Cola. It's political correctness gone mad.

T.O'Neill, Glasgow

MOTHER Nature doesn't seem to be as tough as she used to be. Grimsby has a magnitude 3.9 earthquake, yet the massive overhang on the tuppenny falls machine at a Cleethorpes amusement arcade still defies gravity. On a completely unrelated subject, superglue is really strong, isn't it?

Jenx, Lincoln

TWITCHER'S CORNER

ON PAGE 120, David Smallbone asked for help identifying a bird in his garden from its distinctive "w-wurrr-woo, w-wurrr-woo" call. And the eagle-eared Viz twitching fraternity have been writing in in their droves...

...**I THINK** Mr Smallbone's bird is a pigeon. I have them sitting in the tree at the bottom of my garden, going "w-wurrr-woo, w-wurrr-woo" all the time, and pooing on my compost bin.

Charles, email

...**I BELIEVE** the mystery bird that goes "w-wurrr-woo, w-wurr-woo" is a wood pigeon. As a keen twitcher, I have spent many an afternoon watching and listening to these magnificent creatures. My wife has not left me for the postman yet, but I feel it is imminent.

P Wilkinson, Withernsea

...**I CAN** confidently say that it is probably called a Wurrr-Woo bird or something. And I'll take a fiver instead of a pen. A pen will do though, if you're a bit skint this month.

Paul Fallon, Halifax

...**IN** order to identify the bird with any certainty, Mr Smallbone must be more specific. "W-wurrr-woo, W-wurrr-woo" gives no indication of the speed of the sound made by the bird. If it was slow and lazy it could be a wood pigeon. But if it was more chippy and upbeat, it could be a collared dove (although a collared dove sounds more like it's saying "uniii-ted, uniii-ted"). So, unless you correspondent can provide more accurate information, he can just fuck right off.

Reginald Twitcher, Devon.

...**REGARDING** David Smallbone's letter enquiring as to which garden bird makes the w-wurrr-woo, w-wurrr-woo sound. It's the call of the collared dove, as opposed to the wood pigeon that goes w-wurrr-woo. So fuck off.

Chris Baylis, email

...**HAS** Mr Smallbone considered the possibility that there's just a couple of teenage burglars at the end of his garden imitating bird noises at certain times, so they can track his movements? Eventually they will probably break into his house, taking everything he owns, shitting on his carpets whilst they do so.

Andy Lyons, Birmingham

★ So there you have it, Mr Smallbone. Your mystery bird is either a wood pigeon, a collared dove, neither, or some teenage burglars with the turtle's head. We're glad to have been of service, and don't hestiate to write in again with any more ornithological related questions.

LAMES TO FAME

A BLOKE borrowed my mate's glasses the other week, and it turns out his cousin is Zach Galifianakis, one of the blokes who was in *The Hangover*. He borrowed a pen as well, but that was off my mate's mate.

Ian Nanford, London

MY BROTHER'S missus's mum taught Arthur Askey to ride a horse for a pantomime. That was when he still had legs.

Dennis Farmer, Cheshire

A FRIEND of mine brought Eddie "The Eagle" Edwards a drink a few years ago at a football match. He had a Diet Coke and my friend said he was the nicest bloke you could meet, even though he didn't buy him a drink back.

Martin Scoltock, Matlock

THE bathroom at the place where I work is so small that I can easily reach the sink while sitting on the toilet. In fact, I save precious time by washing my hands at the same time as taking a dump, leaving me free to simply wipe and get back to the kitchen for another challenging shift.

Howitt, Bedford

I SUPPOSE the liberal elite will queue up to call me a racist for this, but I'm not a fan of these Russian nerve agent poisonings. I'm sure the Islington Set would sneer at me for speaking my mind, but that's how I feel.

Pete Cashmore, Wolverhampton

I HAVE just tripped and fallen on a broken bottle. Fortunately it was a plastic bottle, which goes to show that pollution isn't always a bad thing.

Lew, Birmingham

THEY say that you are never more than twenty feet from a rat. Surely, if we could orchestrated it so everyone in the world moved twenty feet to their left or right, we could eradicate the rat problem by 50%.

Morton Bell, Deal

BRAD PITT AND EDWARD NORTON ARE THE SAME PERSON IN FIGHT CLUB.

CAR SPOILER

TOP

WHEN you have mislaid something around the house, asking your spouse "where have you put…(the object)?" rather than "have you seen…?" helps provide the kind of frisson needed to keep a relationship healthy.

D Cooper, Malta

PRETEND you're an angry vegan for a day by putting a piece of Lego in your sock in the morning and tutting at everything that isn't made of quinoa.

Gareth Thomas, Redhill

SAVE money at the supermarket by peeling your bananas before weighing them. This will also mean you have less rubbish to throw away at home, saving you more money in bin liners.

Mr S Andrews, Bristol

IMPROVE the quality of your online ads by googling the price of a Rolls-Royce once a week.

Adrian Horsman, Banbridge

BAILIFFS. Play the song *Someone's Knocking at my Door* when you need to repossess people's meagre belongings. They will think that they have won some money on the postcode lottery, thereby saving you the need to threaten debtors with powers you don't have in order to gain access to their property.

Jonathan Daykin, Langport

TIPS
toptips@viz.co.uk

WHY don't footballers wear plaster strips across their noses anymore? I'm starting to suspect it was perhaps a bollocks idea in the first place.

T. Rusling, Cottingham

IT is said that a family that plays together, stays together. Yet when I was caught playing with my sister-in-law's tits, the wife fucked off and I haven't seen her since. I'd like to hear the so-called 'experts' explain that one.

Adam, Newport

PLEASE find enclosed a picture of a strawberry that looks like Finbarr Saunders. Do I win £200?

Doug, Biggleswade

* *It does indeed look like Finbarr Saunders, Doug, but where on earth did £200 come from? Most readers conclude their letters with "do I win £5?" or "do I win a tenner?" Frankly, we find your upping the correspondence-ending financial request stakes in this way to be over the top, not to say a little disappointing.*

I ASKED the young man working in JD Sports today if he knew the price of a rucksack, and he replied pleasantly with a definitive and final-sounding "I'm sorry, I have no idea." It's quality customer service like this that makes visiting shops rather than shopping online an absolute pleasure.

Jane Hoole Garner, St Ives

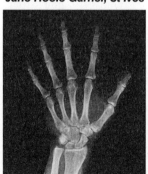

IF X-rays are so safe, how come doctors and dentists always hide behind a door whenever they switch them on?

Tarquin Armlock, Goole

CONSIDERING that my daughter is planning to do an English degree, I find her inability to agree with anyone without using the phrase "innit though?" slightly worrying. If three years of university can knock that out of her, it'll be £50k well spent in my book.

Steve Crouch, P'borough

MY wife reckons that XTC's 70s hit *Making Plans for Nigel* is the song that mentions the name Nigel the most number of times. However, I reckon there is probably a song out there somewhere which mentions Nigel even more times. Can your readers settle the argument please, as I'm living in a Travelodge until it's all sorted, and she's threatening to get a solicitor involved. And it's not the kids' fault, at the end of the day.

Jock Boofuss, Pontypool

* *Well, readers, time to don your marriage guidance counsellor hats and save Mr Boofuss's marriage by coming up with a song that mentions the name Nigel more times that that XTC record. Actually, don't bother. If he's in a Travelodge over such a paltry argument, his relationship's fucking doomed anyway.*

BBC news presenter Sophie Rayworth was on *BBC Breakfast* this morning talking about her grandfather, who lied about his age in order to become an RAF pilot in the First World War. I have to say, if I found out my grandfather was a liar I certainly wouldn't go on national television boasting about it.

Stanley Cheesecake, Hull

THE government's approach to reducing crime has clearly not worked over the years as the crime rate is still soaring. So, instead of punishment, why don't we try a more positive approach to law and order, and introduce a rewards system for good behaviour? For instance, if you go into a shop and don't steal anything, you receive a gift voucher. Drive under 30mph in a 30 zone and you get a nice box of chocolates. Go out on the piss and don't smash someone's face in and receive a Supercar Racing Track Experience. Such a 'carrot' approach may be far more effective than the punitive 'stick' system we currently have.

Rick Riley, Manchester

MY mate thinks it would be great if crabs could talk, but only in a foul-mouthed manner. Whenever you went rock-pooling they could say things like "put me back under that rock, you big fat bastard" or some such profanity. It would add a touch of hilarity to an otherwise dreary pastime.

Tim Buktu, Timbuktu

I DON'T know why foxes have the reputation of being cunning. I was watching one through the window last night and rather than simply walking through my neighbour's open front gate, the silly little bastard leapt up and jumped over the five-foot railings. He could have easily ripped his bollocks off. Not particularly cunning in my book.

Alf Dill, Kent

My Arse Has Cost Me My Dreams

ASK ANY schoolboy what he wants to be when he grows up and chances are he'll say a footballer, racing driver, film star or an astronaut. For the vast majority of us, such exciting jobs remain mere pipe dreams, and we end up settling for more mundane careers with a sanguine shrug of the shoulders.

But one Leeds man feels the disappointment of his lost opportunities more keenly than most, because during the past forty years he has come tantalisingly close to making his childhood dreams a reality. But frustratingly, each time a thrilling job offer has come within the grasp of 58-year-old Tollerton Ponds, it has been cruelly snatched away at the last moment due to bottom trouble.

"My dodgy backside has been my Achilles heel time after time," Tollerton says ruefully. "Whenever I've been on the point of landing a job that the average Joe in the street would kill for, my anus has always blown it for me one way or another."

Ponds's troubles began when he left school and joined the employment market. "I was an Easter leaver,"

EXCLUSIVE!

Tollerton's heartbreak after anus repeatedly scuppers career

he told us from his bedsit above a Crossgates fishmongers. "All the teachers told me I would pass my exams with flying colours, so there was really no point sitting them as I would simply be wasting mine and everyone else's time."

estate

"I'd been left school for a couple of months and me and some of the other Easter leavers were having a kick around on some waste ground on the estate. We were having a good game; it was three against three with rush keepers and I had scored about 25 times, when I noticed somebody watching us from a flashy car that was parked nearby."

"Eventually, the driver got out and wandered over. I was amazed to see that it was none other than Don Revie, the former Leeds United manager who was now in charge of the England team. He took me to one side."

sports

"He told me he'd been watching me play and he'd been impressed by what he'd seen. So impressed, in fact, that he wanted to sign me up there and then to be the new Captain of the national side for the following year's World Cup campaign. I simply couldn't believe it; I'd always wanted to be a professional footballer - what

Sweet FA: Career as soccer star was scuppered by laxative effects of Smints.

schoolboy hadn't - and this was the opportunity of a lifetime. I thought he must be a wind-up merchant pulling my cock. But then he pulled a £10,000-a-week professional player's contract out of his sheepskin jacket and handed it to me to sign."

clown

"It was like a dream come true for a young lad just out of school. I couldn't wait to scribble my name on the dotted line and begin my new life as a sports star."

"That morning I had eaten two packets of Smints on my way to sign on and another couple on the way home, and I've since learned that it says on the packet that excessive consumption may cause laxative effects. Unfortunately, those laxative effects suddenly made themselves known at that exact moment. It felt like there was about a hundredweight of thin gravy about to burst out of my browneye."

bowling

"I told Mr Revie that I had to dash off for a minute, but to wait there and I would be straight back. I dashed behind the nearest bush, unbuttoning my Oxford bags as I ran. I got them down just in time, a

split second before my freckle erupted like a dirty geyser. It went on and on and on like a rooster tail; every time I thought it had stopped, it would start up again, even worse than before."

"Eventually, after what seemed like an age, my bowels finally ran out of fuel. Thankfully, I found a crisp bag and used it to clean myself up as best I could, and pulled up my kegs. I emerged from behind the bush to sign my contract and my heart sank as I saw Mr Revie's car driving off. He'd clearly got fed up of waiting for me while I was having my Smint-powered clearout."

village

"A year later, as I watched Kevin Keegan proudly leading the England team out onto the field in Argentina to start their 1978 World Cup campaign, I choked back tears of regret at what could have been. At that moment, I vowed never again to let my bottom come between me and my dreams."

Although countless young lads dream of chasing glory behind the wheel of a Formula One racing car, very few actually make the grade. So when Tollerton got an unexpected chance to prove his mettle on the

race track, he was determined not to let his golden opportunity slip through his fingers.

"I'd always had a very specific idea of the sort of career path I wanted to pursue; I wasn't prepared to take just any old job that was offered to me. As a result, I'd been signing on for about four years when I suddenly got a letter off the nash to say that they were going to stop my benefits if I didn't start actively looking for work."

arthur

"The next afternoon, as I half-heartedly browsed the Situations Vacant boards in Gipton JobCentre, my eye was drawn to a dog-eared postcard tucked away in the corner of one of the racks. 'Grand Prix racing team seeks driver,' read the ad. 'Apply in person at the Lotus garage, Silverstone Circuit, Northants'. "

"I'd always wanted to be a Formula One racing driver - what schoolboy hadn't - my ambition had always been to join the ranks of my heroes James Hunt, Niki Lauda and Emerson Fittipaldi on the glamorous, high octane, international motor racing circuit. This was my big chance, what all those years on the rock & roll had been leading

Piles per hour: Haemorrhoids put paid to chance of Grand Prix stardom.

up to; a chance to take my most outlandish dream and turn it into a one thousand horsepower reality."

"I bought a ticket on the next National Express to Northamptonshire. It was a terrible journey down from Leeds, with the bus stopping everywhere. I had been suffering from really bad piles for the past few weeks, and the eight hour coach trip along the A1 really brought the buggers down something rotten. As I hobbled up the Silverstone pit lane towards the Lotus garage, I was in agony."

paper

"Team boss Colin Chapman answered the door. He explained to me that he wasn't interested in paper qualifications, only raw talent behind the wheel. Basically, if I could drive the car around the circuit in less than seventy seconds, the job would be mine. I knew I could do it. At that time, I used to spend half my dole money at an arcade in Garforth, driving for hours on a racing game called Jackie Stewart's Grand Prix Champ, so I knew every twist and turn of the Silverstone circuit like the back of my hand."

"The job was as good as mine. I couldn't wait to slip into that racing car and show the boss what I could do."

chip

"But it was not to be, as my bottom once again conspired to thwart my ambitions. As I slipped into the cockpit and lowered myself behind the wheel, I screamed in pain. The hard bucket seat was putting so much pressure on my farmers that it felt like I had a broken bottle sticking up my jacksie. Each movement of my feet on the pedals was a fresh wave of torture to my poor chocolate starfish."

"As two mechanics hoisted me out of the car, I spotted the next interviewee standing in the corner of the garage, a fresh-faced youngster named

Nigel Mansell. He slipped into the cockpit, gunned the engine and tore off round the track in a cloud of burning rubber, eventually taking the flag in an impressive 69.6 seconds. I knew I could easily of beat his time if I had only of been free from the misery of galloping bumgrapes, but sadly that was not to be."

"My chances of getting the job of my dreams evaporated before my eyes, and with it my hopes of a jetsetting lifestyle, seven-figure salary and a supermodel on my arm with big tits. It was back to signing on in Crossgates for me."

Back in Leeds, another four years of unemployment passed. Tollerton had almost given up hope of securing an exciting, glamorous career, when he read something in the paper that gave him new hope.

"I was flicking through Titbits in the barbers, and there was a story about how Roger Moore was retiring as James Bond. I'd always wanted to be a film star - what schoolboy hadn't - and now the role that every actor dreams of was suddenly up for grabs. I knew the casting call for a new 007 would be going out soon, so I decided to steal a march on my rivals and set off for Pinewood studios, where I hoped to secure an audition in front of Cubby Broccoli."

"The legendary producer saw me straight away. He asked me if I could lift one eyebrow up, which I did, and he told me I'd got the job. He explained that the shooting on the next movie, *A View to a Kill*, would start the very

A poo to a kill: Large stool led to catastrophic anal fissure on brink of achieving 007 stardom.

next day, and my fee would be a million pounds plus 50% of the gross box office. To say I was over the Moon would be an understatement."

sex

"My first scene would require me to ski off the Alps wearing a Union Jack parachute, so I would have to be at the studios first thing in order to learn how to ski and parachute. I booked myself into a nearby boarding house, aiming to get a good night's sleep before my big day. However, things didn't go to plan."

"For the previous three weeks or so, I'd been living mainly off a diet of eggs and black puddings, so I was really having to push when I went to the toilet. On the morning of the first day's shooting, I went for my number two and suddenly felt a sharp pain shoot straight up my back passage. When I looked in the bowl, I had passed a motion that was the size of a thermos flask, and I'm not exaggerating. That big bugger had split my ringpiece wide open."

book

"Now we all get a little anal fissure now and again, but this one was so bad I had no alternative but to go to the nearest hospital to get it seen to. There was a big queue in the A&E department and I didn't get seen until dinner time, when they put three stitches in it and told me to eat soup and fruit for the next week."

"I got the next bus back to Pinewood, all ready to apologise to Mr Broccoli for my late showing and assure him it wouldn't happen again.

But when I got there, the crew had got fed up of waiting and the director had given the role of James Bond to Timothy Dalton instead."

fish

"As I gingerly duckwalked off the studio lot, wincing with every step, I reflected ruefully that once again, I had had my dream job in the palm of my hands, only to see it snatched away by my errant bottom."

Still refusing to settle for anything less than his ideal career, Tollerton spent the next eight years on the dole.

He told us: "I would pop into the local JobCentre every few weeks to see if there were any vacancies for professional jetskiers, lion tamers, or Red Arrows pilots, but such job opportunities were few and far between, particularly in the Crossgates area."

kid

"I'd always wanted to become an astronaut - what schoolboy hadn't - so on a whim, I decided to send my CV to NASA. I'd got grade 4 in the mock CSE science test I'd done just before leaving school at Easter, so I thought I was in with a shout of a ride to space on the next Shuttle. And NASA clearly thought I had the right stuff too, because I got a letter back by return of post, saying I'd got the job and asking me to report for astronaut training at Cape Carnival, Florida in a week's time."

"The offer was subject to a clean bill of health, so I booked an appointment with my GP for a medical the next morning. Then I went out to celebrate my good news with a few jars in Leeds. I must have had a few too many, because when I came out of the pub in the early hours, I took a wrong turning and fell into the canal."

"I managed to scramble out onto the towpath, but

We have blast-off!: Ponds's foetid Scotch egg wind shattered dream of flying on Space Shuttle.

not before I'd swallowed half a gallon of the putrid canal water. It must have reacted with the ten pints of Scotch Bitter that was already in there, because in the morning my guts were absolutely rotten. They were making a noise like a cappuccino machine and I was doing some of the tripiest, most lethal farts I've ever had the misfortune of smelling."

cat

"Things hadn't improved by the time I got to the doctors; if anything they'd got worse. After I dropped a couple in the waiting room, the receptionist told me to stand in the car park and said she would shout me in when it was time for my check-up."

"The doctor gave me the once over. She said she was a bit worried about my excessive flatulence, but I explained it was simply due to a combination of canal water and, to a lesser extent, Youngers bitter. However, she must have mentioned her concerns in her medical report, because the next day I got a letter from NASA withdrawing their previous astronaut job offer."

fire

"Apparently, the mission director thought that the enclosed, highly pressurised environment of a Space Shuttle was no place for someone who was dropping their guts every few seconds."

"I could have been the first man from my estate to fly into space. It would have been one small step for man, one giant leap for a man from Crossgates. But alas, once again my dream lay in tatters at the hands of my pestilential anus."

Next week: A septic anal fistula that erupts the night before his first stadium gig as Queen's new lead singer puts paid to Tollerton's dreams of rock stardom.

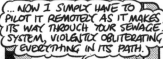

CLINT IN A TIZZ

Hollywood star upset by tiny bird tree find

PALS of CLINT EASTWOOD say the Tinseltown star has recently been "in a right tizz" after he found a baby bird at the bottom of a tree in the garden. The star of movies such as *A Fistful of Dollars*, *Dirty Harry* and *Every Which Way But Loose* was out playing when he spotted the chick at the base of a tree.

Do you feel plucky?: Hollywood hard-man Eastwood was left in a flap after finding featherless bird.

"He looked up the tree but he couldn't see the nest it must have fell out of," said Eastwood's close friend and *Bronco Billy* co-star **SONDRA LOCKE**. "It didn't have no feathers on, and he was all worried the cat would get it if he just left it."

oscar

The 2-times Oscar winner ran inside to alert his mum to the bird's predicament. "I asked her if I should climb up the tree and put it back on a twig but she said just leave it because its mam would be watching and if she smelt me on it she would kick it out the nest anyway," he told satellite entertainment news channel TMZ. Mrs Eastwood also cautioned her son, 88, against climbing the tree in case he ripped his best trousers.

The *Outlaw Josey Wales* star was still worried about the bird, and decided to give it something to eat. "I put it out a saucer of milk with bread in but it didn't want it," he told the channel. "It was just sat there squawking at me with its yellow beak."

big bird

Not long afterwards, Eastwood's best pal and Spaghetti Westerns co-star **LEE VAN CLEEF** turned up to help him build a den. "Lee knows loads about birds because he found a swallow that had flown into the front window and he kept it in a box and fed it off the end of a pencil until its wing mended," the *Magnum Force* star said. "He let it go up near the woods and it flew off."

"Lee said I shouldn't of tried to give it milk and bread as it was too small and instead I should of give it chopped up worms like what its mam would do," Eastwood added.

Bad Bob The Randy Wonder Dog

IT WAS a dark, snowy Christmas Eve in Glenpeebles, and Sergeant Greenock had just taken a worrying call. "That was Auld Jock the shepherd's wife," he told his terrier Bob. "She says he's nae returned frae the moors. Come on laddie, we're awa' oot tae find him. We'll tak a flask o' tea wi' a wee nip o' somethin' stronger tae warm 'im up."

THE PAIR were soon out searching on the bleak, snow-covered moors above Glenpeebles. The sergeant pushed his way through the deep drifts, calling the shepherd's name. "Auld Jock! Whaur are ye?" he shouted. Suddenly, he heard a faint cry in return. "Did ye hear that, Bob?" he said. "I think it came frae Braveheart Crag!"

AULD JOCK had slipped down the crag whilst rescuing a lamb. He had landed on a narrow ledge, but his leg was badly broken. "Quickly, Bob," said Greenock. "Tak yon flask doon tae him, an' I'll lower the rope tae rescue him!" Gripping the flask tightly in his jaws, the nimble-footed terrier skittered down the steep slope to the injured shepherd.

BUT WHEN he got down to the ledge, Bob suddenly forgot all about his mercy mission and clamped himself tightly onto the lamb's back. The little dog humped away for all he was worth, as Greenock vainly commanded him to behave himself. "Staup that, ye mucky wee bugger!" the sergeant shouted. "Bad Bob! Staup it richt awa', d'ye hear me?!"

GREENOCK threw a snowball in an attempt to put the amorous terrier off his stroke. "Tak that, ye randy wee fud!" he shouted. But the sergeant's aim wasn't true, and the snowball's impact took the orphan lamb's feet from under it. As the poor creature toppled off the ledge, Bob released his grip and somehow managed to scramble to safety.

WITH THE lamb fallen to its doom in the glen far below, the lust-filled mutt turned his romantic attention to Auld Jock's broken leg. "Aargh! Ma leg!" screamed the shepherd. "Get yon dirty wee bas aff ma feckin' leg! Aaargh!" "Bad Bob! Nae biscuit fair ye!" shouted Greenock. "Let go or I'll tak a bluidy newspaper tae yer wee snoot, so I will!"

JOCK SECURED the rope around his chest and Greenock began hauling him up the crag to safety. "Bob, will ye nae leave go o' the puir mon?!" shouted the sergeant. But Bob was nearly at the Billy Mill roundabout, and he was deaf to this master's commands. Jock screamed in agony as the priapic pooch hammered away at his compound fracture.

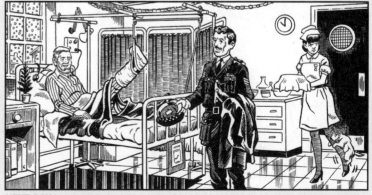

NEXT DAY in hospital, the injured shepherd had a pair of very special visitors who came with compliments of the season. "Merry Christmas, frae me an' Bob," said Sergeant Greenock. Jock smiled. "It's thanks to ye twa that I'm here at a'," he said. Suddenly, the nurse screamed. "Eek! Get this mucky wee fecker auf ma leg!"

The Twelve Days of Christmas

Whether it's not decorating the tree until Christmas Eve, wearing comedy jumpers on December 25th, or toasting the Queen's Speech with a sip of sweet sherry, every family has its own set of quirky and eccentric Christmas traditions … and our favourite stars are no exception. We were originally intending to ask a dozen top showbiz celebrities called Day to tell us about the origins of their own families' much-loved Christmas customs, but we could only think of ten. One of them was dead and two others wouldn't reply so, to fill up the page, we thought of a few other household names and asked them as well.

DARREN DAY *Ex-serial love rat*

"AT my house, we tie grandad up with a washing line and lock him in the shed from Christmas Eve until Boxing Day. Our family have been tying up the eldest male member and putting them in the shed for Christmas for generations, and nobody can remember why the tradition started. It's a bit of fun that everyone looks forward to all year, except grandad, obviously. I'm fully aware that one day it will be my turn to be tied up and put in the shed, and I only hope I'll be able to meet that horrible ordeal with good humour and a twinkle in my eye."

DAVID VAN DAY *Ex-Dollar, ex-Guys'n'Dolls, ex-a-version-of-Bucks Fizz singer*

"CHRISTMAS wouldn't be Christmas in the Van Day household without us putting washing-up liquid on our turkey. One Christmas when I was little, my mother accidentally filled the gravy boat with Fairy Liquid, and before we realised, we had all poured the bright green detergent on our dinners. As you can imagine, we all fell about laughing at mum's daffy goof, and it was such a happy family memory that we've done it every year since. It wrecks the meal, and we have to throw it all away and have a Pot Noodle or beans on toast instead, but I think these traditions are worth keeping."

GREEN DAY *US pop group*

"BEFORE we were famous, we couldn't afford a real Christmas fairy, so we would draw straws to pick one of us to sit on top of the tree until twelfth night, when the decorations came down. Thanks to all the pop hits we've had over the intervening years, we could now afford to buy any number of Christmas fairies, but we still keep up our old tradition. Sure, the real thing would look just swell, but it simply wouldn't be the same as having one of us up there with the top of the tree stuck up his fanny, which is what we Americans call an arse."

YOU are FATHER CHRISTMAS The Ref

Test YOUR Festi
top North Po

1 AN attacking player passes the ball forward to a team mate, and your linesman raises his flag to indicate an offside offence. However, you spot a defending player hanging up his stocking in the back of his goal. What do you do?

2 A goalkeeper in possession throws the ball out to a team mate on the wing. However, before the ball reaches him, he collides with a small table with a mince pie, a glass of sherry and a carrot on, which have been left for you and your reindeer by one of the opposing team, and the ball rolls into touch. How do you restart the game?

3 A centre half is sitting on your knee just outside the penalty box telling you what he wants for Christmas when an attacking player with a clear run at goal takes a shot. The centre half deliberately reaches out with his hand and deflects the ball out of touch. What action do you take

DANIEL DAY-LEWIS *Tall-hatted Gangs of New York actor*

"WHEN I was little, one Christmas my dad, the Poet Laureate Cecil Day-Lewis, decided to dress up as Santa Claus, climb up on the roof, and come down the chimney to surprise us all. However, somewhere between the first and second floor, he got stuck and my mother had to call the fire brigade to knock a big hole in the chimney breast to get him out before he suffocated. He tried the same stunt the next year, and the year after that, and every year till he died. And I have carried on the same festive tradition every year since. The firemen are here every December 24th, knocking a big hole in the chimney breast and pulling me out in a big cloud of soot, before enjoying a warming glass of sherry and a mince pie. I like to think it's become as much a part of Hampstead Fire Brigade's Christmas as it is the Day-Lewises's."

FELICIA DAY *Buffy sidekick*

"WHEN I was little, every Christmas morning Mom and Pop would walk us to our local park in Huntsville, Alabama, before walking us back home to open our presents. And now I am a parent myself, that's a tradition I have carried on with my own daughter. We live in Los Angeles, so after breakfast every December 25th, we set off on the 2,000 mile walk to the park in Huntsville, Alabama. Once there, we have a little play and a little walk round the pond before excitedly setting off to walk 2,000 miles back to open our presents. We usually get to open them some time in the middle of May."

DORIS DAY *96-year-old girl next door*

"MY Pop grew up on a farm, and he always said that on Christmas Day his parents made him go out and milk all the cows in the barn before he was allowed to open his presents. And that lovely story from his childhood became a festive family tradition that I still carry on to this very day. Of course, I don't milk 40 cows like dad used to have to, that would simply be ridiculous. I just have 6 brought round to my New York apartment first thing every December 25th, and I milk them all into a bucket. Then, after opening my presents, I tip all the milk down the bog because I'm a vegan."

THE LATE SIR ROBIN DAY *Former Question Time curmudgeon (speaking via a Ouija board)*

"WHEN my children were growing up, every year we had a Christmas tradition that we called 'Trick or Carol'. The whole family would go down our street, carol singing from door-to-door. We weren't the most musical family in the world, but what we lacked in close harmony we more than made up for with our good humour and enthusiasm. What's more, we were collecting donations for local good causes as we went. And if any of our neighbours didn't answer the door to us, we would key their car, put a window through or push dog dirt through their letterbox."

SIMON DAY *Fast Show funnyman*

"WHEN I was a kid, I accidentally opened a present from my dad that was intended for my mum – it was a bra, and everyone laughed at me. The next year, they bought me another bra as a joke, and you won't be surprised to learn that giving me bras as presents has become a family tradition. These days, my wife and kids buy me bras for Christmas and birthdays, and I've got hundreds of the things that I keep in boxes all around the house. Honestly, I could set up a bra shop if the acting work ever dried up. Come to think of it, the acting work is drying up a bit, so you never know, I might start thinking about setting up a bra shop. I think I'll call it *Day's Bra Shop* or *Bras By Simon*."

DR HANNAH FRY *TV Mathematician*

"ONE Christmas when I was little, our TV aerial fell down and we could only get BBC 2 because the man wouldn't come out until the new year. Ever since, the whole family has only ever watched BBC2 over the festive season, and it's a tradition I carry on to this very day in my own home. As a result, over the years we have missed some great programmes and watched some right old shit. But it's important that quirky customs like these aren't allowed to die out."

IDRIS ELBA *James Bond actor*

"ON Christmas morning when I was eight, I was so excited about opening my presents that I put my underpants on back to front before running downstairs. Everybody fell about laughing, so the next year I did it again as a joke. You won't be surprised to hear that today, 38 years later, I still put my underpants on with the Y-shaped tassel flap at the back every Christmas. Nobody knows I'm doing it because I've got my trousers on, but I'm determined to keep this tradition going for future generations."

DAVID BECKHAM *Brand*

"WE'VE never had any festive traditions in our family, so I tried to start one last year. On Christmas Eve, I sat down with the whole family to read them Clement Clarke Moore's *The Night Before Christmas*. To be frank, the exercise wasn't a big success; when it comes to reading, I've got a bit of a monotonous voice, and it wasn't long before the kids got their iPhones out and started going on Facebook and Instagram, and so did Posh. If I'm honest, I only got about half way through the poem before I got my iPhone out as well. I might give it another go this year, but if it doesn't go down any better, that's it, I'm knocking it on the head."

JACOB REES-MOGG MP *Utter bellend*

"I HAVE always stressed the importance of family life to whomever I am employing to raise my children, and I would imagine that, consequent upon that earnest injunction, they may possibly perpetuate several Yuletide traditions."

Footballing Knowledge with Football Association Referee Santa Claus

Christmas morning.

Question 1: Despite being over the goal line, his stocking is still deemed to be involved in play. He is therefore playing the attacker onside, so over-rule your linesman and allow the game to continue. When play stops, caution the defender for leaving the field of play without permission.

Question 2: Bringing anything onto the field which may cause injury to a player is deemed reckless play and can result in dismissal. However, since it was a nice gesture, you could downgrade the offence to dangerous play and caution the player who left it. Restart the game with a throw-in to the opposing team, requesting them to give it back to the keeper.

Question 3: In deliberately handling the ball, has denied a goal-scoring opportunity, an offence which warrants an instant dismissal. You tell him that he has been very naughty, and that only footballers receive a visit from Santa. You show him a red card and leave him a piece of coal on Christmas morning.

ANSWERS

mr. LOGIC

hmmm

Cobley's Bank

THIS IS A STICK-UP! PUT YOUR HANDS IN THE AIR!

I SAID... PUT YOUR HANDS IN THE AIR!

hm...

IN THE SENSE THAT THEY ARE PRESENTLY CONTAINED WITHIN THE PLANET EARTH'S BREATHABLE ATMOSPHERE, MY HANDS ARE ALREADY "IN THE AIR".

IT IS GENERALLY AGREED BY THOSE WHO STUDY THE SUBJECT - AEROLOGISTS - THAT AIR IN SOME DETECTABLE FORM CEASES TO EXIST AT AN ALTITUDE OF APPROXIMATELY 100 KM ABOVE SEA LEVEL... AT THE SO-CALLED "KARMAN LINE"..

...HOWEVER...

...BOTH MY HANDS ARE SITUATED INSIDE THE PLANETARY BOUNDARY LAYER OF THE TROPOSPHERE, WHERE THE AIR IS IN A STATE OF HYDROSTATIC EQUILIBRIUM...

TROPOSPHERIC AIR IS COMPOSED AS FOLLOWS.. 78·09% NITROGEN, 20.95% OXYGEN, 0.93% ARGON...

0·04% CARBON DIOXIDE, PLUS VARIOUS TRACE...

BLAM! BLAM! BLAM!

HOORAY!

FARMER PALMER

PIG SHIT

Borsetshire Land Registry

DEEDS

OI! YOOMZ TWOOOZ..!

GET ORF MOY LAAAAAND!

DEEDS

The **REAL ALE TWATS**
5.2 ABV
D.J. '18

SATURDAY LUNCHTIME
THIS IS A RARE TREAT FOR US, CASKETEERS!

IT HAS BEEN SOME TIME SINCE WE INDULGED IN A SPOT OF AFTERNOON QUAFFING!

BUT BEWARE! WE MUST PACE OURSELVES AND REMEMBER THAT THIS IS NOT ONE OF OUR USUAL EVENING BOOZING SESSIONS!

THERE IS NO NEED TO HURRY THE PINTS DOWN OUR NECKS IN A RACE AGAINST THE LAST ORDERS BELL!

NO, DAYTIME DRINKING REQUIRES A VERY DIFFERENT APPROACH...

IT IS A QUIET, LEISURELY AFFAIR — A TIME TO PERUSE THE NEWSPAPER AND SLOWLY SUP OUR ALES IN THE TRANQUIL ATMOSPHERE OF AN ALMOST-DESERTED LOUNGE BAR...

WHAT ON EARTH —※?

HI! HAVE YOU BOOKED A TABLE?

NO WE HAVE NOT "BOOKED A TABLE." WE ARE HERE TO IMBIBE ALE!

I WAS UNDER THE IMPRESSION THAT THIS WAS A PUBLIC HOUSE, RATHER THAN A RESTAURANT WITH A CRÈCHE!

COME, CASKETEERS. LET US PROP OURSELVES UP AGAINST THE BAR AND TRY TO IGNORE THE CACOPHONOUS DIN OF CUTLERY UPON PLATES!

I'M AFRAID THIS IS THE FOOD SERVICE AREA, IF YOU WOULDN'T MIND MOVING AROUND THE BAR A BIT...?

WELL REALLY!

TSSCH! THE CURSE OF THE "FAMILY FRIENDLY PUB" STRIKES AGAIN!

ONCE MORE, WE HONEST-TO-GOODNESS DRINKERS ARE MADE TO FEEL LIKE SECOND CLASS CITIZENS IN OUR OWN HOME!

JUST LOOK AT THIS PLACE! KIDS RUNNING AMOK, THE PEACE AND QUIET SHATTERED BY THEIR CRIES AND JUVENILE CHATTER!

WHATEVER HAPPENED TO THE TRADITIONAL BRITISH ALEHOUSE?

WHEN I WAS A NIPPER, CHILDREN WERE MADE TO SIT OUTSIDE THE PUB WITH A PACKET OF CRISPS AND A GLASS OF POP.

ANY OF US WHO DARED TO POKE OUR HEADS AROUND THE SALOON BAR DOOR WOULD BE MET WITH DISAPPROVING GLARES FROM THE DENIZENS WITHIN!

BUT WE RESPECTED THAT RULE, BECAUSE WE KNEW THAT THE PUB WAS A PRIVATE SANCTUARY FOR ADULTS...

...A GROWN-UP PLACE, WHERE THEY COULD SUP GROWN-UP DRINKS AND ENGAGE IN GROWN-UP CONVERSATION!

NEE-OWW!

MY KLINGON SPACESHIP CAN GO INVISIBLE!

NO IT CAN'T.

IT CAN TOO! KLINGON SHIPS HAVE GOT CLOAKING DEVICES WHICH CAN MAKE THEM GO INVISIBLE!

YES, BUT THAT MODEL IS BASED ON THE DESIGN FOR THE KLINGON SHIP IN THE NEW STAR TREK DISCOVERY SERIES...

'DISCOVERY' IS A **PREQUEL**, WHICH IS SET IN A TIMEFRAME YEARS BEFORE THE KLINGONS DEVELOP CLOAKING TECHNOLOGY...

5 MINUTES LATER —

YOU'RE NOT LISTENING TO ME! KLINGONS GET THEIR CLOAKING TECH FROM THE ROMULANS IN THE 2260s, WHICH IS A DECADE **AFTER** THE EVENTS OF STAR TREK DISCOVERY...

...ERGO, THESE SHIPS CANNOT TURN INVISIBLE!

BUT THEY **CAN!** I'VE SEEN IT ON THE PROGRAMME!

WELL THAT JUST PROVES MY POINT THAT 'DISCOVERY' IS NOT FUCKING CANONICAL!

MUM! TELL HIM!

TSK!

A LESSON IN MODERN TECHNOLOGY *with* BBC Radio 4's JOHN "JETPACK" HUMPHRYS

D.I. '18

A GROUP OF TEENAGERS ARE ON A CAMPING HOLIDAY IN THE COUNTRYSIDE.

WE'LL SET UP CAMP IN THIS FIELD!

HEY, LET'S LISTEN TO SOME MUSIC!

COOL! I'LL PLAY SOME POP TUNES ON MY MOBILE PHONE!

STOP RIGHT THERE, KIDS! 21ST CENTURY GADGETS SUCH AS MOBILE PHONES CAN BE FUN — BUT ONLY IF YOU USE THEM SAFELY!

WOW! IT'S JOHN "JETPACK" HUMPHRYS FROM RADIO 4'S 'TODAY' PROGRAMME!

MOBILE PHONES NOWADAYS ARE EQUIPPED WITH MINIATURISED COMPUTERS CALLED "INTERNETS."

EACH INTERNET CONTAINS HUNDREDS OF "WEB-SITES" WHICH ARE KIND OF LIKE THE PAGES OF A MAGAZINE — BUT MADE OUT OF ELECTRICITY!

WHENEVER YOU USE YOUR MOBILE PHONE OUTDOORS, IT AUTOMATICALLY "DOWNLOADS" CLOUDS FROM THE SKY

THE CLOUDS ARE DRAWN TOWARDS YOUR INTERNET, MUCH AS IRON FILINGS ARE ATTRACTED TO A MAGNET.

NOW WE ALL KNOW THAT CLOUDS CONTAIN A LOT OF MOISTURE — AND WATER AND ELECTRICITY JUST DON'T MIX!

IF ANY WATER DROPLETS GET INSIDE YOUR MOBILE PHONE'S WEB-SITES, YOU COULD RECEIVE A NASTY ELECTRIC SHOCK!

ALWAYS USE YOUR MOBILE PHONE INDOORS, IN A DRY ROOM WITH THE WINDOWS SHUT!

AFTER ALL, THERE'S NOTHING "COOL" ABOUT ENDING UP IN HOSPITAL WITH ELECTROCUTION INJURIES!

THANKS, JOHN "JETPACK" HUMPHRYS! I GUESS I WON'T PLAY POP TUNES ON MY MOBILE PHONE AFTER ALL!

YES — WE'LL MAKE OUR OWN MUSIC INSTEAD, WITH THIS GOOD OLD-FASHIONED 14TH CENTURY LUTE!

BBC TELEVISION AND RADIO VACANCIES

Question Time Panelist

A vacancy has arisen for an uncomfortable, out-of-their-depth non-politician to sit on Fiona Bruce's extreme left on Question Time.

YOU ARE...

* A footballer with large Twitter following...
* A stand-up comedian with political leanings...
* A crime author with a new book to sell...
* Not doing anything on Thursday nights...

Whoever you are, you will like the sound of your own voice, but be unable to put your thoughts into order sufficiently to make any sense. You will also be unable to do that thing that politicians do where they can talk for five minutes without actually answering the question.

Apply in writing to: Fiona Bruce, Question Time, BBC Television Centre.

BBC Meteorological Office
LOCAL WEATHER FORCAST PRESENTER

A vacancy has arisen for a presenter to read the weather on a regional BBC network. The sucessful candidate will be an attractive, pregnant blonde woman or a dapper young man in a jacket that's far too tight.

The ability to sweep your left hand across a map of the UK while pressing a small hand-held button with your right hand is essential.

Send your cv, including details of any relevant experience you have of talking about the weather to: BBC Meteorological Office, Television Centre, London.

Travelogue Presenter

We are looking for a former member of parliament, comedian at the end of their career, or ageing actor to present an insipid documentary series in which they travel about an area of Britain in an unusual form of transport (eg. Gypsy caravan, canal boat, traction engine, Model T Ford)

The sucessful applicant will make their way circuitously around all parts of the British Isles, but mainly the south east and will:

• *Chat to a local cheesemaker about their craft*
• *Take part in a ploughing competition*
• *Pretend to be interested whilst visiting a provincial lawn mower museum*
• *Be exaggeratedly bad at throwing a pot*

Apply by old fashined post to: BBC TV, Television Centre, London

BITTER, PURPLE-FACED TV ANCHORMAN REQUIRED FOR LOCAL STATION

A vacancy has arisen for a bitter, purple-faced local TV anchorman who will never make it onto national television.

The sucessful applicant will have at least forty years experience of TV Broadcast Journalism but will be completely unknown outside his BBC region.

You will have extensive experience in...

• *Presenting a local magazine programme.*
• *Getting pissed every night in your regional BBC bar.*
• *Opening fetes, signing autographs for old ladies and starting fun runs.*

You will also be able to talk for hours about how the cabal of fuckers in London are working to keep you out of the big time and wouldn't know fucking talent if kicked them in the fucking arse.

Apply online at:
www.bbc.co.uk/goingnowhereanchorman

An exciting opportunity has arisen for a Religious Gobshite to spout bollocks in the Thought for The Day slot on Radio 4's flagship *Today* programme.

The successful applicant will have a proven track record for talking wank without actually making any sense or coming to any point. The ability to liken any situation, (e.g. buying a car, falling down a manhole, being overcharged in a shop) to our relationship with Jesus would be an advantage, but is not essential, as all listeners will be off making a cup of tea when you are broadcasting.

Salary £35k pa (men) £10k pa (women)

The BBC is an Equal Opportunities Employer

152

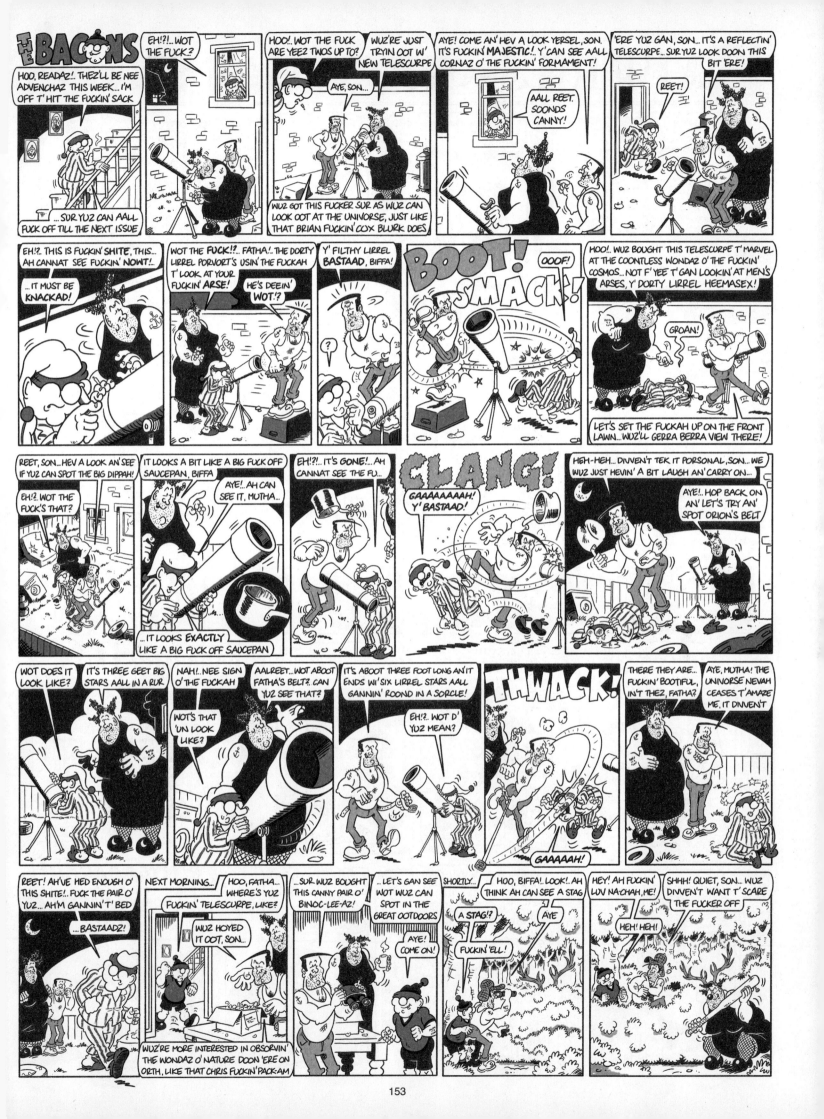

153

RAFFLES THE GENTLEMAN THUG

RAFFLES AND BUNNY ARE AT CHATSWORTH HOUSE, ATTENDING AN "AT HOME"..

BRAVO, LORD BUNNINGTON! WHAT A CAPITAL PENUMBRAL SIMULACRUM!

...AND NOW PERHAPS LORD RAFFLES WOULD CARE TO ENTERTAIN US?

I THINK NOT.

COME COME, SIR! WE ARE REQUIROUS OF NOTHING MORE THAN A TRIFLING DIVERTISSEMENT!

INDEED. DO YOU NOT HAVE A PARTY PIECE, YOUR GRACE?

MY PARTY PIECE? YOU WOULD LIKE ME TO PERFORM MY PARTY PIECE, YOU SAY?

THAT IS SO.

VERY WELL. BUNNY - KINDLY BE IN RECIPIENCE OF MY COAT, WILL YOU, OLD CHAP..?

CERTAINLY, RAFFLES.

‡A-HEM‡ MY FELLOW LORDS, LADIES AND GENTLEMEN... I GIVE TO YOU...

"...THE LATTERMOST PHEASANT IN FORTNUM & MASON..!"

NOBBY'S PILES

AT THE SUPERMARKET...

AH, SMASHING. I NEED A NEW PHOTO FOR MY BUS PASS. HAVE YOU GOT ANY MONEY FOR THE MACHINE?

YES. I GOT FOUR POUND COINS CHANGE FOR THIS PINEAPPLE.

I'LL JUST POP IT HERE WHILE I GET THEM OUT OF MY BAG.

YOU GO IN THE BOOTH AND SIT DOWN, NOBBY. I'LL PUT THE COINS IN THE SLOT.

THANKS.

NYAAAARGH!

FLASH!
ME FUCKIN' BONNY MARYS!

A WEEK LATER...

WELL THAT'S NO GOOD IT DOESN'T LOOK LIKE YOU AT ALL, PAL..!

'ERE... WHAT'S THE RUDDY 'OLD UP?!

JAB! JAB! JAB!
GET A RUDDY MOVE ON..!

NYAAAARGH! ME FUCKIN' BONNY MARYS!

AYE. ON YOU GET.

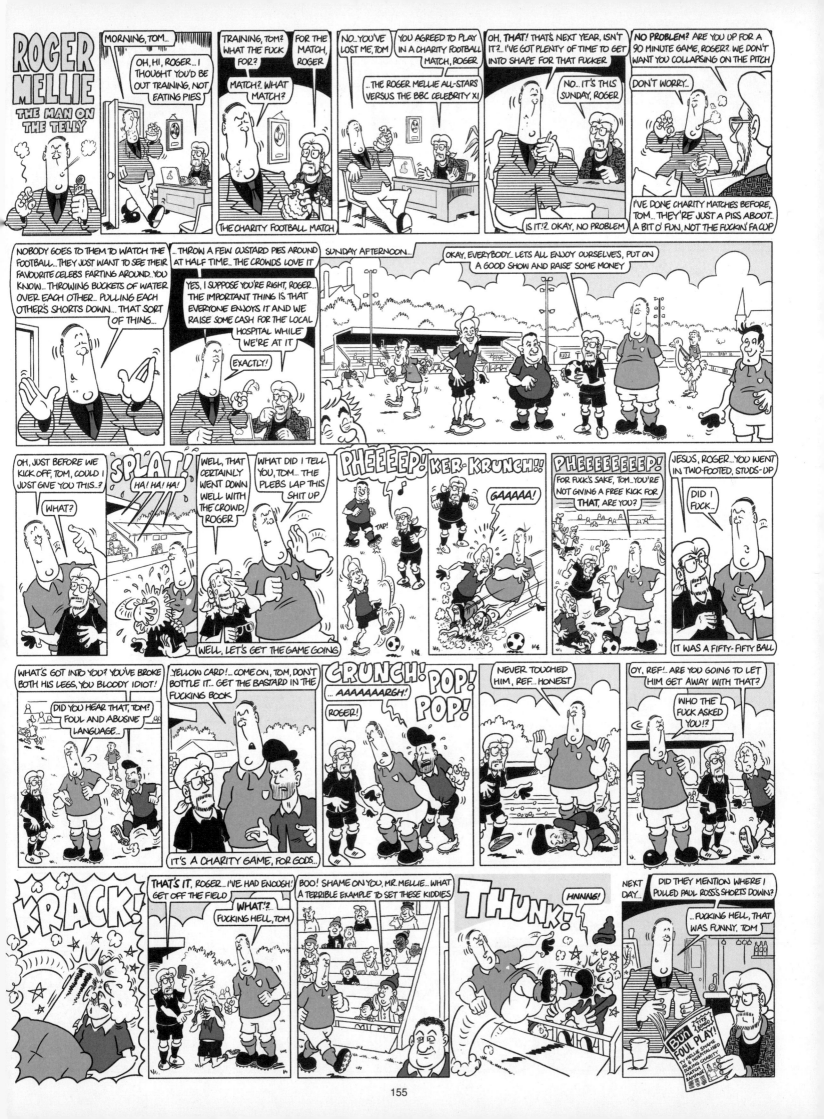

The AB of C
Dr Justin Welby

ANSWERS *YOUR* ECCLESIASTICAL PROBLEMS

Dear Justin,

I GO TO church every week but I squashed one of my plums sitting on the pew, and now I'm worried that I'm going to Hell.

I am 34 and my wife is 36. We have been married for 12 years and attend the Sunday morning service at our local church every Sunday without fail.

Last week, I stood up to do the Lord's prayer, and after saying Amen I sat down. However, I was wearing an old, unsupportive pair of boxer shorts at the time, and as I did so I accidentally squashed one of my bollocks, like men do sometimes. It really knacked, and made my eyes water.

I immediately thought of Chapter 21, verse 20 of Leviticus where it states quite clearly that no man who has been *"injured in the stones"* shall be admitted to the Assembly of the Lord. And that made me worry that all my good works and all the time I've spent praying, singing hymns and raising money for the church roof are all for nothing, simply because I accidentally

Faith tested by testes

squashed one of my clockweights.

Please put my mind at rest, Justin. I don't want to go to Hell.
Mr B., Rutland

•Justin says...

It would be a very a harsh and capriciously judgemental God indeed that punished a faithful believer simply because he sat funny on one of his plums. Unfortunately, however, that is exactly the sort of God that He is.

But don't worry. Reading between the lines of Leviticus, it says that you shouldn't "enter" His congregation if you have crushed or damaged stones. Presumably, your nads were tickety-boo when you arrived at church that morning, so, in my opinion, you should probably be alright. Only go back to church next week if all the swelling has gone down, the throbbing has subsided a bit, and your poor old nads have been restored to their factory settings.

Cheap slacks cost dear

Dear Justin,

MY HUSBAND got a bargain at Boundary Mills, and now I'm scared he will burn for all eternity in the Lake of Fire.

I am 58 and my husband is 61 and we have been married for 38 years. He recently went out to Boundary Mills at North Shields and came back with a pair of trousers from the sale.

He was very pleased with them, because they were drip-dry, didn't need ironing, and had an elasticated waist. However, when I looked at the label, I was horrified, because it said they were made from a 60%/30%10% Polyester, linen and wool-mix fabric.

I won't need to remind you that Deuteronomy Chapter 22 verse 11 clearly states: *"Thou shalt not wear a garment of divers sorts, as of woollen and linen together."* I waited until my husband had gone out and I threw his trousers on the fire.

When he found out, he blew his top. He explained that they had cost £19.99 and he is now refusing to speak to me. Please Justin, can you explain to him that I did what I did for the best reasons?
Mrs J., Hull

•Justin says...

For reasons best known to Himself, the Lord prohibited the wearing of mixed fabrics many years ago, and there is no reason to suppose that He has changed His views during the intervening 3 millennia or so.

God is not an unreasonable deity. He has nothing whatsoever against linen trousers. He has nothing whatsoever against woollen trousers. It is only when these two materials are combined in the same raiment that His wrath is provoked.

Take your husband back to Boundary Mills and treat him to a new pair of trousers, but this time make sure he reads the label carefully before taking them to the till. £19.99 may be a good price, but an eternity spent burning in a pit of fiery excrement and dead men's bones is a long time to reflect that those slacks may not have been such a good bargain after all.

Justin's Advice Lines Ecclesiastical counsel you can trust

Hubby makes baldness between his eyes for the dead *(Deuteronomy 14)*	**01 811 8055**
Wife happy to suffer a witch to live *(Exodus 22)*	**0 1811 8055**
Husband wants to clip the edges of his beard *(Leviticus 19)*	**018 1180 55**
Boyfriend went near tabernacle whilst not being a priest *(Numbers 1)*	**0181 1805 5**
Wife ate of the waters that which hath not fins or scales *(Deuteronomy 14)*	**0 1811805 5**
Vaginal dryness *(Genesis 18)*	**0181 1 8055**

Calls cost £1.50 per plus the Lord God's standard network charge and terminate in St Paul's Cathedral

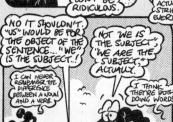

158

MEGHAN'S FAIRYTALE LIFE

A VIZ ROYAL EXCLUSIVE!

Ex-schoolfriend lifts lid on Markle's storybook upbringing

EVERYONE agrees that the romance between the dashing prince and the glamorous American starlet is like a fairytale come true. But according to one of the royal bride-to-be's former classmates, the 36-year-old *Suits* actress's whole life has been a fairytale. Now, in a hastily written biography, Humberside-based **PAIGE MUNCHAUSEN** has lifted the lid on Markle's remarkable life story, a story that has finally culminated in a proposal of marriage from a real life Prince Charming.

Grimm story: Markle's childhood was full of woe.

"I knew we were friends the first time we met on our first day at Kindergarten," recalls Munchausen, 58. "The teacher asked everyone in the class to draw a picture of their house. I drew a picture of the trailer where I lived, whilst Meghan's picture was of a gingerbread cottage in the middle of an enchanted forest."

"She explained that she'd been found abandoned in a basket by a woodcutter and his wife, who was barren. And it was true, because I used to go round to her house sometimes after school and we'd just eat bits of the house when we got peckish."

According to Munchausen, Markle's idyllic childhood came to an end when her adoptive mother died after being eaten by a talking wolf. She remembers: "Her father remarried to a wicked stepmother who had two ugly daughters of her own. They treated her badly, no better than a servant, making her clean out the fireplace and do all the chores before coming to school."

Harr-ily ever after: Markle bagged ginger bred man.

"She would regularly turn up for class with bare feet, wearing tattered rags and with soot on her cheeks. The other children would taunt her, laughing at her threadbare clothes and dishevelled hair."

sleep

Markle used to confide in her best friend, telling Paige how she was mistreated at home. "She told me how her stepmother would make her live in the barn with the animals, and how she would often cry herself to sleep," she said.

hussey

One day in the fourth grade, Paige remmbers, Markle failed to turn up for her lessons. "Meghan was always a straight As student, so it was unusual for her to skip school. After class, I went round to her house to see if she was okay."

"When I got there, I was shocked to discover that her wicked stepmother had locked her in the attic, and was refusing to let her out until she had spun some straw into gold."

"I told her mom that I would report her to the police for child cruelty, and she eventually relented and released her."

lineker

Eventually, Markle could bear her ill treatment no longer and ran away deeper into the forest, where she was given shelter by a group of dwarves who worked in a diamond mine. Paige remembers: "Meghan was very happy throughout the time she spent living with the dwarves. Her grades went up at school, and she often had a bluebird on her finger."

But her happiness was not to last. "We went to lunch one day and we noticed a new dinner nanny. She had a long hairy chin, a hooked nose with a wart on it, and long bony fingers like gnarled twigs. And whereas most dinnerladies wear a white trilby with a hairnet, she had a tall black conical hat, with a brim."

rooney

"Meghan went up to the counter and asked for her favourite, a hot dog and fries, but the new dinner nanny beckoned her closer in and said she had something special for her - a shiny red apple."

"I was a little suspicious, but Meghan was so pure of heart and trusting that she took the apple and bit into it. Immediately she fell to the ground in a deep sleep. The dinnerlady was actually a witch, and the apple was enchanted!"

Chore blimey!: The dirty kitchen Markle was forced to work in by her wicked stepmother.

According to Munchausen, Markle was immediately taken to the medical room, where the school nurse examined her. "The nurse announced that the only way to break the spell and wake Meghan from her sleep of death, was if she was kissed by a handsome prince," she remembers.

mouse

Paige remembered that the Invictus Games were taking place in a nearby sports centre, and alerted a member of staff who immediately went round to see if the games' patron, Prince Harry, could pop over to the school to kiss a tragic pupil out of a wicked witch's spell. He gallantly agreed.

Paige remembers: "By the time Harry arrived in the nurse's office, a load of woodland creatures had turned up after hearing what had happened to Meghan. They were gathered around the glass case where she had been laid, and were standing with their heads bowed in sadness. Harry walked through the door and instantly fell in love with Meghan."

door

"He bent over her sleeping form and kissed her tenderly on the lips. She immediately woke up from her dreamless sleep. The witch's spell had been broken, and the animals danced around the room with joy."

Meghan went back to her classes and Harry went back to his royal duties, but Paige knew that the seeds of romance had been sown, and that nothing could now keep the pair apart. "True love always finds a way," she says. "I knew that one day they would be married and live happily ever after."

table

Munchausen, now working on a zero hours contract at an all-night petrol station in Hull, now hopes that her former schoolfriend will think of her when compiling the guest list for her forthcoming wedding ceremony in May. "I just hope she remembers that it was me what brought her and her Prince Charming together all those years ago," she smiles. "If it wasn't for my quick thinking, she'd still be lying in a glass case in the school medical room, still under the witch's sleeping spell."

"I'm looking forward to getting an invite to the wedding. I hope I get to sit next to the Queen, so we can have a nice chat. Like her, I've got lots of dogs, so we could have a good old natter."

Fairytales Can Come True: The Life of Meghan Markle by Paige Munchausen (Cash-In Books, £13.99), will be published on February 2nd, or possibly sooner if she gets it finished in time.

PORN TO BE QUEEN

Shipley driving instructor reveals sordid X-rated past of Harry's bride to be!

DESPITE the squeaky clean image that royal fiancee Meghan Markle has been so keen to promote, a West Yorkshire driving instructor says he has cast iron proof that she once starred in a hardcore pornographic movie. And now 58-year-old **CLIFTON RADFORD** is involved in a race against time to produce the evidence that he claims will prevent Harry from making the biggest mistake of his life.

SEXCLUSIVE!

Radford, who has a collection of more than 10,000 erotic videos and DVDs stored in the attic of his Shipley home, told us: "If they get married and then this explicit footage comes to light, God knows what damage could be done to the British monarchy."

Meghan whoopee: Markle took part in saucy ninesome.

"This bongo flick will lead to the biggest constitutional crisis this country has ever faced."

"When Harry and Meghan appeared on the news to announce their engagement, I knew I had seen her before," he said. "Then it came to me; I recognised her from one of the mucky vids in my collection."

"I must have last watched it fifteen years ago or more; a petite woman with long dark hair, getting gang-banged off eight men in the back of a Winnebago. It was definitely her. Definitely. She must of made the film when she was a struggling actress."

Poking gun: Video will prove Markle had seedy past.

"I remember, it particularly caught my attention at the time, because it was the first time I'd ever seen a DVDA double spitroast with downhill skiing," he continued.

Now Radford has vowed to search through his entire library of erotica to find the elusive hardcore sequence. He told us: "I've got less than six months to sift through more than thirty thousand hours of scud, looking for a five-minute clip. That's a big ask."

"I'll have to approach the task systematically, fast forwarding through anything lesbianny, anything with blondes, or anything with fewer than eight blokes."

But Clifton's marathon quest has hit hit an unexpected hitch early on. He told us: "I've got most of my films in boxes up in the loft, but I've put quite a lot of weight on just lately and I can't get through the hatch."

TONY PARSEHOLE

WHEN I heard the news of Prince Harry's engagement to American starlet Meghan Markle, I am not afraid to say that I wept. I wept and I wept. I wept and I wept and I wept.

And then I wept some more.

But I wasn't wepping out of sadness. In fact, I was wepping for the opposite of sadness. For those tears that poured down my cheeks like a salty Niagara when I heard the news of Prince Harry's engagement to American starlet Meghan Markle were tears of joy.

Joy that our nation's Prince Charming had finally found the fairytale princess of his dreams.

Joy that the fifth in line to our country's guilded throne had chosen such a noble and elegant consort.

And joy that I could cut and paste large chunks of this column from the 500 words I churned out when his brother got hitched to his piece.

And so it is with happiness in my heart and the greatest pride and the utmost humility that I speak on behalf of the 65 million people of this proud land when I say: Welcome to our nation's favourite family. This island opens its heart to you, ma'am, and gladly embraces you in its bosoms.

Of course, the naysayers, moaning minis and mongers of doom have come out of the woodwork to draw parallels between the divorced Suits actress and another glamorous American who once came to our shores intent on bagging herself a Prince of the Royal House of Windsor.

But Meghan Markle and Wallis Simpson could not be more different. Indeed, Meghan Markle and Wallis Simpson are as different as chalk and cheese. As different as night and day. As different as salt and pepper.

They are as different as two peas in different pods.

Markle is young and beautiful. Markle is all woman from the tip of her head to the bottom of her toes.

Welcome to our Nation's Favourite Family, Ma'am!

Mrs Simpson was old and hatchet-faced. According to some sources, she even had a cock. Back in the 1930s, Simpson got her claws into the Duke of Windsor and did her level best to rent the monarchy in twain. Her scandalous relationship with the hair to the English throne brought the country to the very brink of civil war.

In contrast, Meghan Markle is set to heal the rifts that have beset the royal family for so long. Where there is discord, she will sew harmony. Where there is despondency, she will sew hope. And where there is sadness, she will sew there thats 500 wds pdf inv attched w a/c no. pay by return

Who's got the tastiest tush?
Meghan Markle or Princess Pippa?

BATTLE OF THE ARSES

IT'S the debate that's splitting the nation up the middle like a tight thong; **PIPPA MIDDLETON** or **MEGHAN MARKLE** - just which royal hottie has the most delectable derrière? We went out on the street to find out where the Great British Public's allegiance lies...

"...WHILST both these derrieres are delectable, we Britons should show a bit of patriotism and back Pippa's Great British backside to the hilt."
Hilton Buscel, ophthalmic surgeon

"...PIPPA Middleton's arse is alright, but time doesn't stand still. Now Pippa Middleton's arse has to move over and make way for Meghan Markle's arse. Your moment in the sun is over, Pippa Middleton's arse. There's a new arse in town - Meghan Markle's arse."
Peter Paul Roget, Thesaurus compiler

"...AS AN AMERICAN, Meghan Markle's chuff will have been nipped, tucked, botoxed and bleached into a state of unreal perfection. Pippa's dirtbox, on the other hand, has developed as mother nature intended and gets my vote over Markle's pampered and preened plastic monstrosity any day of the week."
Cuthbert Creme, Community Support Officer

"...THERE'S far too much conflict in Britain these days, and in the wake of the Brexit referendum, the last thing we need is yet another argument to come between us. Let's just agree that Pippa has the best left cheek, Meghan has the best right cheek, draw a line under this whole fractious debate and move on."
Peter Victor Andrew Woodglue, English teacher

"...AS AN ENGLISH teacher, Mr Woodglue should be aware that, when describing the relative merits of two things, such as the right or left arse cheeks of two women, the correct word to use is "better", not "best". God help his pupils."
Prof A Gowans-Whyte, university don

"...DON'T get me wrong. Princess Meghan's got a lovely arse, but I'll never forget the moment I first caught sight of Pippa's shitter in that tight white dress as it made its way up the steps of St Paul's Cathedral. It was like two hard-boiled eggs in a handkerchief."
Rev J Foucault, Truro

"...AS A SCIENTIST, I know that it is impossible to compare two entities unless all extraneous variables are kept the same. Until we see Meghan Markle's arse in a tight white dress, sashaying its way saucily up the steps of St Paul's, any comparisons with Pippa's muckspreader are scientifically meaningless."
Jim Al-Kalili, Eggheaded egghead

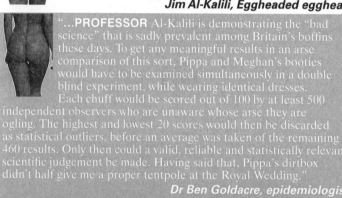
"...PROFESSOR Al-Kalili is demonstrating the "bad science" that is sadly prevalent among Britain's boffins these days. To get any meaningful results in an arse comparison of this sort, Pippa and Meghan's booties would have to be examined simultaneously in a double blind experiment, while wearing identical dresses.
Each chuff would be scored out of 100 by at least 500 independent observers who are unaware whose arse they are ogling. The highest and lowest 20 scores would then be discarded as statistical outliers, before an average was taken of the remaining 460 results. Only then could a valid, reliable and statistically relevant scientific judgement be made. Having said that, Pippa's dirtbox didn't half give me a proper tentpole at the Royal Wedding."
Dr Ben Goldacre, epidemiologist

♛ *Your Cut Out n' Keep Royal Arse Fact File* ♛

Pippa Middleton's Arse

Age: *34*
Number of Cheeks: *2*
Occupation: *Farting, shitting, sitting on, etc.*
Piles: *No*
Firmness quotient: *Good*
Bummability: ★★★★★
Wow factor: *Pert*
Bootyliciousness alert: *Severe*
Final rating: **98%**

Meghan Markle's Arse

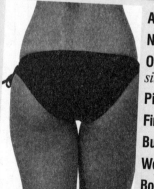

Age: *36*
Number of Cheeks: *2*
Occupation: *Farting, shitting, sitting on, etc.*
Piles: *Unknown*
Firmness quotient: *Good to Fine*
Bummability: ★★★★★
Wow factor: *Peachy*
Bootyliciousness alert: *Critical*
Final rating: **98%**

Figures © Oxford University/YouGov

After examining all the evidence, the two royal bots are tied. We couldn't get a cigarette paper between their regal cheeks, so it's down to YOU to decide which bottom comes out top.

Text 'PIPPA' or 'MEGHAN' to 018118055 to make your voice heard
The lines are now closed and your vote will not be counted, but you will still be charged £2 plus your provider's standard text rate.

ALDRIDGE PRIOR
THE HOPELESS LIAR

NO I'M NOT!

DJ '18

ST MUNGO'S PARISH CHURCH ✝

ST MUNGO'S PARISH CHURCH ✝

I AM THE TRUTH

DO FEEL FREE TO COME INSIDE AND LOOK AROUND OUR CHURCH!

I AM THE TRUTH

OUR DOORS ARE ALWAYS OPEN!

OH, I'VE SEEN ENOUGH CHURCHES TO LAST ME A LIFETIME. I USED TO BE THE POPE'S PERSONAL DRIVER, SEE.

DROVE HIM ROUND HUNDREDS OF CHURCHES ALL OVER THE WORLD. THOUSANDS, ACTUALLY.

I'LL TELL YOU ONE THING ABOUT THE POPEMOBILE, THOUGH — YOU KNOW, HIS CAR WITH THE BIG WINDOWS?

WELL THE POPE HAD IT FITTED WITH A MCLAREN M838T ENGINE. STRAIGHT UP! IT CAN DO OVER 200 MPH ON AN OPEN STRETCH.

HE NEVER LET ME FLOOR IT WHEN THE TV CAMERAS WERE AROUND, BUT WHEN WE WERE ALONE HE'D SAY "PUT YOUR FOOT DOWN, MY SON."

ONE TIME I WAS DRIVING HIM ACROSS AMERICA AND HE SAYS "LET'S SEE WHAT THIS BABY CAN DO!"

WELL IT WAS FINE UNTIL I HIT THIS KANGAROO — IT WAS IN AUSTRALIA, ACTUALLY — AND I FLIPPED THE POPEMOBILE OVER ON ITS ROOF.

JUST MANAGED TO PULL THE POPE OUT OF THE WRECKAGE BEFORE IT BURST INTO FLAMES. HE WAS PISSING HIMSELF, THOUGHT IT WAS HILARIOUS. TRUE STORY.

YES, WELL I HAVE TO PREPARE MY SERMON NOW...

YEAH, I NEARLY BECAME A VICAR MYSELF. WENT TO VICAR TRAINING SCHOOL AND EVERYTHING...

YOU MEAN THEOLOGICAL COLLEGE?

YEAH. I CAME TOP IN ALL THE EXAMS, ACTUALLY. THEY SAID I WAS THE BEST STUDENT VICAR THEY'D EVER HAD...

THEY WANTED TO FAST-TRACK ME TO BECOMING AN ARCHBISHOP, BUT I COULDN'T BE ARSED WITH ALL THAT GOD STUFF SO I JACKED IT IN.

I WAS DATING THIS SUPERMODEL AT THE TIME. SHE WAS A COUSIN OF STEVEN SEAGAL'S. WE USED TO GO AND SPEND CHRISTMAS AT HIS PLACE IN BEVERLEY HILLS.

I'M REALLY VERY BUSY...

'COURSE, I'VE GOT NOTHING AGAINST CHRISTIANITY...

BUT I'LL TELL YOU WHO IS A DEVIL-WORSHIPPER — DAME JUDI DENCH! YEAH, WOULDN'T THINK IT TO LOOK AT HER, WOULD YOU?

STRAIGHT UP, JUDI DENCH IS AN ACTUAL SATANIST! WHENEVER SHE MAKES A FILM SHE HAS A BLACK COCKEREL SENT TO HER DRESSING ROOM, AND SACRIFICES IT BEFORE SHE GOES ON.

MY BROTHER IN LAW IS A CAMERAMAN FOR PARAMOUNT AND HE SEEN IT WITH HIS OWN EYES.

BLOOD AND FEATHERS EVERYWHERE, HE SAID. AND THAT'S GOD'S GOSPEL TRUTH.

PLEASE DO NOT BLASPHEME IN THE HOUSE OF THE LORD!

THE BIBLE TELLS US THAT LYING IS A SIN, AND AN OFFENCE TO GOD!

DO YOU NOT KNOW THE NINTH COMMANDMENT? "THOU SHALT NOT BEAR FALSE WITNESS."

FUNNY YOU SHOULD MENTION BEARING WITNESS. DON'T BREATHE A WORD TO ANYONE, BUT I'M ACTUALLY ON THE WITNESS PROTECTION SCHEME.

I TESTIFIED AGAINST A NEW YORK MAFIA BOSS AND THE FBI GAVE ME A NEW IDENTITY. SEE THIS? IT'S NOT MY REAL SKIN, IT'S A VERY REALISTIC LATEX MASK.

I MUST ASK YOU TO LEAVE! YOUR LIES ARE AN AFFRONT TO THIS CHURCH, AND YOU WILL BRING UPON YOURSELF THE WRATH OF GOD!

REMEMBER THAT STAR TREK FILM, THE WRATH OF KHAN? THEY FILMED SOME OF THAT IN MY MUM'S BACK GARDEN.

RUMBLE!

KAP-OW!

MERCIFUL HEAVENS! IT'S HAPPENING!

YOU HAVE INCURRED GOD'S ANGER, AND HE IS COMING TO PASS JUDGEMENT!

YEAH, YOU DON'T WANT TO MAKE ME MAD.

I ONCE GOT SO ANGRY THAT I HEADBUTTED THE SUN AND IT EXPLODED IN MY FACE. HAD TO HAVE A BIONIC EYE FITTED.

I'M A BLACK BELT IN KUNG FU, AND ALL. I WAS ACTUALLY JACKIE CHAN'S STUNT DOUBLE IN THAT FILM RUSH HOUR!

YEAH, I CREATED THE UNIVERSE IN SEVEN DAYS. WELL, SIX ACTUALLY.

FIVE.

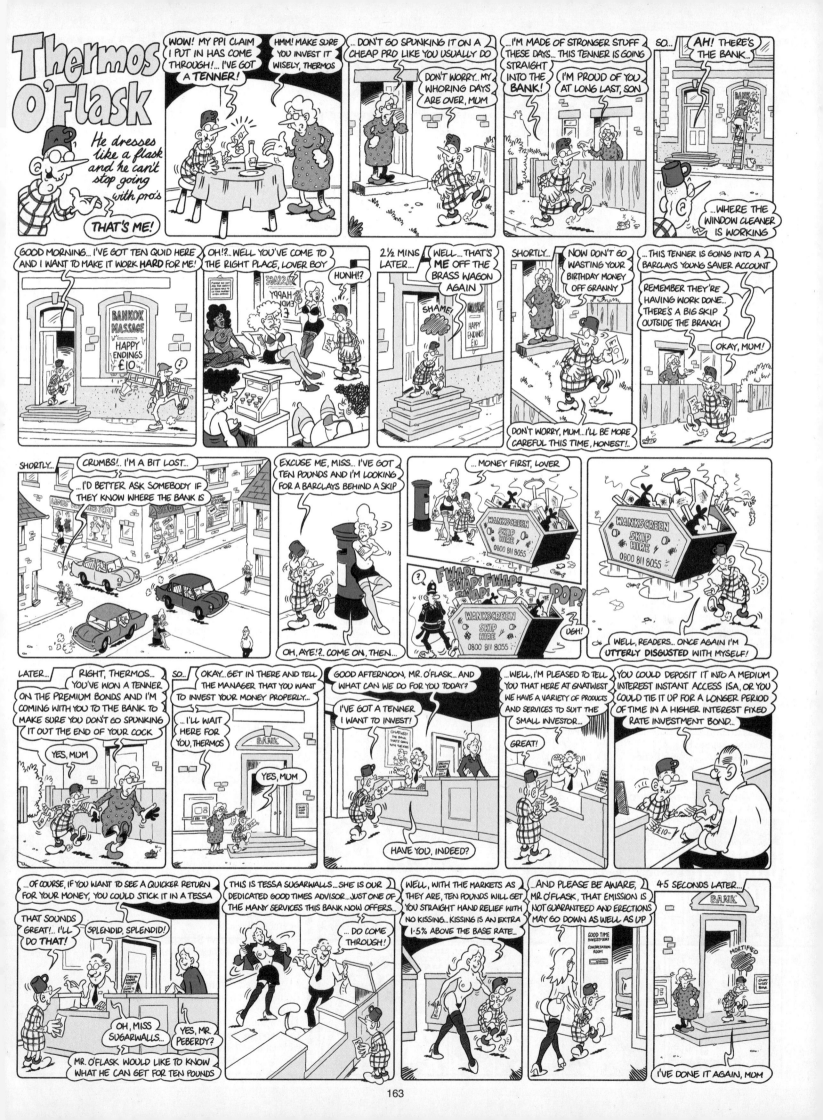

163

letterbocks

Viz Comic, P.O. Box 841 Whitley Bay, NE26 9EQ : letters@viz.co.uk

ST★R LETTER

I'VE just realised that the words "Stick it up your arsehole. Shove it up your bum" fit perfectly over alternate lines of the song *Land of Hope and Glory*. Imagine if they could get the whole audience at the Albert Hall to join in lustily with these lyrics. What a memorable Last Night of the Proms that would be.

Peter Hall, Dorking

MY dog recently made a rather tasteless joke about deceased pop legend David Bowie. When I protested that it was still 'too soon' for that sort of thing, he reminded me that in dog terms it has been over 14 years since the warbling space weirdo popped his clogs. So I had to admit that he had a point.

Josh Cluderay, Wensleydale

IT seems that, these days, it's impossible to pick up a newspaper or switch on the television without being informed that plastic is killing all the fish in the oceans. How ridiculous. As a child, I won a goldfish at the fair which I took home in a plastic bag and kept in a perspex bowl with no ill effects whatsoever. The creature only died when I got bored with it and flushed it down the toilet, yet nobody seems to suggest that porcelain should be banned. One wonders what the loony lefties and scaremongers will claim is destroying the planet next.

Roland Rolloff-Ferry, Truro

I THINK that it is reasonable to surmise that, given his diet, Count Dracula would pass a stool very similar to a black pudding. I find this particularly galling, as whenever I eat a black pudding, I am afflicted with acute diarrhoea. Once again, it seems there's one rule for un-dead Transylvanian noblemen, and another for us mere mortals.

Pam Fried-Seabass, Truro

WHY is it that whenever describing certain films, people say, "It was very dark"? Of course, it was dark. I don't know many cinemas that leave the fucking lights on when there's a film on.

Hector Balls, Ely

WHY do laboratories test shampoo in rabbits' eyes? We all know it stings like fuck.

Adrian Kenyon, Sarlat

"A MAN. A plan. A canal. Panama" is probably the most famous palindrome in the English language. But "A man. A plan. Anal. Panama" works just as well, but you never seem to hear about it.

Joe Williams, Leeds

FOR as long as I can remember I've always wondered why birds have white shit. I can't see how this is possible, or what it is in their diet that causes it. It leads me to wonder whether any of your readers have ever seen a house martin chowing down on a tin of Dulux Brilliant White Matt Emulsion. Or any other type of white paint. I'd really appreciate an answer.

Adam George Forman, Derby

PEOPLE say that wasps serve no useful purpose, but that's not true at all. I just watched one chase a bloke round a beer garden and it was fucking hilarious. Thanks for the laughs, insect friends.

Joe Williams, Leeds

IT'S a strange paradox that you have to be 18 to buy *Viz*, but my daughter has just turned 18 and considers herself too grown-up to read it. It's almost as if women mature more quickly than men, but I'm sure that can't be the case. Come to think of it, she no longer laughs when I fart into my hand and throw it in her face, and she used to find that hilarious 10 years ago, so maybe it's just her.

Steve Crouch, P'borough

YOU always hear about this leopard or that leopard being endangered, but when you see them on wildlife shows, they're usually just lying around, licking themselves. I'm no authority on leopards, but I do wonder if they might not be quite so endangered if they stopped lounging about and got on with some serious shagging. Come on leopards, do yourselves a favour, you lazy arses.

Carlos, Portstewart

CAN anyone think of an item of furniture that contains more sexual innuendos than a chest of drawers? I can't and I've been trying for weeks.

Tim Briffa, London

POLITICAL correctness has gone well and truly mad. These days you can't even make fun of somebody because of their cultural ethnicity or the colour of their skin without someone calling it 'racist'.

Ben Nunn, Caterham

I WISH someone would take a picture of a fit bird kissing MY arse for once. But even if it did happen, it's unlikely there'd be a *Viz* reader on hand with a camera. Typical.

Warren Stumper, Milford Haven

THE other night I slipped a couple of Rohypnols into my wife's Slimming World Bolognese. That evening I ate 5 Creme Eggs and had two wanks without a peep from her.

P Roller, Liverpool

I LOVE that bit in the Bible where the woman said she got pregnant by magic or something, and the husband actually believed her! Priceless.

Snouter Harris, Borehamwood

I AM disgusted that a family store can package their goods in this way. What's more there were several of them, all standing to attention.

Phil Graham, Knaresborough

NOW that Chrissie Hynde isn't doing much by the way of the hit parade, I think starting her own baked beans company would be a shrewd move. Hynde's Baked Beans has a certain ring to it and she couldn't be sued by rivals for a variety of reasons - fifty-seven in fact. Do any other readers know of any other rock stars that could start their own food production companies? Sorry, Kraftwerk Cheese Slices and Ali Campbell's Soup are already taken.

Renton Duckworth, Leeds

COSPLAY SMALLPIECE

NEC FULCHESTER COMIC-COS-CON '18

BEEP! BEEP! BEEP!

BOINK!

SLAP!

KNICKERS KNACKERS KNOCKERS!

SPOING!

What would the youthful stars do if they went...

grey for a day?

EVERY fresh-faced celeb has wondered at some point what it would be like to spend 24 hours with their normal hair replaced with aged, silver locks. We rounded up three of our favourite youthful A-Listers and put the simple question to them: *What would YOU do if you went Grey For A Day?*

Ed Sheeran, ginger troubadour

GOING Grey For A Day would be a career ender for me. As we can see with squirrels, people absolutely adore the red-haired ones, finding them inherently cheeky and lovable. But when the same creature has grey hair, they round it up and cull it. With that in mind, I would spend my silver-locked 24 hours keeping a very low profile indeed, remaining indoors and wearing a big hat at all times. Then, when the clock struck midnight and my flame-tinged follicles miraculously re-sprouted, I could once again venture out safely into the world to enjoy my vast and utterly inexplicable popularity.

Kim Jong-un, supreme leader

I'M ABSOLUTELY *Bake Off* bonkers, so if I went Grey For A Day, I'd probably spend 24 hours pretending to be the silver fox himself, Mr Paul Hollywood! I would draw on a goatee with silver felt pen and then gather my top advisors, allocating each of them a different *Bake Off* role: Noel Fielding for my deputy director, Sandy Toksvig for my treasury secretary and my war minister would play Prue Leith. We would then invite Pyongyang's finest bakers to knock us up a selection of sweet treats, while I hovered about in the background, offering advice in a Scouse accent. The winner would be rewarded with their own state-sanctioned cookery series, while the losers would be swiftly and brutally executed.

Justin Bieber, Canadian pop fave

ONE OF the advantages of being old and grey is that you are able to benefit from more competitive home buildings and contents insurance. Companies typically offer special discounts for customers aged sixty-plus, since the elderly are likely to make fewer or smaller claims, and generally reside in low-crime areas. So if I went Grey For A Day, I would head straight down to my nearest security provider, posing as a doddery old pensioner, and pick up an absolutely *STONKING* deal on buildings insurance. Then, the next day, when my youthful brown locks had returned, I could throw a wild party and trash my gaff to my heart's content, safe in the knowledge that I would be paying well under the going rate for repairs.

ON my packet of Mini Cheddars, Jacobs claim that they contain 547kJ of energy. However, according to Einstein, 25g of Mini Cheddars should actually contain 2,246,887,946,842 kJ of energy. So who's lying? I bet even Prof Jim Al-Khalili couldn't explain that one.

Kevster, Tiptree

I WAS recently listening to *Siegfried's Funeral March* and *Finale* from the opera *Götterdämmerung*. I didn't think it was as good as T. Rex. There was no beat or clever rhymes or hidden meaning to it at all. No wonder Richard Wagner never makes the charts, whilst forty years after his death, we are still grooving to Marc Bolan.

Alan Heath, Germany

IT'S a long way to Tipperary they say. Not for me - I live in Limerick, so it's only about half an hour away on the train.

Paul D'Arcy, Limerick

SO much for getting a rescue dog, I say. I've had mine six months and let's just say it isn't exactly Lassie. Far from barking to tell people that someone is trapped down a well, saving drowning people from rivers, or pulling people out of house fires, all it does is sit around licking its cock and bollocks all day long. And don't even get me started on the farting.

Molton Reesdale, Crewe

LESS than half a mile from my house there's a Sainsbury's store. Yet three miles away on the other side of town there is a Sainsbury's Local. I'd like to see the so-called experts explain that one.

Fred Mudflaps, Twatt

IN reply to James Thompson (*Letterbocks page 120*), dinosaurs were not "pretty fucking amazing lizards" at all. Dinosaurs came from a group of reptiles called Archosauromorphs, whereas lizards come from a distantly related reptile group called Lepidosauromorphs. So whilst they are related - much like your parents - they are not actual fucking lizards.

Trim McKenna, Surbiton

✱ *Thank you for the information, Mr McKenna. At Viz Comic, we pride ourselves on accurate reporting and are always happy to correct our mistakes. However, we thought that your incestuous jibe insult towards our parents was a little unnecessary. And a bit rich, coming from someone whose mum, we know, sucks tramps' cocks behind the Surbiton Odeon for a pound a go.*

I DON'T trust Formula One drivers. During one race they pull off the track saying they're retiring, then the following week there they are again on the starting grid. There should be some sort of punishment for this sort of continual lying.

Monkey Boy, email

I SEE the obesity problem this country is having has now spread to machines.

DJ Green, email

THEY say 'the cream always rises to the top.' But a pint of whipping cream burst in my shopping the other day, and it went fucking everywhere. Bastard of a thing to clean off.

Stuart McDonald, Melbourne

GIVEN that the Penny Farthing bicycle was modelled on the penny and the farthing, I suppose we have to be thankful that it was invented before decimalisation. I can only imagine what an uncomfortable ride it would have been if the fifty pence piece was used as the inspiration for the front wheel.

Mitchel Brantub, Gotham

I LOVE documentaries, but I'm fed up with them being aimed at sportsmen. Something is always 'bigger than ten football pitches' or 'the size of eight Olympic swimming pools'. Such comparisons are completely meaningless to me, as I am a couch potato and I have never swam in one or played on the other. If they said it was six times the size of my back garden I might get some idea.

Rob, Nantwich

I WAS under the impression that no two fingerprints are the same. So you may be surprised to hear that I'm currently serving 4 years at Her Majesty's pleasure, as apparently my fingerprint is the same as one found on the window ledge of one of my neighbours.

Andrew Burnstein, Pentonville

LAMES TO FAME

THE bloke I work for says that, as a child, he was once chased by a Great Dane belonging to Carol Decker out of T'Pau. At the time, he thought that the dog was going to eat him, but as an adult he realised that it was probably going to try to bum him.

Shenkin Arsecandle, Llareggub

TOP

EXPECTANT mums. Make giving birth easier by simply spraying the inside of your flaps with WD40.

John Owens, Glasgow

VICARS. Employ higher quality builders so you can focus more on spirituality and less on constant roof repairs.

Jimmy, Manchester

CATCH a glimpse of post-Brexit hyperinflation by buying a loaf of bread at a Center Parcs ParcMarket.

Chris Sleight, Cousldon

ACTION film lovers. Driving through motorway roadworks at 50mph is an ideal time to practise climbing out of your car and onto an adjacent HGV with a gun in your hand.

Andrew Underpants, Widnes

WEAR a stopped watch at all times. Then, when you ask someone the time and they wittily reply "time you got a watch," you can respond by showing them the watch, but explaining that it has stopped.

D Cooper, Malta

MEN. Trick people into thinking your penis is longer than it is by drawing vertical stripes on it. Draw horizontal stripes for the impression of a thicker girth.

David Craik, Hull

PROTECT your new carpet by putting your old carpet over the top.

Michael Thompson, Wales

ENSURE first class treatment for your grandad in the care home by wearing a dark suit, kissing his signet ring and calling him Don whenever you visit him.

Tony Corleoni, Crawley

toptips@viz.co.uk

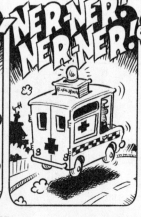

YOUR FABULOUS, FREE APP

TO everyone's great joy, the latest series of *The Apprentice* is back on our screens. The top-rated show, with its amazing £250,000 investment first prize, is a chance to watch hungry young entrepreneurs battling across Sir Lord Sugar's boardroom table for the chance to make it big in the business world.

But just in case you're doing something else for the next ten Wednesday nights – such as de-fleaing the cat, unblocking the shower plug, or watching whatever's on the other side – don't despair. Because we've teamed up with the scrotum-faced Amstrad billionaire himself to bring you this fantastic **FREE** *The Apprentice* board game!

INSTRUCTIONS: It's a game for two players. Firstly, pick an overblown name for your team. Below are a few suggestions, but feel free to choose another word from slightly beyond your own vocabulary. Cut out the five candidates that make up your team and place them on the START square. Take it in turns to throw the dice and advance one of your candidates along the board. With each throw of the dice you must move the candidate that is in last position. The candidate that reaches the *YOU'RE HIRED* square is the winner.

Suggested Team Names:

- Transcendence
- Primacy
- Paramount
- Imperium
- Preponderance
- Predominance
- Prometheus
- Olympus
- Primus
- Superlative
- Tremendum
- Subsidence
- Triumphator
- Vanquish
- Subjugation
- Excelsiorium
- Excalibur
- Millennium
- Suppositive
- Certitude
- Infallable
- Apollo
- Suppository
- Cocksure
- Trojan

Cut-out candidates:

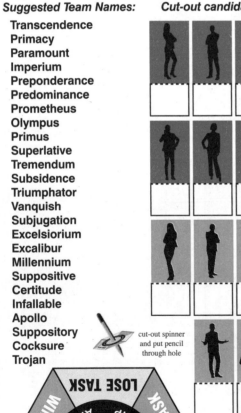

cut-out spinner and put pencil through hole

APPRENTICE WHEEL OF ENTREPRENEURSHIP
LOSE TASK / WIN TASK / LOSE TASK / WIN TASK / LOSE TASK / WIN TASK

fold base under candidate to stand up

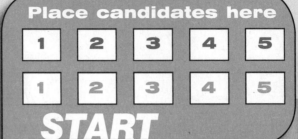

Place candidates here

| 1 | 2 | 3 | 4 | 5 |
| 1 | 2 | 3 | 4 | 5 |

START

You accidentally use the word "I" instead of "myself" when talking to Sir Lord Sugar.

Miss a turn

Even though you are a bellend, this week's filmed task has been edited to make you look like even more of a bellend than you actually are.

Move Back 1 space

Task:

Invent, brand and produce a shit TV advert for a new kind of drug to treat an under-active thyroid. **Spin the Apprentice Wheel of Entrepreneurship** to see whether you win or lose.

You pick a superficially impressive-sounding team name – such as *Team Ostentatious*, *Team Meretricious*, or *Team Superfluous* – but the word doesn't mean what you think it does. After he is told the real meaning by researchers, Sir Lord Sugar berates you ungrammatically for your foolishness.

Miss a turn

You lose your task, and are filmed arguing vociferously about whose fault it is (not yours) in a specially constructed 'greasy spoon' café on the BBC studios lot.

Move Back 2 spaces

YOU'RE FIRED!

Regretfully, Sir Lord Sugar has to tell you that you will take no further part in the process. Thank him for the opportunity, put on a big scarf and an overcoat, and wheel your little suitcase to a waiting taxi.

Task:

Organise a corporate bonding session away-day at Alton Tow[er] for the General Synod of the Church of England. **Spin the Apprentice Wheel of Entrepreneurship** to se[e] whether you win or lose.

You make an on-camera arseh[ole] comment of such moronic magnitude – something along [the] lines of "Penguins aren't birds, [are] they?", "what's the main ingred[ient] in an omelette?", or "Was Henry [—] alive in Victorian times?" – tha[t] gets used in the trailer announc[ing] the whole series, in the openi[ng] highlights montage of every epis[ode] and also becomes a popular run[ning] joke on *The Apprentice: You're* [Fired] with Rhod Gilbert on BBC2.

Miss 2 turns

You win your task and your tre[at] to go ten-pin bowling with form[er] Liverpool, Spurs and Englan[d] goalkeeper *Ray Clements*.

Miss a turn

You win your task and your tr[eat] is to go to a bird-watching hi[de] on Romney Marshes and ha[ve] your own signature cocktail mi[xed] up for you by *Chris Packha[m]*.

Miss a turn

You've survived the boardroo[m] **Move forward** [1] **space** as you hug the pers[on] you just slagged off, lied abou[t to] Lord Sugar, and got fired.

"As a factory worker in a fish packing plant, I never thought of myself as an entrepr[e]neur. However, playing this game has showed me just how much drive, ambition and passion to succeed in business I have .[..]"

Mrs J, Hu[ll]

During a boardroom meeting you make a boast about your performance on the previous task that causes Baroness Karren Brady to pull a face like someone just stuck their arse under her nose and farted.

Move Back 2 spaces

The director makes [you] come down the st[airs] in your pants, yaw[n] and pretend to ans[wer] the phone, even tho[ugh] it's three o'clock in [the] afternoon.

Miss a t[urn]

168

RENTICE BOARD GAME!

You win your task and your treat is to go on a flight simulator with **Ainsley Harriott**.

Miss a turn

YOU'RE FIRED!

Regretfully, Sir Lord Sugar has to tell you that you will take no further part in the process. Thank him for the opportunity, put on a big scarf and an overcoat, and wheel your little suitcase to a waiting taxi.

You're one of the final three in the boardroom, and Sir Lord Sugar starts making a speech, repeatedly using words such as *"I'm sorry to say…"* and *"regretfully, I have to tell you that…"* so it sounds for all the world like you're for the chop, before turning to someone else and firing them out of the blue.

Have another turn

You win your task and your treat is to go to a 5-star health farm for an hour-long sauna with **Ricky Tomlinson**, **Andy "The Viking" Fordham** and **Johnny Vegas**, after they've stuffed themselves with beef and egg pies.

Miss a turn

YOU'RE HIRED!

Although a glittering career as Sir Lord Alan's trusted business partner now awaits you, you will never be heard of again.

A mild exaggeration of your own business's turnover that the show's researchers insisted that you include in your CV, is uncovered in the last episode by Claude Littner.

Move Back 2 spaces

Task:

You have 24 hours to invent a new type of clothing that has never been thought of before, and try to sell it to supermarkets. **Spin the Apprentice Wheel of Entrepreneurship** to see whether you win or lose.

You win your task and your treat is to go on a luxury candle-making course with **Bob Carolgees** at a country house hotel very near the *Apprentice* studio.

Miss a turn

In a shock move, Sir Lord Sugar sacks TWO candidates in the same week, explaining that they have not showed him any of the qualities he is looking for in a potential business partner, and also because a scheduling clash means that this series has to be one episode shorter than the last one so it doesn't clash with the *Strictly Come Dancing* semi-final.

Miss a turn

You win your task and your treat is to spend an hour on the *EastEnders* set, learning the kazoo with **Joe Swash**.

Miss a turn

Your team is given a task that requires four of you to spend two days developing a new fish bait at a Catford maggot farm, while the fifth member flies to New York to attempt to sell the product to Madison Avenue business magnates at a swish cocktail reception. **Miss three turns** while you bicker acrimoniously about which of you has the best "skillset" to do the pitch.

YOU'RE FIRED!

Regretfully, Sir Lord Sugar has to tell you that you will take no further part in the process. Thank him for the opportunity, put on a big scarf and an overcoat, and wheel your little suitcase to a waiting taxi.

"I was penniless when I started playing your Apprentice board game. Now I run my own business with an annual turnover of £8.5 million."
Mr B, Derby

"After playing this game, I told my boss at the carpet cleaning company where I work to shove his job up his arse because I don't like liars, I don't like bullshitters and I don't like schmoozers. I now intend to set up my own multi-million dollar digital media company."
Mr F, Sheffield

"Business is boon-ing!"
Mrs B, Essex

You win your task and your treat is to go offroad driving with the **Brotherhood of Man**.

Miss a turn

Your team, comprising five of "Britain's finest young business brains", spends 18 hours developing, branding and making twenty small pots of unpalatable smoky bacon-flavoured cottage cheese, which they then sell in Leadenhall Market to passers-by who want to get their faces on the telly. After initially deciding a price-point of £12.50 a tub, you eventually flog the last dozen tubs for 10p each. You have turned a total profit of 8p, beating the other team, who only managed to make 60p.

Move forward 2 spaces

Whilst being driven round in the back of a black people carrier, you shout at someone through the end of a horizontal mobile phone, and come over like a right fucking twat.

Miss a turn

The crew forget to bring the box that Sir Lord Alan stands on to make himself look taller than Karren and Claude. **Miss a turn** while a runner is sent to find a milk crate.

During a task, you make a suggestion that causes Claude Littner to roll his eyes like someone has just begun working a baby pineapple anti-clockwise up his ringpiece.

Move Back 2 spaces

Drunken bakers

One morning in June

They got let down last minute now they're totally fucked –

– that's why they called us.

And we're expected to just *drop everything* and kiss their sodding arse?

This could be good for us.

They organise all these posh private parties...

This is for a do at a bloody *regatta!*

They want Coffee Renoir and Strawberry Pavlova for 20 – for tonight!

I bet they do the *cheeky bastards*.

I'll go and see what we need.

I need another Teacher's.

Soon

I'm off the cash 'n' carry.

What do we need?

We have nothing.

You're going to *burn*...

What do we know about reggae...

Four hours later

How's it-*eh*?

Fuc-gh...

I'm nearly done here.

Whaaa'sa booze is in it then?

Nah, ain't no booze in meringue.

I've saw off all the Teacher's...

So can't... no that...

Get your dirty fingers out of it.

PLOP

Mmmmmm, neev voov...

What?

I said, it needs boo-*GWAAWK!*

Time to make another?

No.

Where's the masher?

Sorry, crossed wires. We made Eton Mess.

Our own recipe that though.

Big splash of whisky. And a few carrots.

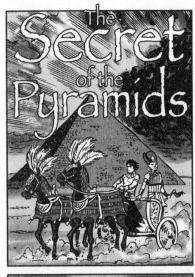

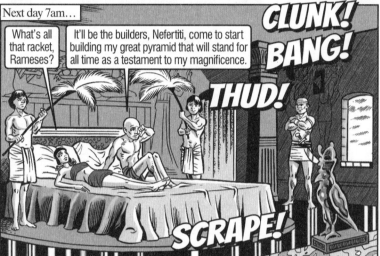

The End

THE PYRAMIDS are the only remaining Seventh Wonder of the World. Ever since the Pharaohs of Ancient Egypt's 3rd Dynasty first began erecting these giant stone tombs to contain their mummified remains nearly five millennia ago in 2649 BC, nobody has known who built them, what their original purpose was, or for how long they have been standing. And although the truth may lie somewhere amidst this tangled web of supposition, conjecture and myth that has grown up around them, the only real certainty is that the mystery of the Pyramids will endure long after these eternally unchanging monuments have crumbled to dust. Here are…

THINGS YOU NEVER KNEW ABOUT THE
20 PYRAMIDS

1 ANYONE hoping to knock up a pyramid in their garden over a weekend had better think again. That's because an average one contains an estimated 2,500,000 cubic metres of rock – meaning you'll have to make at least a million trips to your local builders' yard in a rented flatbed truck to pick up materials… and that's before you even start digging the foundations.

2 ALSO, obtaining local authority planning permission is likely to be a stumbling block. At nearly 500 feet high, a pyramid will block significant amounts of light from your "nimby" next door neighbour's garden, and they will almost certainly lodge an objection.

3 ALTHOUGH they like to bang on about them, Egypt isn't the only country to have pyramids. There's also one in Las Vegas, which is even better than the real thing. That's because, instead of being full of dusty old tombs, crumbly hieroglyphics and boring sarcophagii, the Luxor Las Vegas pyramid contains a luxury hotel with a swimming pool and spa, a high-end shopping mall, and an amusement arcade with 2,000 fruities.

4 THE Great Pyramid of Ghiza was originally designed with three sides. However, halfway through construction, the Pharaoh Khufu decided that 'The Great Tetrahedron of Ghiza' didn't sound grand enough to be his eternal resting place, so he ordered his slaves to add a fourth side.

5 THE tiniest ever pyramid constructed in Ancient Egypt was approximately the same size as a modern medium-sized greenhouse. The magnificent tomb was the resting place of the mummified remains of the world's smallest Pharaoh, Calvin Phillips-Hotep III. His body, tightly wrapped in bandages the thickness of dictaphone cassette tape, was placed in a secret chamber in the depths of the pyramid, housed in a golden sarcophagus the size of a peanut husk.

6 MANY people believe that the pyramids are mysteriously arranged in such a way as to mirror the constellations of the cosmos. But they're not.

7 ARCHAEOLOGISTS claim that evidence from texts and hieroglyphics shows that the Ancient Egyptians had a sophisticated pyramid building system which involved tens of thousands of men working round the clock for decades. According to this theory, firstly water from the Nile was diverted into a barricaded area in order to achieve a level worksite, before basic geometry was used to mark out the base dimensions of the proposed construction. Millions of stones cut by teams of masons were brought in on barges and lifted to their final position by slaves using inclined earth ramps, A-frame pulleys and wooden rollers. Despite this, no-one really knows how the pyramids were built and what's more, no-one ever will.

8 MANY people believe that the Pyramids are actually evidence of alien technology. Nobody knows why, but it seems that beings from the other side of the galaxy flew unimaginable distances through space, possibly even warping time, to get to Egypt. Once there, they constructed three big pointy piles of rock – one big one and two smaller ones – and then pissed off home.

9 IF you dismantled a pyramid, you might think you'd have enough stone to build two pyramids half as high. And you would be right. But amazingly, when you'd finished building them you'd have enough stone left over to build another six more! "We simply don't know why that should be," says TV mathematician Professor Marcus de Sautoy. "It's just another one of the mysteries of the pyramids."

10 WHAT'S more, if you dismantled one of these half-size pyramids and built some quarter-height ones, you'd have enough stone to build another eight. "You think I'm shitting you, but it's true," says TV mathematician Dr Simon Singh. "It does my bleeding melon in, this stuff."

11 IF the Great Pyramid of Cheops had been built on the seabed mid-way between Dover and Calais, it is estimated that the top 300 feet of it would stick out of the water. Scientists are undecided over whether this demonstrates how tall the pyramids are or how shallow the English Channel is.

12 IT would also present a hazard to shipping, and add approximately 14 minutes to the average ferry crossing. However, a mid-channel Great Pyramid of Cheops would be a welcome sight for Channel swimmers, who could clamber onto it to get their breath back and enjoy a warming cup of Bovril.

13 BEING a worker on a pyramid building site was a thankless task. Not only was there very little in the way of health and safety, but they were also unpaid, forced to work long hours, and were routinely whipped. If that wasn't bad enough, at the end of their 70-year shift they were sealed in the pyramid and left to starve to death.

14 5,000 years ago, if you were a roofer in Ancient Egypt, you may as well have packed up your tools and gone home. That's because a pyramid is the only sort of building that doesn't have a roof. "The walls just sort of slope in and meet in a point at the top," says Kevin McCloud of TV's *Grand Designs*.

15 THERE have been many hit records that take Egypt as their theme, such as *Walk Like an Egyptian* by the Bangles, *Egyptian Reggae* by Jonathan Richman and the Modern Lovers, and *Night Boat to Cairo* by Madness. But strangely, none of these records mentions that country's most popular tourist attraction, the Pyramids. "It's probably because nothing rhymes with the word pyramid," says veteran *Hit Man & Her* songwriter and producer Pete Waterman.

GELLER IN A TIZZ OVER PYRAMID THREAT

16 UK adult star Lara Latex has never filmed one of her saucy videos at the Great Pyramid of Cheops. "I've had it off on camera in many exotic locations, such as Romney Marsh, underneath the pier at Cleethorpes and in the back of a Seat Alhambra in a car park in Wigan, but never in the shadow of these mysterious and majestic monuments on the plains of Ghiza," she told *Desert Island Discs*'s Kirsty Wark.

17 THE same can't be said of veteran porn actor Ben Dover, whose DVDs *Ben Dover's Pork Like an Egyptian*, *Ben Dover's Cheops Housewife Gangbang*, and *Ben Dover's Anal Pyramid Cum Bath vol. 23* have all topped the adult entertainment charts.

18 THE Pyramids are famous for their dreadful curses, which promise death to anyone who enters them. Chillingly, every single person who was involved in the first systematic archaeological exploration of the Great Pyramid of Cheops in 1872 has since perished.

19 THE curse of the pharaohs also befell Terry's Pyramint – a pyramid-shaped chocolate confection with a mint fondant centre that was discontinued in the 1990s due to falling sales.

20 IF you took all the chocolate and fondant from a Terry's Pyramint, you might expect to have enough to make two 'fun-size' Pyramints. But in fact you'd have enough to make eight. "Straight up, I'm not pulling your cock," says TV mathematician Dr Hannah Fry. "Stuff like this does my fucking crust in."

VETERAN 1970s psychic **URI GELLER** yesterday slammed pyramid bosses over their claims that the 5,000-year-old monuments had the power to bend spoons. Geller, 71, rubbished an announcement by the Cairo Tourist Board that, during scientific tests, pieces of cutlery had been spontaneously deformed by mysterious forces emanating from the summits of the ancient structures.

"These charlatans claim to have taken ordinary spoons to the tops of pyramids, where they have mysteriously curled up, gone all wibbly-wobbly, and in some cases even snapped in two," Geller told reporters at a hastily convened press conference in Cairo. "But the evidence for these so-called experiments is flimsy at best."

neck

Geller went on to list a number of ways in which he believed the results may have been falsified. "They could have been using a trick spoon with a pre-weakened neck, or there could be a spoon that is already bent that has been left under a rock at the top, and they swapped them over," he said. "Either that, or they bent the spoons with their hands while they were climbing up the pyramid and no-one was looking."

However, tourist chief Anwar Sazwar later demonstrated the effect to the world's press by carrying an ordinary soup spoon to the top of the Great Pyramid of Cheops.

Geller: "Flimsy" spoon evidence.

When he came down again an hour later, he showed reporters the exact same spoon, which was now almost bent double. He said: "That's been in my pocket all the time. That's the forces off the pyramid that's done that, not me."

"I've never touched it, and that's God's honest truth," he added.

spoon

And Sazwar's claims were supported by eminent US sceptic James Randi. "Believe me, I know every way of bending a spoon that's ever been invented, and I simply can't explain what I have witnessed today," he said. "I can only conclude that the pyramids indeed have some mysterious, magical force emanating from their summits that bends spoons."

Geller later carried out a demonstration of his own spoon-bending ability. Holding a spoon loosely between his thumb and forefinger, he began to rub it gently. After about thirty seconds, he suddenly pointed behind the reporters and shouted: "Quick! Look at the sphinx!" When everyone turned back round, Geller had mysteriously bent the spoon using the power of his mind.

"Look at that, it's like plastic," he added.

Pyramid Soapbox

Experts have told us how, when and why the pyramids were built. But as fish-faced arsehole Michael Gove rightly says, the public have had enough of experts. So we asked the only people whose opinions really matter – the Soap Stars – for their take on the enduring mysteries of the Pyramids.

Jennifer Metcalfe, 'Mercedes McQueen' in *Hollyoaks*

"I think the pyramids aren't anything; they're just the places where the ancient Egyptians stored stones in big triangular piles. They kept them there for when they needed them to build Sphinxes, Colossi of Memnon, obelisks and Temples of Hapsetshut and stuff. Any topologist will tell you that a quadrilateral tetrahedral stack with an incidence angle of 45° is the most efficient way to store right-angled blocks. Their civilisation must have fallen before they got round to using them."

Danny Dyer, 'Danny Dyer' in *EastEnders*

"I seen this documentary on the internet, and they said that the Pyramids were like alien petrol stations, where flying saucers can come down and refuel. They've been soaking up the sun's rays for millions of years, ain't they, and it all comes out the point on the bleeding top, don't it. You look at pictures of UFOs, and they've all got an adapter on the bottom the shape of the top of a pyramid. Coincidence? Do me a favour, you melt."

Patrick Mower, 'Rodney Blackstock' in *Emmerdale*

"I think that if you put food in the middle of a pyramid, it would stay fresh forever. Even very perishable things that go off really quick, like avocados, hummus and chicken portions, would remain perfectly edible if they were stored in a pyramid for hundreds or even thousands of years. I've got no evidence for what I think, but I strongly believe this to be the case."

Helen Worth, 'Gail Platt' in *Coronation Street*

"I believe that the measurements of the pyramids contain hidden within them the answers to questions that we earthbound humans cannot yet fathom. For example, if you divide the height of a pyramid by the length of one of its sides, you get another number which may well have magical properties. In fact, if you take any measurement of a pyramid – such as the diagonal of the base – and divide it by any other measurement – such as the corner to the top – you'll get another magical number. Let's see the so-called scientists explain that one away."

RAJ OF THE LIGHT BRIGADE!

ASK anyone from Land's End to John O'Groats to name their favourite Crimean War catastrophe and the answer will always be the same: *The Charge of the Light Brigade*. This iconic 1854 Battle of Balaclava blunder - which saw 107 British soldiers killed in combat with the Russian Empire - has lived long in the UK's collective imagination, and each of us harbours our own views on who exactly was to blame for it.

But did you know that where YOU lay the responsibility for this military catastrophe speaks volumes about how good you are at sexual intercourse? "It's true, it does," says TV shrink, **DR RAJ PERSAUD**. "The only way to find out whether a prospective partner is hot to trot or a flop between the sheets is to ask them who, precisely, they think was at fault for the Charge of the Light Brigade."

Here Dr Raj takes a look at the four most common candidates to blame for the calamitous 'Charge into the Valley of Death', and what we can learn about their accusers' sordid sexual secrets.

"Who you blame for botched 1854 cavalry manoeuvre says A LOT about how good you are at sex", says telly shrink Raj Persaud

Rode the sex hungry: What does your choice of light bridgade scapegoat say about your sex drive, asks Raj Persaud (above left)?

LORD RAGLAN

Dr Raj says: "FitzRoy Somerset, the 1st Baron Raglan, remains the most obvious guilty party on that fateful day of 25 October 1854. Raglan was the commander-in-chief of British forces in Crimea, and as such the calamitous order to attack the Russian guns was his and his alone to deliver. Blaming Raglan has long been the traditional, conservative choice, and for Raglan blamers, those values extend into the bedroom. These bland and timid sexual performers rarely stray from tedious missionary-style spousal intercourse, performed with grinding rigidity once a week inside a darkened room."

Celebrity Raglan blamers:
Joe Swash, P Diddy, Mark Lawrenson

EARL OF CARDIGAN

Dr Raj says: "Reports indicate that the 7th Earl of Cardigan openly expressed doubts about Raglan's order to charge, but then proceeded to obey it anyway. In other words, he failed to stand up for himself - a problem that Cardigan blamers are all too familiar with between the sheets. These hapless sexual incompetents find it almost impossible to achieve full penile turgidity, and any amount of physical or mental stimulation will still leave their miserable members as limp as the 7th Earl's backbone."

Celebrity Raglan blamers:
Mark Zuckerberg, Nick Clegg, Kim Jong-un

CAPTAIN NOLAN

Dr Raj says: "Captain Louis Nolan was among the first to realise that the British cavalry were attacking the wrong target, but he fatefully miscommunicated the order to turn back. And "turning back" is very much the order of day for Nolan blamers, who enjoy frequent and frantic anal intercourse. The struggle to communicate plays a large part in their bedroom antics, too, with cheeky mouth-stuffing ball gags and zip-lined leather gimp masks a near-constant presence on their bedside tables."

Celebrity Raglan blamers:
Charlton Heston, Abu Hamza, James May

EARL OF LUCAN

Dr Raj says: "Those who blame George Bingham, the 3rd Earl of Lucan, for the Light Brigade's heavy casualties display a clear interest in chains of command. The order to attack was passed from Raglan to Cardigan via Lucan - who found himself awkwardly sandwiched between the two. And Lucan blamers seek to recreate similar "sandwiches" in the sack, due to their burning passion for group sex. Threesomes, orgies and DVDA gang-bangs are all music to the ears of these sexual socialites, who enjoy nothing more than regular anonymous intercourse with multiple partners."

Celebrity Raglan blamers:
Boutros Boutros-Ghali, Mike Pence, Dan Walker

NEXT WEEK: *Raj-ent Pepper's Lonely Hearts Club Band! "Your favourite 1967 Beatles song says A LOT about the type of sex toy you would take to a wife swapping party."*

MEDDLESOME RATBAG

BRITAIN'S JUICIEST GRAPE FORUM, HOSTED BY FAMOUS FILM ACTOR TIM ROTH

THE GRAPES OF ROTH

Hi, **TIM ROTH** here. You'll know me as 'Mr Orange' from the hit film *Reservoir Dogs*. But to be honest, I'd much rather of been 'Mr Purple', because that's the colour of my all-time favourite fruit... grapes! Or 'Mr Green', I suppose, because some grapes are green. Yes, believe it or not, I'm pathologically obsessed with these juicy little non-climacteric berries. And judging by the size of this week's *Grapes of Roth* postbag, you lot are fairly keen on them, too. So, what are we waiting for? Let's start 'raisin' the curtain on a selection of the 'grape' letters I've received this week.

Yours grape-obsessedly, Tim xx

WHOEVER was in charge of naming the different types of grape did a pretty shocking job, if you ask me. So-called 'white' grapes are actually pale green, so-called 'red' grapes are typically purple, and so-called 'black' grapes are actually dark blue. Perhaps whoever was in charge of naming oranges 'oranges' could supervise this initiative, as he or she seems to have their head screwed on correctly.
Chester Benelux, Scholes

I FANCIED making a spotted dick the other day so I asked my husband Brian to nip out and get me some currants. Imagine my surprise when he returned with several flows of electric charge carried by ions in an electrolyte. My spotted dick turned out to be inedible as it was full of magnetic fields and had a potential difference of 300 volts across it. He laughed so hard at this simple misunderstanding that he had an accident in his trousers. Needless to say, I shan't make the mistake of asking Brian for help again!
Agnes Barrelscraper, Stamford Brook

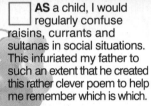

AS a child, I would regularly confuse raisins, currants and sultanas in social situations. This infuriated my father to such an extent that he created this rather clever poem to help me remember which is which.

Raisins are dried white Moscatel grapes,
They're squashy and come in all sizes and shapes,
Sultanas are golden and plump as can be,
You put them in cakes that you bake for your tea,
Currants are black; from the Corinth grape strain,
Now don't fucking mix them up ever again!

He still forces me to recite it at gunpoint ten times a day.
Sebastian Carstairs, Chiswick

WITH regard to Mr Carstairs' letter/poem *(above)*, I've always found it incredibly unfair that grapes are permitted THREE different words for their dried incarnation, whilst other fruits don't even get a single one. Sun-dried tomatoes, for instance, are simply referred to as 'sun-dried tomatoes', rather than having their own specially invented title. I think grapes should share the wealth a bit and donate two of their dried incarnation monikers to other fruits who have been less fortunate than they in the dried incarnation naming stakes.
Selwin Digfeather, Moseley

> ### Top Grape Tips
> **AN EXTREMELY** over-ripe grape makes an ideal water balloon for a mischievous hamster.
> ***Del Gripplecheek, Surrey***

WITH regard to the many previous letters about the naming of fruits, it's always struck me as strange that a grapefruit is called a grapefruit. Yes it's a fruit, but it's absolutely nothing like a grape. It's about a hundred times bigger for a start, and bright orange.
Ethel Acetate, Sunderland

I HAVEN'T drunk foreign wines since I discovered that the winemakers tread the grapes in their bare feet. I bet the dirty pigs don't even bother getting out of the barrel when they need a wee. I know I wouldn't.
Tollerton Ponds, Luton

WHEN I was nine years old, I ate sixteen packets of raisins for breakfast and then shat myself in school assembly. Ever since this mortifying event occurred, I've been looking forward to the sweet embrace of death so I can forget all about it.
Emilio Bad-Chests, Haslingden

> ### Top Grape Tips
> **SAVE** money on expensive grapes by simply buying some raisins and injecting each one with a small amount of water.
> ***Dennis Ataraxia, Warwick***

I AM a vintner, and with summertime fast approaching, I wanted to pray for my grape yield to be successful. However, when I went online to find out which particular God I should be praying to, I discovered that Dionysus – the God of the grape harvest – is also the God of several other things, including ritual madness, fertility, theatre and religious ecstasy. With such a large and diverse portfolio, I'm now unsure as to whether Dionysus will have either the time or the expertise to ensure my grape harvest is sufficiently bountiful. I mean, I've heard of multitasking, but this just beggars belief.
Murray Cravencock, Devon

IN REFERENCE to Mr Cravencock's letter *(above)*, I wonder if he has considered praying to a Catholic saint, rather than an Ancient Greek deity? I've heard good things about St Vincent of Saragossa – the Catholic patron saint of wine-making – who apparently specialises exclusively in grape-specific prayers, and has no interest – either professional or personal – in ritual madness, theatre, fertility or any other non-grape-based activity.
P Francis, Vatican City

> ### Top Grape Tips
> **CUT** eleven grapes in half and stick an 00-gauge toy soldier into each gooey centre. Hey presto: your very own Army Subbuteo team!
> ***M Lawrenson, Merseyside***

MY father was a greengrocer during the war, and grapes were strictly rationed as they had to come in on the convoys. However he was a soft-hearted old thing and he felt very sorry for young mums trying to feed their growing families with the meagre amounts of fruit available during those difficult times. If a lady came in for her weekly ration, he would always slip in a few extra grapes in return for sexual favours such as a hand job or fellatio.
Irene Sheldon, Louth

WE have a large grapevine growing on a pergola in our garden, and last week my husband told me'd heard a mistle thrush that was sitting on it, singing "You could say, I heard it on the grapevine," he quipped. I had to laugh, and what made it even funnier was that my husband is Motown singer Marvin Gaye.
Ada Gaye, Detroit

MRS Gaye *(above)*, if that's her real name, must think we were born yesterday if she expects us to believe her anecdote. In the first instance, mistle thrushes are not native to the state of Michigan, so it is highly unlikely that one was singing in her garden. Secondly, the title of the song in question is I Heard it "Through" – not "on" – the Grapevine, which Marvin Gaye would surely have known. Thirdly, she maintains that the episode in question happened last week, even though Marvin Gaye has been dead for 34 years after his dad shot him.
Mavis Bats, Tooting

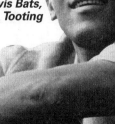

> ### Top Grape Tips
> **LADIES.** A raisin glued to the side of your mouth with a dab of honey makes for an ideal Cindy Crawford-style 'beauty spot'. And it can be removed quite easily at the end of the night by simply sliding your tongue across for a tasty treat!
> ***Ada Covetous, Hull***

I WAS very disappointed when they invented seedless grapes, as the seeds were always my favourite bits off a grape. I used to eat the pips and then spit out the juicy flesh that everyone else likes. The bitter, astringent taste combined with the unpleasant woody texture was always a proper treat.
M Contrary, Tipperary

Kids say the funniest things...about grapes!

"NANA, those grapes look a bit dry," my 3-year-old grandson said to me last week. I had to chuckle – he was pointing at some raisins!

Agnes Mousepractice, Hulme

"NANA, those raisins look a bit moist and tumescent," my 3-year-old grandson said to me last week. I had to chuckle – he was pointing at some grapes!

Agnes Mousepractice, Hulme

"NANA, those grapes look a bit crushed, blended with yeast and then fermented over a period of several weeks before being siphoned periodically off the resulting sediment," my 3-year-old grandson said to me last week. I had to chuckle – he was pointing at some wine!

Agnes Mousepractice, Hulme

Has a kid said the funniest thing to YOU about grapes? Write in and tell us about it. Each letter we print wins a lifetime's supply of grapes for you and the kid that said the funniest thing to you about grapes.

GRAPE BLOOPERS
Big screen grape gaffes with grape-bonkers cinephile, *Mark Commode*

● IN THE 1940 BUSTER KEATON film *Nothing But Pleasure*, the iconic silent comedian disastrously attempts to make a romantic meal for his spouse. His ingredients include a string of onions, a live cat and a whole bunch of grapes, including the stems. The film is set three decades before the invention of electronic time-keeping technology, yet Keaton can clearly be seen wearing a digital watch as he adds the grapes to the saucepan.

● IN ONE scene during the 1963 masterpiece *Cleopatra*, the Egyptian queen – played by ELIZABETH TAYLOR – is being fed grapes by a lowly slave. The film is set in 48 BC, yet each grape clearly has a digital watch wrapped around it.

● IN THE 1995 romantic drama *A Walk In The Clouds*, KEANU REEVES'S character joins a family of Mexican vintners in a traditional raucous 'grape stomp'. The film is set just after the Second World War, yet we can clearly see Reeves and his co-stars are all wearing digital watches, stomping on a huge pile of digital watches, and chanting the words 'Digital watch' over and over again.

● IN THE popular wine-themed comedy *Sideways*, we see two friends (PAUL GIAMATTI and THOMAS HADEN CHURCH) strolling happily through a sun-kissed vineyard. The film is set in 2004, more than three decades after the invention of the digital watch, and yet neither actor is wearing – or evens mentions – a digital watch.

More silver screen grape fuck-ups next time, Vitis vinifera fans! *Mark x*

Raisin d'Etre

YOUR metaphysical dried grape queries answered by raisin-lovin' telly philosopher **ALAIN DE BOTTON**

Dear Alain de,

I RARELY eat raisins as I think they taste fucking awful. However, according to Buddhist philosophy, suffering gives our life meaning. Should I perhaps be consuming raisins on a regular basis in order to give my existence some vague sense of purpose?

Nigel Want-Brass, Cambridge

Alain de says: *"It's a nice idea, Nigel, but no. The Buddha certainly taught that all life is suffering, but he also taught that suffering can be eliminated by extinguishing selfish craving and personal desire. As such, your selfish craving to eat raisins as a means of imbuing your pitiful existence with meaning will only lead to more suffering. I would suggest that your true path to enlightenment lies in meditation and the doing of good deeds, rather than constantly obsessing over whether or not you should be eating raisins."*

Do YOU have a question about the general fundamental problems concerning existence, value and reason that is also in some way connected to raisins? Why not write in to: 'Alain de Botton's Raisin D' Etre' c/o Viz Comic, PO Box 841, Whitley Bay, NE26 9EQ

GRAPES, THE LAW AND YOU

with Grape Barrister *Quercus Petraea Q.C.*

MY NEIGHBOUR has a large grapevine in his greenhouse that produces bunches and bunches of succulent grapes every year, whilst I have to pay through the nose for mine at the supermarket. It simply isn't fair. Unfortunately, the vine doesn't block my light or overhang my property and its roots aren't affecting the drains. Are there any legal grounds upon which I could compel him to cut this vine down, so that the smug bastard has to pay for his grapes like the rest of us do?

Nigel X., Surrey

Indeed there is. Living without stress, strain or anguish is a fundamental human right, and your neighbour's grapevine is clearly causing you great mental distress. Go to your doctor and get him to sign a note to the effect that you are suffering anxiety and depression as a result of your neighbour's overly bountiful grapevine. Lay it on thick, saying that you are now harbouring suicidal feelings because of it. Then, use the note to apply for a court order compelling him to cut his vine down and dispose of it. If he comes round to try and reason with you, shout that if he touches you, you will treat it as an assault. Then get a restraining order to prevent him coming within 20 yards of your front door so that you can have him arrested next time he comes home from work.

Do YOU have a grape-related legal query? Write to: Quercus Patraea QC, Viz Chambers, PO Box 841, Whitley Bay, NE26 9EQ, enclosing 600 guineas plus disbursements.

ROYAL AFFAIR SHOCK

Historians forced to rethink after North Shields woman's announcement

ACADEMICS are being forced to re-examine historical documents after a North Shields woman cast doubt on conventional thinking about a 19th Century royal marriage.

Historians have long believed that King William IV's wife, Adelaide of Saxe-Meiningen, remained faithful to her husband despite rumours that she conducted an affair with her Lord Chamberlain in the 1830s. Documents show that the consort queen was extremely close to Richard Curzon-Howe, but the rumours of a fling, which led to his dismissal from the post, have long been understood to have been politically motivated.

However, after reading an historical fiction novel, 45-year-old Janice Bunions has cast doubt on the theory. "I think she had an affair with him," she told *The Journal of Contemporary History*. "I've just finished reading *Victoria in the Wings* by Jean Plaidy, and I reckon she might well have done the dirty on her husband."

howe

According to Janice, the novel paints a picture of Lord Howe as a tall, handsome, dashing gentleman with chiselled features and a pencil moustache, and the Queen as a fragile, sensitive woman trapped in a

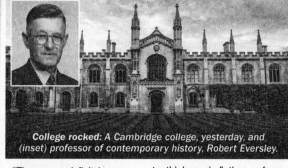

Written evidence: Bunions discovered clues in Plaidy's historical novels (above).

loveless marriage of state. And whilst the novel shows the King and Queen were fond of each other, it describes an irresistible chemistry between the Queen and Howe. "After all, she was only flesh and blood," said Bunions.

She told us: "In chapter seven, there's a bit where the King takes Adelaide on a ride in his carriage in Regents Park and they're both all lovey-dovey. But then she sees Lord Howe riding past on a big white horse and she goes all quiet and starts to cry."

College rocked: A Cambridge college, yesterday, and (inset) professor of contemporary history, Robert Eversley.

"There was definitely something going off," she added.

"We certainly need to look again at the facts," said Robert Eversley, professor of contemporary history at the University of Cambridge. "We have long believed that Adelaide supported the Tory government, and the public believed she was trying to influence the King to halt the passage of the Reform act of 1832."

"As a result, the press began to circulate rumours about an affair in order to destabilise their relationship and weaken her influence. But the entire court knew she was extremely pious and faithful to her husband. The Whig Prime Minister Earl Grey had Howe removed from the queen's household simply to quell the rumours," he said.

father

"That's the current thinking, but it looks like we might have to think again," the professor added.

Bunions, who has read almost every historical novel Jean Plaidy has written, says that her other books back up her theory.

"In *The Goddess of the Green Room*, William conducts an affair with an actress, Dorothy Jordan, and has ten kids by her," she explained. "And when he marries Adelaide, he's still got the picture of Dorothy up in the house. Well, if that's not enough to make her want an affair, nothing is."

But not everyone agrees with Janice's theory. Sharon Balmcake, her friend who borrowed the book after she had read it, said she held with conventional academic thinking. "I don't think she had an affair. I mean, yes, she might of, but I don't think she did," she told *Comparative Studies in Society and History*.

Woman Finds Dead Rat in *Viz* Profanisaurus!

A *Viz* reader who is pregnant with quads got more than she bargained for when she bought a copy of the brand new *Viz Profanisaurus: War and Piss*. While perusing the famous dictionary of bad language, 23-year-old Maureen Mimblehulme turned the page to find a *DEAD RAT* squashed inside the book!

"I felt physically sick," the Northants canning factory worker, who is expecting four babies in December, told her local paper *The Silverstone Lodestar & Beacon*. "I'd already read quite a bit of the book before I found it. It was absolutely disgusting."

wonder

"It makes you wonder what the hygiene policies at Viz are like, when they can sell a heavily pregnant woman a book with a dead rat in it," she continued.

The popular comedy magazine's editor, Hampton Doubleday, said he was at a loss to explain how the decomposing rodent came to be lodged in the book. He

Horrible surprise for Viz reader

told us: "Here at our offices in the North-east, the issue of cleanliness takes top priority. In fact Viz is one of the few magazines in Britain to boast a five-star hygiene rating."

shower

"We simply can't imagine how this dead rat slipped through the net and got inside one of our books," he said. "We were hoping that War and Piss, a fully updated, revised and re-edited 624-page Profanisaurus including 20,000

Mouse about that, then?: Maureen finds dead rodent in copy of War and Piss, on sale now.

definitions and a foreword by Professor Brian Cox, was a going to be a sales success."

"Sadly, this kind of publicity is only going to harm its prospects of becoming a best-seller," said Doubleday.

shot

He continued: "As a mark of how seriously we take this issue, we have offered to replace Miss Mimblehulme's book with a fresh copy that

we have carefully checked for dead rats."

retriever

"In addition, as a gesture of goodwill we have also offered her an ex-gratia payment of £250 and told her to fuck off," Doubleday added.

But last night, *Viz* found itself embroiled in a fresh controversy after a used condom was found inside a copy of the magazine's

Doubleday: Dreadful publicity will almost certainly effect sales of book.

brand new, bumper 220-page annual *The Pieman's Wig*, which is available from all good bookshops.

THE STAG NIGHT is as quintessentially British as St Paul's Cathedral, the Changing of the Guard, and Brexit. It's the jolly rite of passage that every young man must undergo as he prepares to leave behind his carefree, irresponsible bachelorhood and embark upon endless decades of marital bliss with the same, ageing woman.

Over the centuries, this institution has progressed from a simple night at the local inn with a few close pals to a complex ordeal involving a series of spiteful, booze-fuelled revelries that often ends with the groom-to-be chained naked to a park bench in Dundee or laid up with liver failure in a foreign hospital on the morning of his wedding.

Today's stag is unrecognisable from its humble antecedent, and there is no reason to expect that it will not continue to change, progress and evolve in the future. But what exactly will the Stag Night of the year 2020 look like? Join futurologists *Martin Alookahead* and *Jeff Totwentytwenty* as they take a peek into their crystal balls.

THE ENTERTAINMENT. In the future, it is still traditional for all those in the stag party to embark on some adventurous pursuit as an hors d'oeuvres to a night of heavy drinking. But gone are today's old-fashioned stag-do pursuits suc

THE STRIP CLUB. In 2020, strip clubs have become a virtual reality experience, with visitors donning headsets in order to watch exotic CGI dancers bump and grind in super-high definition 3D. The experience has been designed to be as convincing as possible, with every single element of a traditional evening in a strip club recreated. The exotic and tantalising lap dance, the paying 50 times the going rate for a glass of coke and being kicked senseless by a couple of bouncers for touching one of the virtual girls are all brought vividly to life with immersive, 360 degree realism.

ATTIRE. As with Stag Do's in 2018, the stag of the future must be dressed in a ludicrous outfit. However, in 2020, the development of futuristic metamorphic garment technology means that the groom-to-be can be dressed in a multi-purpose, shape-shifting Invisi-Poncho, which is controlled by an "app" that metamorphs it into whichever embarrassing novelty outfit the party desire - be it a Borat-style 'Mankini', a Litt Bo-Peep costume or a baby's nappy, bonn and dummy. It can also be transformed to resemble just a pair of underpants for th end of the night when the stag, by now suffering from acute alcohol poisoning, is tied to a laser lamp-post using futuristic electro-magnets. And whilst we all love wearing fake novelty breasts on a Stag D the women of tomorrow will all have th tits like in *Bladerunner*, so this must also now be taken into account.

THE DIRTY PINT. In the dark ages of 2018, Stag Do parties traditionally concocted a 'Dirty Pint' for the stag to consume, a heady brew made from the dregs of various alcoholic drinks, as well as any additional condiments and/ or bodily fluids they felt inclined to include. In the futuristic world of 2020, however, all food and drink is in the form of a pill - so attendees can simply add a specially formulated 'Dirty Pint Pill' to a glass of water, and hey presto - an instant, utterly repulsive beverage that tastes of lager, gin, whisky, absinthe, mustard, ketchup, phlegm, vomit, Pot Noodle, curry powder, knobcheese and shower gel.

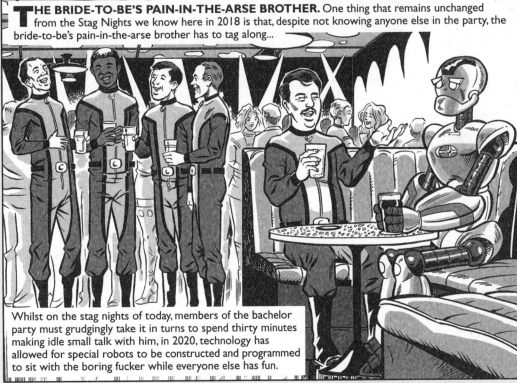

THE BRIDE-TO-BE'S PAIN-IN-THE-ARSE BROTHER. One thing that remains unchanged from the Stag Nights we know here in 2018 is that, despite not knowing anyone else in the party, the bride-to-be's pain-in-the-arse brother has to tag along...

...Quaser Laser, paintballing and karting. Here in 2020, [the] groom-to-be and his coterie will spend the afternoon [go]-kart racing in futuristic, driverless vehicles that use [state]-of-the-art computer technology to ensure they [t]ravel at exactly the same speed and remain a safe [dist]ance from each other as they hurtle round the track.

Whilst on the stag nights of today, members of the bachelor party must grudgingly take it in turns to spend thirty minutes making idle small talk with him, in 2020, technology has allowed for special robots to be constructed and programmed to sit with the boring fucker while everyone else has fun.

PRANKS. Whether they don balaclavas and bundle him into the boot of a car in a mock kidnapping, gaffer tape him to the underside of a bus shelter, or wait until he's unconscious and shave his eyebrows off, today's stag fully expects to be pranked by his fellow revellers. And the stag of 2020 will be subjected to similar ritual hilarity, being bundled into the boot of a driverless hover car, affixed to the ceiling of a holographic bus shelter with electrostatic graphene ribbons, and de-eyebrowed with a disposible laser-razor.

HILARIOUS MATCHING T-SHIRTS. As predicted in *Back To The Future 2*, all clothing in the future will be self-fitting, self-cleaning and self-drying - a bonus for the members of the stag party, as their T-shirts can be free from spilled lager, vomit or blood in a matter of seconds. They can also be electronically programmed to display amusing nicknames. The Best Man is therefore able to 3D-print these space-age garments at home, before instantaneously downloading a selection of hilarious monickers onto the back of each one from his mobile phone.

Next week in a Look Ahead to 2020:
The Sex Shop of Tomorrow

POPPY BULLSHIT AND ARAMINTA BOLLOCKS ART MAKERS

ARAMINTA... LOOK AT THIS!

HMM... YES. THAT IS CHALLENGING MY PRECONCEPTIONS ABOUT THE INTRINSIC NATURE OF BISCUITS. IT'S A TELLING JUXTAPOSITION OF FORM AND CONTENT.

I'VE ALWAYS REGARDED HOBN AS BEING ROUND... AND YET TH ONE ISN'T. IT'S AN ARTISTIC TOU FORCE DRIPPING WITH DRAMATI ECLAT...!

NO, WAIT... JUST THINK. WE'RE ASSUMING THAT THE MOUSE HAS INVADED OUR SPACE...

YES...?

WHAT IF... IT IS WE WHO HAVE INVADED THE MOUSE'S SPACE?!

GOSH! YOU'VE JUST CHALLENGED MY PRE-CONCEPTIONS ABOUT HOW WE TAKE OWNER-SHIP OF THE SPACES WE INHABIT!

I'D BEST SORT OUT SOME FUNDING RIGHT AWAY!

HELLO? IS THAT THE ARTS COUN WE HAVE A PIECE IN DEVELOPMENT IT'S CALLED "OF MICE AND MEN AND SPACE"...

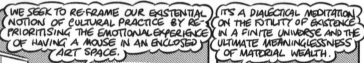

WE SEEK TO RE-FRAME OUR EXISTENTIAL NOTION OF CULTURAL PRACTICE BY RE-PRIORITISING THE EMOTIONAL EXPERIENCE OF HAVING A MOUSE IN AN ENCLOSED ART SPACE.

IT'S A DIALECTICAL MEDITATION ON THE FUTILITY OF EXISTENCE IN A FINITE UNIVERSE AND THE ULTIMATE MEANINGLESSNESS OF MATERIAL WEALTH.

£10,000...? THAT'S A LITTLE DISAPPOINTING.

TSK
PHILISTINES!

IT'S SUCH A COMPELLING PIECE THAT WE'RE HOPING TO EXHIBIT IT TO AN INTERNATIONAL AUDIENCE FOR A COUPLE OF WEEKS AT AN ALL-INCLUSIVE BEACH RESORT IN CANCUN...

THAT NIGHT...

HMM... YES. THERE ARE CLEARLY MULTIPLE LEVELS OF MEANING HERE... THE CHEESE IN THE TRAP IS ESSENTIAL TO LIFE, BUT WILL ULTIMATELY BRING ABOUT THE MOUSE'S DEMISE...

INDEED. IT IS A POTENT DICHOTOMY THAT IS AT ONCE LITERAL AND METAPHORICAL.

IT SEEMS TO ME THAT THE SPRING TRAP EQUATES TO A PALPABLE SENSE OF EMOTIONAL TENSION IN THE AUDIENCE AS WE WAIT FOR THE MOUSE TO ARRIVE...

QUITE.

SCREAM!

JESUS! KILL IT! FUCKIN' KILL IT, SOMEONE!

OOH, FUCK! IT'S RAN UP ME FUCKIN' TROUSER LEG! HELP! HELP! FUCKIN' HELP!

IT'S GONE IN ME KNICKERS KILL IT! FUCKIN' KILL IT!

HOLD ON, ARAMINTA!

Sex Curse of Tutunkhamun

A LEADING Cambridge University Egyptologist says he has fallen foul of a deathbed curse laid almost 5,000 years ago by the boy king **Tutunkhamun**. While exploring a pyramid in the Valley of the Kings, Professor Burton Coggles, 58, came across a sarcophagus bearing ancient hieroglyphics depicting a sad-faced grave-robber holding a floppy snake.

"It was a curse that promised a lifetime of sexual impotence on anyone who dared to disturb the late Pharaoh's eternal rest," Coggles told reporters. "At first I just laughed it off, as I am not a particularly superstitious person. But the very next day I went with a prostitute in Cairo, and I found I couldn't get it up at all."

"Whatever she did, no matter how much she yanked at it or tickled my knackers, it just flopped about like a wet noodle," he said. "I even got her to bring her mate in, to see if a two's-up would put a bit of blood in it, but it was to no avail."

worth

Coggles, whose book *An Analysis of the Culture of the Egyptian Peoples 2558-2532BC* is an authoratative text on the reign of king Khafre, said it was a very humiliating experience. "In the end, I just thumbed it in just to get my money's worth," he said.

He continued: "It had never happened to me before. I'm usually like a rolling pin if I get the slightest whiff of fanny. You just ask my ex-wife or any of the pros I've done over the years."

"I realised there and then that my knob had been jinxed by King Tut, and there was nothing I could do about it," he added. "My blood ran cold."

potter

Now the Professor is planning to take legal action against his employers at Cambridge University in the hope of receiving compensation for his plight.

"I may not have been ran over by a forklift or fell off a ladder in a warehouse, but I've suffered a work-related injury, just the same," he told us. "If the university hadn't

How's your mummy: Coggles was victim of sex curse.

Archaeologist reveals ancient Pharaoh's nookie hex

sent me into that pyramid, I'd still be able to get a stonk-on."

krishna

But the head of the University's Archaeology Department, Sir Chorley Standish, last night told reporters that succumbing to curses was an occupational hazard for Egyptologists, especially those studying 4th dynasty funerary rites.

"It has happened to many archaeologists, including myself. Despite having had no sexual problems before, I began suffering from the embarrassing condition of premature ejaculation after breaking into the burial chamber of Amen-Hotep III," he said.

"Honestly, ever since I've been up and over like a pan of fucking milk before Lady Standish has even got her scads off," he added.

LETTERBOCKS

Viz Comic, P.O. Box 841 Whitley Bay, NE26 9EQ : letters@viz.co.uk

THEY say that if a snooker ball was blown up to be the same size as the Earth, the Earth would be smoother. These so-called scientists have clearly never seen the state of the potholes in the roads around the Cambridgeshire/ Norfolk border.

Thanston Crabb, Wisbech

IT'S always disappointed me that dogs don't piss while they shit. When I shit, I always do at least a bit of wee. Come on dogs, give it a go, see if you like it.

William Mylchreest, Leamington Spa

AFTER recently attending a recording of the *Antiques Roadshow*, I noticed that I actually appeared on the programme in the background. In today's modern age, this now makes me a celebrity. I would like to use your pages to let everyone know that I am available for the opening of local One Stops, guest speaking, or switching on the Christmas lights in Hartlepool.

Michael Thompson, North Wales

STAR LETTER

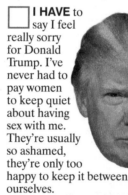

EARLIER in the summer, I went cycling in the Netherlands. The few days I was there were the hottest I can ever remember, and I got quite badly sunburned. I also found myself having to cycle into the wind for most of my ride. In addition, I had two punctures, my chain came off three times, and on the second day I left my water bottle in the hotel. Honestly, the quicker we get on with Brexit and leave the EU, the better.

Monty Claypole, North Shields

YOU hardly ever see those TVs with the big backs any more. Yet microwave ovens seem reluctant to move with times and embrace this more up-to-date plasma technology. Come on microwave companies, let's go flat-screen and drag our kitchens kicking and screaming out of the 90s.

Gustav Fox, Dalston

I HAVE to say I feel really sorry for Donald Trump. I've never had to pay women to keep quiet about having sex with me. They're usually so ashamed, they're only too happy to keep it between ourselves.

Steve Crouch, P'borough

WHY don't animals have breasts? You see nipples on dogs, cats and pigs and the like, but why no breasts? I for one think that seeing large golden retriever with massive tits would be quite astounding. And it would certainly take our minds off of things like Brexit, or the current state of affairs in Washington DC.

Helmet Icepop, Cardiff

WHY is it that classical musicians in orchestras get lauded as being the crème de la crème in the world of instrumentalists, when they all require sheet music to help them remember the tune? I saw Napalm Death a few weeks ago and they didn't have to look at a book once. They could remember all the songs just fine, and most of their ones are loads faster than any Beethoven or Mozart.

Gustav Fox, Haggerston

I'VE often heard it said that a mouse can get into the smallest of holes; in fact, any place where you can shove a pencil. If this is true, then surely the onus is on the pencil industry to help eradicate mice infestations in the home by making their pencils smaller.

Chester Squeezeworth, Hull

IF Geoffrey Boycott ever became a vegan, which do you think he'd bang on about the most; being from Yorkshire, or being a vegan?

Arthur Guff-Whippet, Basingstoke

I PUT a Fruit Pastille in my mouth in 1987 and I still haven't chewed it. I don't even like Fruit Pastilles.

Ian Webb, Bury St Edmunds

HOW come countries like Japan get to be 9 hours ahead of us here in the UK? It hardly seems fair. I've just started work here, but if we too were 9 hours ahead, I'd be on the bus home. If I wasn't unemployed.

George Charles Hill, Elephant and Castle

WITH so many people these days ordering their drugs online via the dark web, it can only be a matter of time before drug pushers vanish from our streets. Yet another part of our familiar British high street disappearing before our eyes in the name of 'progress'.

Phil Kitching, Isle of Jura

I HEARD something on a documentary the other day that apparently we know more about the surface of the Moon than we do about our oceans. Frankly these so-called "oceanographers" need to pull their fucking fingers out and get some real work done.

P. I. Staker, Minster On Sea

I'VE never understood the saying "It goes like stink" to indicate that something is very fast. Whenever I drop one in a crowded room, it generally takes a good 8 to 10 seconds before the people at the back start to retch.

John Foster, Liverpool

STOP the bloke at the next urinal from looking at your cock by complimenting him on his own. Works every ti...

Steve Crouch, P'boro

DRAPE a tea towel over your shoulder and polish a glass when saying farewell guests so as they think yo... are a former pub landlord.

Billy Grayson, Bundab...

DETER wild birds from yo... covered bird table by naili... plastic or metal spikes to the roof and gluing pieces of broken glass around the platform. A cardboard cut-of a cat on the ground add... an extra level of security.

Mrs Birdie Num-n... Durh...

HOW come whenever we have a heatwave, the authorities impose a hosepipe ban, yet whenever we have torrential rain there is no opposite rule to make sure we all turn our hosepipes on daily? Come on, water companies, get your act together. It seems there's one rule for droughts and another for extreme flood events.

Richard Bowen, Pontardawe

I WONDER how many animals we jumped on the back of before we realised that horses were cool with it.

Ross Kennett, Kent

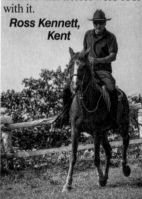

I TOLD my wife that she was so good at hoovering that she ought to try mowing the lawn since it involves essentially the same action. Instead of being flattered by my compliment, she reacted very angrily. There's no pleasing some people.

Phil Kitching, Isle of Jura

186

...TOGRAPHERS. Refer ...urselves as an 'artist' ...king ridiculous close-... absolutely any old ...while asserting that it's ...out having an eye for ... things.

Chris Francis, Oxford

...TEND you work for Sky ...s by adding "the worst ...l be yet to come" to the ...f everything you say.

Gustav Fox, Toddington

...TORS. Fool patients ...thinking you're a safe-...er by listening to their ...ts with a stethoscope ... turning their nipples.

Michael Thompson, North Wales

WHAT with the latest fad for remaking old ...novies, isn't it time they ...emade *Confessions of a ...Window Cleaner?* They could ...ring it bang up to date, and in ...the new version we could even ...et to see it going in. If they ...ren't going to show it going ...n, then I don't know why they ...re wasting their time.

Douglas Pouch, Tiverton

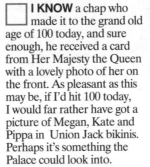

I WAS shocked and appalled to see a recent newspaper headline announcing: 'Putin's Hitmen on British Streets'. What's the world coming to when even Russian assassins can't afford to pay their rent? Come on Mr Putin, do the decent thing and sort your hitmen out with some proper digs.

Ethel Perestroika, Salisbury

BRUCE Springsteen famously sang "Tramps like us, baby we were born to run". Almost all the tramps I've seen have worn-out shoes, carry lots of carrier bags and probably couldn't run more than two steps before their trousers fell down. So much for the boss's "Socially Aware" lyrics.

Michael Féaux, Kusterdingen

DENTISTS make their living fixing people's bad teeth, so why would I buy toothpaste recommended by 4 out of 5 dentists? It seems to me that they've got a nice little scam going on there. In the future I won't bother brushing my teeth at all, see how they like them apples.

Ivor Cummin, Broadbottom

I WILL always buy a manual car because the act of changing gear provides the perfect conditions for forcing out a trapped fart. Depressing the clutch as hard as possible while pulling the gear stick is all you need to free an incommodious frump. And you can ride the clutch for a while if it's a long 'un.

Lawrence, Duff

I KNOW a chap who made it to the grand old age of 100 today, and sure enough, he received a card from Her Majesty the Queen with a lovely photo of her on the front. As pleasant as this may be, if I'd hit 100 today, I would far rather have got a picture of Megan, Kate and Pippa in Union Jack bikinis. Perhaps it's something the Palace could look into.

Mike Oxlong, Hexham

NOWHERE in the Bible does it say that Noah ever applied for planning permission to build his ark, it seems he just built it. Yet when I wanted to build a small granny flat above my garage, the council fucked me over good and proper. Once again, there's one rule for some Old Testament prophet of doom and another for the rest of us.

Hector Niecelybig, Truro

"ONE minute he was there, the next minute he was gone". This phrase is often used by someone to describe the supposedly instant disappearance of a person from where they were standing. In my opinion, however, sixty seconds is quite a long time to take your leave of someone. If it took me sixty seconds to walk away from a person, I would consider myself either very, very old, or lost.

Terry Farricker, Blackpool

CONTRARY to the usual advice, whenever I leave the house I make sure I'm wearing my oldest, shittiest underwear possible. If I get hit by a bus, the shame of having the doctors see my skiddy pants would probably kill my mother, and I stand to inherit quite a tidy sum.

Steve Crouch, P'borough

IT beggars belief how gullible some people are about the so-called "pollution" caused by discarded refuse, plastics and other non-recyclable packaging. When you consider the fact that absolutely everything we use is made from chemicals and elements extracted from the earth in the first place, it puts quite a different slant on the argument. These so-called 'scientists' can't pull the wool over my eyes.

T O'Neill, Glasgow

THE other day I was watching TV news with the sound off when I saw a somewhat attractive middle-aged woman giving an interview. I thought it might be Donald Trump's pornstar girlfriend, Stormy Daniels, but I couldn't be sure as I've only ever seen her with jitler dribbling down her chin. Have any of your readers got a picture of Stormy Daniels without jitler dribbling down her chin so as I can tell if it was her or not?

Steve, New York

I SPOTTED this on the label of some pink tonic water. It looks impressive, with its picture of an old-fashioned sailing ship and the reassuring statement *'Since MMXVII'*. Impressive, that is, until you work out that MMXVII is 2017. Has anyone seen a more blatant exploitation of the public's inability to count in Latin?

Bikkus Dikkus, Newbury

IF you believe their slogan, Gillette is "the best a man can get". However, I just got a blowjob and I would take that over a pack of razors any day of the week.

Brian Saxby, Chicago

Are You So-and-So?

No. 84. At the Train Station

WE'VE had a deluge of letters from readers who have seen famous people at a train station and have asked them if they were them. Here are some of the best we've received.

I SAW Robbie Coltrane getting on a train in Amsterdam in 1990. I said "are you Robbie Coltrane?" and he said "fuck off" to me. Have any other readers seen a fat celebrity getting on a train?

Dan Bamboo, Exeter

I ONCE saw wavey-armed telly scientist Magnus Pyke at Kings Cross station. I said to him "are you Magnus Pyke?" and he replied "Yes, but I've got to catch a train." I thought it was an odd response from a scientist, as it seemed to imply that his being Magnus Pyke and his need to catch a train were in some way linked, almost as if by not catching the train, he would cease to be Magnus Pyke.

Colston Bassett, Tyne & Wear

* Have you spotted a celebrity at a train station and asked them if they were them? If so, what was their response? Write in to the usual PO Box or email address and tell us about it. Mark your envelope or email subject 'I saw a celeb at a station and I asked them if they were them.'

MY Grandmother, who was happily married for over 70 years, once told me to find someone who feels the same way about me as I feel about them, and we'll be happy forever. However, my wife and I hate each other and have done for some time and, quite frankly, neither of us are happy. My 'wise' Nan needs to get her fucking act together.

Walter Trout, Grimsby

AIRPORT PARKING

EXTORTIONATE | DAYLIGHT ROBBERY | HOW FUCKING MUCH?!

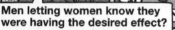

DOWN THE TUBES!

"WHITE PUNKS ON DOPE"

Vieux Tube: Band too old say fans.

PROTO-PUNK band The Tubes have been slammed by their fans after ageing forty years since their late seventies heyday. The San Francisco-based nine-piece, who were known for their rebellious, anti-establishment stance and fast-paced, aggressive songs such as *Mondo Bondage*, *Don't Touch Me There* and *White Punks on Dope*, are now more than four decades older than they used to be. And their fans aren't happy.

"These guys used to be in their twenties," said disappointed Tubes fan Ted Carpet, 58. "They were young, angry and full of energy."

"But just look at them now. These days Fee Waybill is getting on for seventy. Quite frankly, he's let us all down," said Carpet.

pass

He also slammed other members of the group for being much older

EXCLUSIVE!

than they used to be. He told us: "I'm not just singling out Fee for criticism. The others are just as bad as him, if not worse."

"Drummer Prairie Prince has had a free bus pass for at least three years now, and keyboardist Vince Welnick is so old that he's been dead since 2006," Carpet con-

tinued. "Honestly, talk about selling out."

"It makes you think that all that youthful fire and anger on stage was just an act."

down

A spokesman for Fee Waybill yesterday apologised to anyone who felt let down by the Tubes' advancing years. "The band tried

Californian rockers panned for getting old

to stay in their twenties, but time simply caught with them," he said. "Fee feels really guilty for letting everyone down."

"He'd be here to say sorry himself, only he's got the mobile chiropodist coming round this afternoon to do his feet," the spokesman added.

mr. LOGIC — HE'S AN ACUTE LOCALISED BODILY SMART IN THE RECTAL AREA.

A DAY AT THE M

EVERYONE loves a trip to the museum. Nothing beats the thrill of shuffling from display case to display case, peering at flint arrowheads, Roman brooch pins and bits of broken pottery while repeatedly being told not to touch anything. But it's not just the exhibits that are worth looking at; to a seasoned observer, the staff and the visitors are often just as fascinating and exciting. It's time to spend a day at a typical museum and ask the age-old question...

What Can You See when you spend...

- A man who has taken a wrong turning and got his museum audio guide out-of-sync, and is now confused because he's looking at a stuffed dodo while being told about a Ming vase

- An old couple who are determined to read the information card on every single exhibit, including the catalogue numbers

- A security guard who also does nightclub door work, itching for someone to start a fight near a display of Saxon cooking implements so he can wade in and crack some heads

- A family who scooted round the whole museum in five minutes and have so far been in the gift shop for an hour-and-a-half

- A tramp who comes in every day because it's free and it's somewhere nice to go for for a shit

- A pretentious twat with an easel doing a really bad charcoal study of a suit of armour

- A perspex box labelled "Suggested Donations" seed with £5 notes by the museum staff to make you think you're the only person not contributing

- Visitors walking past the "Suggested Donations" box, thinking to themselves: 'There's a lot of fivers in there. The clearly doing quite well, so I'll not bother donating anythin

- A coin-squeezing machine that turns a penny into a sr Pringle-shaped piece of copper imprinted with an incompl and barely legible version of the museum's previous logo

- A man who likes to stand next to the coin-squeezing machine and point out that it's a criminal offence to def

USEUM

...oin of the realm, and any child using it could be arrested
...sent to prison for five years

...A guard who has been dead for 4 months without
...body noticing

...A party of school-children in hi-viz jackets who have
...en given worksheets in order to sap every last vestige of
...and interest out of their visit

...Two teachers whose school party are fully occupied
...ng worksheets so they are contemplating an affair

...A café with a cloying smell of spilled milk

...A guard playing Clash of Clans while someone sticks a
...uable Viking amulet under their coat

...Children frantically pushing buttons, pulling levers and
winding handles in the hands-on experience gallery where
every single exhibit is out of order

● An empty case from which the most exciting exhibit that
features on all the publicity material, has been removed to
go on loan to another museum for the next four years

● A single man who wants to knob a classy piece and,
having so far failed to pull anything at the art gallery and
opera house, is trying his luck at the museum instead

● A gaggle of old women looking at the fire extinguisher,
and chatting about how it looks just like a modern one

● A display of antique agricultural implements that isn't now,
never has been, and never will be of any interest to anyone

● A brightly coloured banner featuring a hashtag that has
only appeared on Twitter twice in the last five years.

● A gift shop with exactly the same stock as every other
museum gift shop in the country, only with this museum's
badly designed logo stamped on it

● A divorced dad who operates on a three-weekly cycle of
taking his kids to the museum, the sea-life centre and the
zoo, followed by McDonald's

● An elderly man who keeps pointing at exhibits and
saying "Eeh, I used to have one of them. I should have kept
it, I should," standing in front of the Golden Death Mask
of Ahmenhotep III and saying "Eeh, I used to have one of
them. I should have kept it, I should."

● A toddler being told off for touching a 2-ton, cast iron
battleship cannon in case her tiny fingers irreparably damage it

● The curator of archaeological exhibits who bitterly
resents the public being allowed in to look at his artefacts

● A man paying £8 for a glossy guide book that he will flick
through once, before folding it in half and sticking it in his
back pocket, later ramming into the door pocket of his car, to
be thrown away three months later when it gets cleaned

● The museum janitor who, having discovered the entrance
to an abandoned gold mine in the basement, has dressed up
as an Egyptian mummy in order to scare visitors away

Next Week: Who's Who at a Hermitage

STING of the DUMP

Charlie Potter was spending the Summer holidays with his grandparents, who lived by a rubbish dump in the West End of Newcastle upon Tyne...

I'm off for a walk by the dump, gran.

Well don't go too close to the edge, Charlie. You might fall in.

Don't worry, grandma, I won't.

Thank goodness they're filling it in this afternoon. And not before time...

The place is a haven for vermin.

Charlie set off on his walk, but as he approached the dump, he heard something strange...

What's that? It sounds like...like ham-fisted lute music... played by someone with a tin ear.

It's got a really mediocre, lacklustre quality, and it's coming from somewhere in the dump...

...I'll go a little closer to the edge to see what bellend is playing it...

CRUMBLE!

Woah! Oof!

Charlie tumbled down...

...down...

...down into the rubbish...

At the bottom, he saw a strange twat...

Wow! It's Sting! What are you doing here?

I fell out of my private jet on my way to an ecological conference.

Luckily I landed on an old mattress, but I've been trapped here in the dump ever since.

Gosh!

The pop arsehole showed Charlie the shelter he had built for himself out of rubbish...

What a great place to live!

Yes. It's not as good as my Tuscan olive farm or my 16th century Wiltshire manor house...

...but during my time here I've become very fond of this dump. This is my home now.

Oh no!

What is it?

The dump is going to be filled in this afternoon!

What?! But what will become of all the rats and slugs who live here? Their natural environment will be destroyed.

We've got to save the dump, Charlie!

But how?

Suddenly, the lute-playing prick had a brainwave...

I know! I'll write a musical!

How will that help?

It will be so awful, so utterly without merit, that as soon as the performance begins, the developers will run away and never come back!

You know, Sting, if anyone can do it, you can.

Yes! Yes, I've got it... It will be about the decline of the Tyneside shipyards or some such bollocks.

Wow! I can already imagine how hackneyed and cliché-ridden it will be!

GOLD! *(CHANG!)* Always believe in your soul! So sang Spandau Ballet frontman Tony Hadley back in 1983. Nobody knew what he meant, but it's an undeniable fact that gold has been one of mankind's most prized and precious commodities since we first crawled out of the primordial ooze back in stone age times. Kings and Queens make their crowns off it, countries secure their economies on it, and pirates of old filled their treasure chests with it. It is a priceless, glittering thread that has run through the warp and weft of our history for millennia, but how much do we really know about this, the 79th element of the periodic table? Here's 24 24-carat facts about our favourite precious metal…

24 THINGS
NEVER KNEW ABOUT
GOLD

79
Au
196.97

1 [79 / 196.97] **IN THE** song *Gold*, Tony Hadley assures the precious metal "You're indestructable." But scientists couldn't disagree more with the old New Romantic warbler, because gold has no less than 18 radioactive isotopes. One of these, ^{198}Au, has a half-life of less than three days, emitting Beta particles and decaying into a stable form of mercury - ^{198}Hg. Other ways in which gold can be destroyed include placing it in front of the proton beam of a cyclotron, bombarding it with gamma rays until it decays into Platinum, or chopping it up into little bits and flushing it down the toilet.

2 [79 / 196.97] **IF YOU** fancy making a cup of tea using gold instead of water, you can forget it. That's because

gold boils at a scorching 2970°C, meaning that your kettle would have boiled away long before the gold inside was even tepid.

3 [79 / 196.97] **IF YOU** were to somehow manage to boil enough gold to brew up a pot of tea, by the time it had cooled down to a drinkable temperature of 60°C, your tea would have stewed. And turned solid.

4 [79 / 196.97] **AS AN** inert metal, gold is perfectly safe to eat; indeed, if you save up and go for a meal at Heston Blumenthal's Fat Duck Restaurant, your shrimps may well arrive at the table sheathed in a shimmering shell of gold leaf. If you get the shits after eating them, it's nothing to do with the gold. You've probably just been laid low by a soupçon of untreated human sewage, just like 500 diners at the exclusive eaterie were back in 2009.

5 [79 / 196.97] **YOU** might expect the chemical symbol for gold to be 'Go', but you'd be wrong, because it's actually 'Au'. *"Nobody knows why,"* says slap-eggheaded TV boffin Jim Al-Khalili. *"It's probably to do with the spelling of the Latin name for it or something. I don't know, because when I was doing Chemistry at the University of Surrey, I missed the lecture on gold because I was selling rag mags in Wolverhampton."*

6 [79 / 196.97] **DESPITE** their name, 'goldfish' only contain about 0.2 microgrammes of gold, worth about half a penny on the bullion market. Yet if you want to buy a goldfish, you won't get much change out of £2.50. That's an eye-watering 50,000% mark-up that the rob-dog owners of pet shops are trousering.

7 [79 / 196.97] **WHEN UK** drum 'n' bass star Clifford Price MBE was adopted by children's TV show *Blue Peter*, viewers were invited to write and propose a stage name for him. The most popular suggestion was "Goldie", after his trademark mouthful of precious metal gnashers. Goldie was then taken home to live with presenter Simon Groom on his farm in Dethick, Derbyshire.

8 [79 / 196.97] **COMEDY AMERICAN** President Donald J Trump famously has a solid gold lift in Trump Tower as

a tawdry display of his wealth. What is less well known is that the POTUS also keeps a solid platinum lift in a storeroom, with instructions that the two lifts should be swapped over if the price of platinum ever exceeds that of gold.

9 [79 / 196.97] **IF YOU** take a piece of gold jewellery to be valued at the *Antiques Roadshow*, the presenters can tell you exactly when and where it was made. That's because each gold item bears a "hallmark" - a tiny series of symbols unique to each

place a[nd] year of manufactu[re.] The experts will examine t[he] hallmark through a jewelle[r's] loupe, stop the cameras a[nd] look it up in a book, then sta[rt] filming again and pretend th[at] they just knew it off the top [of] their head.

10 [79 / 196.97] **AND WHEN** th[ey] have to say what th[e] value is, for insuran[ce] purposes, they stop th[e] cameras and look it up in th[e] 'Completed Listings' on eBay[.]

11 [79 / 196.97] **YOU'LL** never see [a] gold thermomete[r.] That's becaus[e,] unusually for a metal, [it] dissolves in mercury. *"I don['t] know why this happens,"* sa[ys] chrome-domed TV boffi[n] Jim Al-Khalili. *"When I was [at] university, I missed the lectu[re] on mercury because I was o[ut] doing a sponsored bed-push [in] Dagenham."*

12 [79 / 196.97] **'EL DORADO'** was [a] fabled South America[n] city of gold, spoken [of] with awe by returning Spani[sh] Conquistadors. It was al[so] the title of a dismal, ear[ly] evening BBC soap opera th[at] was so bad that even *The O[ne] Show* seemed like a bett[er] replacement.

13 [79 / 196.97] **IN THE** America[n] goldrush of 184[9] thousands of peop[le] descended on the Klondy[ke] in order to pan for gold. Th[e] process involved an aged ma[n] with an unruly beard filling [a] wok with grit from a riverb[ed] and swilling it round whi[le] looking for a telltale spark[le] from a fleck of the elusi[ve] precious metal.

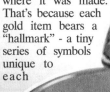

KENWOOD

194

14 196.97 **IT'S** a well-known fact that all the gold in the world, if melted down, would fit in a block between the four feet of the Eiffel Tower. However, security would be an issue as a 200,000 ton block of solid gold sitting unattended in the middle of Paris would be an open invitation to passing thieves.

15 196.97 **IF ALL** the gold in the world was taken from under the Eiffel Tower, melted down, and made into a wire 1mm thick, it would go around the world an incredible 75 times.

16 196.97 **IF YOU** halved the thickness of the wire, you might think it would go round the world 150 times. But you'd be wrong, because according to scientists, when you halve the diameter of a piece of wire, you increase its length by a factor of 4. So it would actually go round 300 times.

17 196.97 **AT THE** end of the iconic movie *The Italian Job*, the gang's getaway coach is left dangling precariously over an Alpine precipice as a large pile of gold bars slides ever closer to its back doors. But scientists from the National Physical Laboratory in Teddington have calculated that such a situation could never occur. *"Assuming that the stack of gold and the bus's engine block are of equal volume, and that the cliff edge forms a fulcrum at a central point along its wheelbase, then allowing for the different densities of the two metals, the gold would have to be 2.44 times closer to the pivot point in order for equilibrium to be achieved. Once the gold overcame its inertial motion and began to slide away from the fulcrum, as it does in the film, it would exert a significant moment that would immediately upset the static equilibrium of the system, creating a dynamic force that would topple the bus down the mountain. So it's bollocks,"* said the Government's chief scientific adviser Professor Patrick Vallance.

18 196.97 **THESE** days, the only people who pan for gold are third-rate celebrities making gentle ITV travelogues, standing in wellies in a Welsh river with a bloke from the local mining museum.

Before going off to shoe a horse, make some cheese and do some dry stone walling.

19 196.97 **THERE** are two types of gold: normal gold, used for jewellery, micro-electronic circuitry and gaudily gilding everything that the Queen owns, and nazi gold, which is all in Switzerland.

20 196.97 **THE WORD** 'gold' features in the title of every James Bond movie, eg. *Goldfinger*, *The Man with the Golden Gun*, *Goldeneye*, and all the others, including *Casino Royale*.

21 196.97 **THE FIRST** actor to play James Bond was Bob Holness, who later went on to host kids' TV quiz *Blockbusters*, where winning contestants got the chance to take part in the 'Gold Run'. Holness also played the saxophone solo on the Gerry Rafferty single *Baker Street*, which, after selling a billion copies, "went gold."

22 196.97 **UNLIKE** most metals, gold does not react with oxygen at any temperature. *"Don't ask me why,"* says billiard-ball-craniumed TV boffin Jim Al-Khalili. *"When we did oxygen, I was hitch-hiking near Arbroath, dressed as a convict and carrying a ball and chain as part of a charity jailbreak."*

23 196.97 **AMAZINGLY,** the word "gold" doesn't appear in the Bible except once in the story of the Nativity as recounted in the Gospel of St Matthew, when the Wise Men bring the baby Jesus gifts of it, frankincense and myrrh. And another 4510 times.

24 196.97 **ASTRONOMERS** believe there may be a planet in the universe that is completely made of gold. All the boulders, rocks and even the sand on the beach on this alien world are pure 24-carat bling. But before you jump in the nearest rocket and blast off to the other side of the galaxy, think again. Because gold is so common on this distant world, it will be utterly worthless. The precious commodities there will be things that are worthless to us on earth, such as old batteries, bottle tops and elastic bands.

It's the Biggest EVER Competition run by a British magazine, with a prize worth £50 MILLION or MORE!

WIN your WEIGHT in GOLD!

~In our 24-carat Gold Wordsearch Competition

Win £50M worth of gold - more if you are clinically obese!

YOU READ IT RIGHT! One lucky reader will be walking away with their weight in solid **GOLD!**

Hidden in the grid are 24 gold- or golden-related words. They may be written vertically, horizontally or diagonally, backwards or forwards. Simply mark each word on your entry form and send it to: *Viz Comic Gold Wordsearch, PO Box 841, Whitley Bay NE26 9EQ* to arrive before July 20th. The first correct entry drawn out of the hat by the magazine editor's wife will win the prize. All other contestants will win a frankly lacklustre *Viz Comic* pen, provided they include a **LARGE LETTER STAMP** with their entry. *No stamp, no pen*. It's that simple!

HIDDEN WORDS

FINGER • EAGLE
SYRUP • EYE OINTMENT
BLEND • BULLION
YEARS • GUN • OLDIES
LABRADOR • TOOTH
RUSH • HAMSTER
STANDARD • MEDAL
VIRGINIA • SOVEREIGN
LEAF • DISC • FISH
NUGGET • TERRY'S ALL
GRAHAMS • SHOWER

```
W Y G V I O S G V T E N L H M U D V X R L Y E F
D A I N I G R I V M E Z G O B Y E J E H G I D L
H E X U I H U O E T B H S I L H I E G N Y I A X
L H F E Y M S A L P E J O L E U T G W E B B R H
E I T W B P H P S T H R Y E A R S E R L R A M L
Q U P O P Y C M H G T M L H V N E U D A W L O H
M U S H O W E R E N R Y N K L J S V D S H O J R
L D N K S T A I E O K M F Y M J A O O L T A P R
K X H I J T F M E                 L R I D S H I M W
D U H N L H T W             P E I O G E J S
E S U D E N H             L P K L G T R
B M K G I W Y R             G P I K H Y T
F L T O X S R             A C D U M T I
A E E T G J C             E K M E L J Y
M Y T N B R L S G       V     B E H K D U K M L
E P T F D Y B D G T P J A     A U T A O L T P A
Z H J V I R T A K L E L H Y M D B L P J U D E D
P M F C H E A C R D H R S M K C Y J L E H R L C
Z H B J G W E R B N E A R L K X B T H I E A W K
W L P G A B H U E R S F G Y P L K Z N Y O D E F
T L U F T I N R E G F U D R S O M L D L X N Z I
L N R H M L D T I B N R V C K A F S D A G A L I
D T Y M I D S M L P A I L T C V L I M A C T L K
A T S Q U M A Y G C J O F P K A E L S B U S L W
A C H V A A V J N T S H O K L S B K S H A B R G
L P G H A V Y F A E L A C H M K D H I P N S T F
```

Name ....

Address ....

.... Post Code ....

I realise I won't get a pen with without enclosing a large letter stamp ☐ so I have enclosed one ☐

Last month's *Win Your Weight in Diamonds* competiton was won by **Mrs Ada Doubleday**, a humorous magazine editor's wife from Whitley Bay, Tyne and Wear, who walks away with 10 stone 4lbs of uncut diamonds kindly donated by the De Beer Diamond Mining Company.

Next Week: 99 Things You Never Knew About Ice Creams with a Chocolate Flake Stuck in the Top.

MEET ABBA'S BIGGEST FAN

Mo devotes life to Supergroup

BACK in the seventies, posters of Abba were plastered on every teenager's wall. Millions of youngsters kept their transistors pressed to their ears 24-7, eager to hear their latest records.

Most of those pop devotees have since grown up and moved on, barely giving their youthful idols a second thought during the intervening three-and-a-half decades since the Swedish group's last hit. But one tragic superfan has devoted her whole life to Agnetha, Bjorn, Benny and Anni-Frid, and has in the process wasted the best part of her allotted span amassing an utterly pointless collection of Abba memorabilia.

Mo Plain, 54, told us: "While all my friends have got married, started families and pursued successful and fulfilling careers, I've been working on my Abba collection."

tat

At the last count, tragic Mo, who lives alone in the Wednesbury, West Midlands house where she was born, had over 40,000 items in her unofficial Abba museum. From LPs and singles to annuals,

A VIZ POP EXCLUSIVE!

mugs, signed photographs and dolls, if it's got anything to do with her Swedish idols, she's probably got it somewhere in the worthless stockpile of tat that stands as a testament to her pitifully squandered time on earth.

knife

"I get up at half-past five to get my collection dusted before breakfast time," she told us. "It takes me at least three hours every morning. Then I hit eBay and start searching for new Abba treasures."

"Being Abba's number one fan is like a full time job for me," she added. "There's no time for anything else."

Fan-d-ABBA-mo-zi! Mo (below left) is plain crazy for the Swedish supergroup (above). And the house where she has lived all her life (below right).

"I've currently got my eye on an Abba picnic box and flask, an Abba colour-changing pen, and a lock of Bjorn's hair," she said. Mo reckons she must have spent more than half a million pounds on memorabilia over the past four decades, money that could have funded a lavish lifestyle of international jetsetting, including round-the-world cruises, first class air travel and stays in luxury five-star hotels.

fingers

Experts recently valued Mo's collection at £150 to £200. "I don't care what my museum is worth, because it's literally priceless to me," she said. "I'm not interested in selling it anyway. When I go, I'm leaving the whole lot to my sister in Australia. Like me, she's a big Abba fan."

When we contacted Miss Plain's sister Doreen, who lives in Melbourne, she told us: "I don't want all that shite cluttering my house up. I'll just get some local firm to put the lot in a skip and then sell the house."

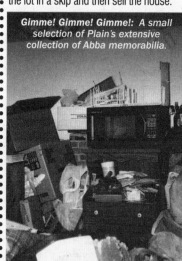

Gimme! Gimme! Gimme!: A small selection of Plain's extensive collection of Abba memorabilia.

FAT, BALDING, MIDDLE-AGED MAN 'DISAPPOINTED' BY ABBA AGNETHA

NEWS that ABBA had reformed to record two brand new tracks delighted the Swedish supergroup's legion of fans earlier this month. But the announcement brought disappointment to one overweight Bolton man suffering from male pattern baldness.

58-year-old Preston Potto said that he didn't think that Agnetha Fältskog had aged as well as he might have hoped.

"She was the best thing going in the seventies, especially when she used to stick her arse out in those tight trousers. Or when she was wearing that short dress with the slit up the side," he told his local paper the *Bolton Prostate Examiner.* "I mean, I certainly would have. Who wouldn't?"

fit

"But when I saw the latest pictures of her, I was disappointed by the effect that the intervening three-and-a-half decades had wrought upon her appearance," he said.

Potto explained that whilst he accepted that Fältskog was now 68, he had

Agnetha now: Potto's in two minds

expected her to look more like a fairly saucy piece in her early-to-mid fifties.

"I thought she would be like one of your mates' fit mums who you hoped would make a pass at you when you was a teenager," the 24-stone unemployed forklift truck driver said. "You know, where you hoped she'd put her hand on your thigh and give you the come-on a bit while your mate was out the room making a cup of tea."

"But to be honest, I saw a recent picture of Agnetha, and she looks to be in her early 60s at best," he said. "She's really let herself go."

drill

Potto, who suffers from piles, halitosis and chronic flatulence, admitted that he was even wondering whether or not he still would.

"To be honest, I'm in two minds as to whether I'd be prepared to give her one now," he vouchsafed.

"I mean, I probably would, but I doubt I'd enjoy it as much as I would have done if I'd given her one back in her heyday," he added.

And Potto said he had no opinions one way or another on Fältskog's fellow Abba vocalist Anni-Frid Lyngstad, now 73. "If I'm honest, I was never that fussed on the dark-haired one," he told the paper.

A ROBOT ABBA IN EVERY HOME BY 2025

Cheshire-based boffin's amazing Sci-Fi prediction

35 YEARS after disbanding, Abba are set to tour again as cyber-holograms. And whilst this sounds like something from a science fiction story set thousands of years in the future, a Crewe-based scientist says this is just the beginning of a technological revolution that will see robotic versions of the Swedish supergroup taking pride of place in every British house by the end of the decade.

"By 2025, no home will be complete without its own android Abba," says independent researcher Professor Gladstone Bagg. "By the end of the decade, lifelike computerised versions of Agnetha, Bjorn, Benny and Anni-Frid will be as much a part of our daily lives as making a Pot Noodle, watching Homes Under the Hammer and walking to the corner shop for a big bottle of Frosty Jack."

animatronic

Working in a state-of-the-art laboratory-cum-potting shed at the end of his garden, Professor Bagg has been working on a prototype lifesize animatronic Abba for nearly six years. He told us: "The project has been a challenging one and I've only done the blonde bird so far, but she's come out even more realistic than I could have hoped."

"When she's finished, she's going to do absolutely anything I want

TECH-SCLUSIVE!

her to. She'll sing all their hits, put on any costume I like, and get into any position I want her to," said the thrice-divorced bachelor, who was recently made redundant from his job in a Nantwich vacuum cleaner factory. "She'll be unquestioningly obedient to my every whim, whether I'm asking her to sing *Dancing Queen*, stick her arse right out like she did at that press conference in that film, or put on a daringly short skirt and thigh-high boots."

washer

"What's more, there'll be none of that backchat you get with real women. That will all be programmed out, believe you me," he said.

"It'll be nothing less than complete compliance. She'll definitely know who's boss alright," he added.

He told us: "And she'll only be

Cyber Touper: *An artist's impression of what the home of the near future may look like, complete with Robo-Agnetha.*

singing at night, of course. During the day, she'll have a lot of spare time to do other things. Other things that aren't to do with being in Abba."

dryer

"A lot of my work has been to do with making her capable of doing these other things. I've had to design a lot of special parts that have nothing to do with singing," he said. "Fine-tuning my design has

been a long and painstaking process, as I want to get the these bits absolutely perfect before I move on to doing the other members of the band."

"Once I've got the blonde one up and running, I'll probably do the dark-haired one, see if I can get the pair of them to work together. Then I might move on to the two blokes after that, if I can be bothered," Professor Bagg added.

KNOWING TEA, KNOWING YOU!

Free Abba Drinks Coasters for every reader!

MAMMA MIA! There's nothing better than sitting in a comfy armchair, listening to your favourite Abba records while enjoying a nice cup of tea. But all too often, that experience is ruined when wet cups leave rings on your best occasional table.

But that annoyance is now set to become a thing of the past, thanks to this *FREE* set of four Abba drinks coasters, yours to cut out and keep.

Instructions: Cut out the coasters along the dotted lines and glue them to something circular and about as thick as a drinks coaster eg. a digestive biscuit, Pringles tube lid or pre-existing drinks coaster.

The blonde one

They're the Scandinavian pop foursome whose toe-tapping hits took the seventies by storm. They're Abba, and nearly forty years after they last performed together, they're still one of the biggest bands in the world. But how much do you really know about Agnetha, Bjorn, Benny and Anni-Frid? Here's...

11 THINGS YOU NEVER KNEWING ME KNEWING YOU ABOUT ABBA

1 IN THE LYRICS of their 1974 Eurovision-winning song, Abba sang: *"My my! At Waterloo, Napoleon did surrender."* In fact, military historians maintain that towards the end of the famous battle, the desperate French Emperor committed his Imperial Guard to a final attack, which was narrowly beaten back. With the Prussians breaking through on the French right flank, Wellington's Anglo-allied army counter-attacked in the centre, and Bonaparte's army was routed.

2 ABBA ARE SO FAMOUS that they have an entire museum dedicated to them in the centre of Stockholm. However, nobody knows what's on display inside because it's forty quid to get in. *Forty fucking quid.*

3 THE FOUR MEMBERS of the group had very different lives before they shot to stardom overnight at the 1974 Eurovision song contest. Agnetha worked in a bookshop, Bjorn was a meatball chef in the Upsala branch of IKEA, Benny was a tyrefitter at Snabb Passform, the Swedish version of Kwikfit, and Anni-Frid was a sales manager for Sweden's leading publisher of farmyard pornography.

4 ABBA ARE ESTIMATED to have sold over 375 million records during their career. If all those records were piled up one on top of another in Trafalgar Square and pushed over by the World's strongest man Geoff Capes, the top of the pile would hit the ground in the village of Revest-les-Roches, 10 miles north west of Nice in the South of France.

5 OTHER THAN the fact that Abba records would land on it if Geoff Capes pushed a pile of them over in Trafalgar Square, there is nothing else even vaguely interesting about Revest-les-Roches. If you type the name of the town's mayor, Rene Goldoni, into Google, nothing comes up.

6 WHEN THEY first formed, the group called themselves "The Swedish Beatles" - "De Svenska Skalbaggarna". However, on the night of their Eurovision debut Katie Boyle was breaking in a new set of false teeth, and every time she attempted to say the band's name, she spat out her top plate. The mortified presenter begged them to change their name to something she could pronounce more easily - suggesting the more denture-friendly "Abba" - and the rest is history.

7 KEYBOARDIST Benny Andersson is terrified of flying. So much so that when Abba go on tour, his bandmates pretend they're going to let him go on the bus, before ambushing him, injecting him with a powerful sedative, and bundling him unconscious onto the plane.

8 ABBA ARE ONE of the few bands to have seen the Loch Ness Monster. While driving between Fortwilliam and Inverness on their 1976 tour of the Scottish Highlands, guitarist Bjorn Ulvaeus spotted what he thought was the monster swimming in the loch. "I was very interested in dinosaurs at the time, and I identified it immediately as a plesiosaur," he told the *NME*'s Mark Ellen. However Ellen, an experienced music journalist, thinks it was more likely that Ulvaeus had actually seen a seal, a cormorant or a semi-submerged log.

9 IN 1978, after their van broke down in the Florida Everglades on the way to perform a concert, the band members and Ulvaeus's Great Dane Scööbygör booked themselves into a run down motel. On the way to their rooms, they saw the glowing apparition of a highwayman, Black Jim, who chased them along a corridor. However, after setting a trap and catching him in a net, the group unmasked the spook as none other than Mr Jenson, the motel's caretaker, who had discovered a diamond mine in the basement, and had been attempting to scare people away by dressing up as a ghost.

10 IT IS SAID that every Swedish person will run down a moose in their car a some point in their lives. Amazingly, however, no member of Abba has ever knocked down a moose.

11 APART FROM ABBA, the only other famous person from Sweden is tennis star Bjorn Borg. At the last count, Borg had mown down over twenty-five mooses since passing his driving test in 1973.

ark-haired one

The one with the beard

The other one

NO THANK YOU FOR THE MUSIC

Abba's least enthusiastic fan 'indifferent to comeback'

Fairbrass: Disinterested in ABBA news, yesterday.

A PENRITH garage mechanic who has been dubbed "Abba's least enthusiastic fan" yesterday announced that he was "not really fussed one way or the other" at the announcement that the band have recorded two brand new songs. And dad-of-three Gary Fairbrass, 56, went on to say that he "couldn't give a toss" that the seventies Swedish supergroup were planning a stadium tour in 3-D hologram form.

Speaking to colleagues at the exhaust centre where he works, Fairbrass said that he supposed some of Abba's songs were alright, but to be honest, he hadn't really given the group a lot of thought since the late 1970s.

Fairbrass has not dedicated a room of his house to his Abba collection,

EXCLUSIVE!

which consists of a double-LP "Best-of" collection that he bought at a car boot sale in the late 1990s. "I don't even know where it is. It's probably in the loft or in a box in the garage somewhere," the not-Abba-bonkers mechanic said. "I've got nothing to play it on anyway."

Speaking to her hairdresser, Gary's not-long-suffering wife Janine, 52, confirmed that her un-Abba-mad hubby's non-obsession had not come between them even to the extent of not threatening their marriage. "It's not Abba-this and not Abba-that, not twenty-four hours a day," she said.

"In fact, to tell you the truth, I can't remember the subject of Abba coming up in the thirty years we've been together," she added.

ABBA TIME TRAVEL COMPETITION

WIN a once-in-a-lifetime chance to appear on stage ★ with ABBA at the 1974 Eurovision Song Contest! ★

A BBA ARE BACK on tour, this time as holograms, but we're giving one lucky reader the chance to appear with the real, flesh and blood Swedish supergroup back in their seventies heyday. That's right, your glam-tastic *Viz* has teamed up with Agnetha, Bjorn, Benny and Anni-Frid, as well as top particle physicists from the CERN research facility, to whisk the winner of this competition *BACK THROUGH TIME* to April 6th 1974, where they will join Abba on stage to perform their first and biggest hit, *Waterloo*, live on the *Eurovision Song Contest* in front of a TV audience of billions!

The winner will be invited to join in on backing vocals and tambourine, wearing a pair of authentically tasteless silver stackheel boots and a metallic jumpsuit that is uncomfortably tight around the crotch.

After the glittering post-show party, where they will mingle with genuine seventies celebrities such as the late **TERRY WOGAN**, the late **KATIE BOYLE** and **OLIVIA NEWTON-JOHN**, it will be back into the CERN time machine to return to nowadays.

It's the prize of a lifetime. The closing date to enter is June 1st 2021, when the prizewinner will be notified. On the offchance that time travel hasn't been invented by then, don't worry. We'll simply wait until it has been, and pop back to 2021 and pick up the winner on the way to 1974.

For your chance to win, simply answer these 3 Abba-related questions and then complete the tie-breaker. The winner will be the entry who, in the opinion of the judges, is the first one out of the hat.

1. What does the first letter "A" in Abba stand for?
- ☐ a. Agnetha
- ☐ b. Anni-Frid
- ☐ c. Alcoholics

2. What do the letters "BB" in Abba stand for?
- ☐ a. Bed & Breakfast
- ☐ b. Bjorn & Benny
- ☐ c. Billy Bookcase

3. What does the second letter "A" in Abba stand for?
- ☐ a. Anni-Frid
- ☐ b. Agnetha
- ☐ c. Anonymous

Tiebreaker: Complete the following sentence in fewer than twelve words: "I think I should be the first one out of the hat because.."

Name.............................Address.......................................…......Postcode.................

Declaration: In the event that my entry is successful, I promise not to tell Abba that they're going to win the Eurovision Song Contest and also to exercise extreme caution at all times so I don't tread on any butterflies while I am in 1974.

NB. If time travel technology is unable to go back as far as 1974, the proprietors of *Viz* reserve the right to substitute the prize for a trip back to play in a similar, more recent Eurovision Song Contest-winning band, such as The Brotherhood of Man (1976), Bucks Fizz (1981) or Katrina and the Waves (1997).

CERN ABBA GIANTS: You could be whizzing back in time to catch the fantastic foursome's most celebrated performance.

SHAGS TO RICHES

ONE OF BRITAIN'S most successful entrepreneurs, who has been romantically linked with a dazzling succession of glamorous showbiz beauties, was yesterday slapped with a £300 fine by Wiltshire magistrates for trading on a public thoroughfare without a licence. 57-year-old **BURTON JOYCEY**, who has built a business empire selling wooden garden ornaments from lay-bys in the Swindon area, laughed off the penalty, telling his local paper: "£300 is peanuts to me. I only asked the court for to let me pay it off over six months for a joke."

Publicity around the case has served to highlight Joycey's love life, which has seen him squiring an incredible rollcall of sexy A-listers he has met while manning his roadside stall. And now he has penned a self-help business guide in which he reveals exactly how he has made his millions while bedding a veritable Who's Who of Tinseltown's most glamorous women.

He told us: "The wooden garden ornament business is very competitive. Even worse, it's full of cowboys; jokers who don't know what they are doing and turn out shoddy goods. But quality always sells for top dollar, and my customers know that my products are of the very best quality. I learned my trade over six months in the fruit crate workshop at Belmarsh prison, so I'm a time-served craftsman."

"And if there's one thing that turns the Hollywood fanny on, it's a successful, self-made man who is good with his hands."

In these exclusive extracts from his book **Boardroom to Bedroom,** *Joycey lifts the lid on his extraordinarily successful career as an entrepreneur and sex machine.*

Theron the make: Charlize settled account in full.

EXCLUSIVE!

Charlize angel

" I remember this one time, I parked up my van in a lay-by on the A419 and set out my wares. Lay-bys are great, because you get a lot of passing trade and there are no overheads like rent, business rates or insurance.

I hadn't been sat on my picnic chair for more than four hours when a top-of-the-range convertible Mercedes pulled up. I couldn't believe who got out of it; it was that **CHARLIZE THERON** out of the hair adverts, and she was clearly interested in some bird tables I had out for a tenner a pop. 'I need three of these,' she said. 'One for my house in Beverly Hills, one for my holiday home in the South of France, and one for my condo overlooking Central Park.'

The way she was eyeing me up and down left me in no doubt how she was proposing to settle her account

loaded

I loaded the tables into the boot of her motor, and held out my hand. 'That'll be thirty quid,' I told her. She fished in her designer handbag and handed me a gold American Express card. I shook my head. 'No, love. I don't take them. It's cash only,' I explained.

Conducting all transactions in cash means that you are exempt from tax and VAT. It's a useful tip for anyone setting up their own business who wants to keep costs down while maximising profits.

'Oh,' pouted Theron, coquettishly chewing her little finger and fluttering her eyelashes. 'I'm afraid I've came out without no money. Perhaps there's another way I can pay for them bird tables.' The way she was eyeing me up and down left me in no doubt how she was proposing to settle her account. Moments later, we were in the back of my van, and while I'm too

All the single lay-bys: Star Beyoncé lured Burton into her limo for more than back seat champers.

much of a gentleman to reveal what happened next, suffice it to say she paid that bill in full.

After I had done her, Theron pulled her clouts up and slid open the side door of the van. 'Burton,' she said. 'Them were the best orgasms I ever had.' She handed me her card, which I later accidentally used as a roach on a rollie, and told me to look her up if I was ever in Hollywood. "

Car boot-licious

The Atomic Blonde star may have been Burton's first taste of showbiz sex, but she certainly wasn't to be the last.

" The filth had moved me on from the A419, so I set up shop a couple of miles on the other side of the White Hart roundabout and unloaded my wares. I'd made some little wheelbarrow planters that I was particularly proud of, so I put them at the front. I'd made them out of scrap pallet wood – as I do all my products. Using discarded materials is a good way to keep overheads down, because you can often find pallets lying at the side of the road or piled up in the yard at this lorry depot near where I live.

Sure, the timber can be a bit rough, but once I've used my carpentry skills to transform it into a thing of beauty, it would grace any garden. Especially from a distance. And sure enough, I'd only had my barrows on display for a couple of hours when a stretch limo

purred to a halt in the lay-by, and the chauffeur climbed out.

esquire

'How much are them wheelbarrows?' he asked me. 'My boss in the back wants one for each side of the front door of her multi-million dollar Bel Air mansion, to put some bulbs in.' I rubbed my chin thoughtfully. 'Tell you what,' I said. 'I'll do her a deal, but I want to speak to her in person.'

The chauffeur opened the car door for me and I climbed inside to start negotiations. My heart skipped a beat when I saw who was reclining on the sprawling white leather back seat, sipping Champagne. It was none other than bootylicious singer **BEYONCÉ**.

'How much for two of them wheelbarrows?' she purred. I told her they were fifteen apiece, but I would do her two for twenty-five cash. She arched a perfectly manicured eyebrow coquettishly. 'How about twenty and a glass of Moët and Chandon with me?' She pulled a crystal glass out of a built-in drinks cabinet with all neon lights in it, and poured me a drink. As I watched the champers fizzing away, something told me that it wasn't just twenty knicker and some bubbly that I was going to be enjoying.

people's friend

Now I've seen plenty of bongo videos where they have it off in the back of a stretch limo, so I'd be lying if I said I didn't have an inkling about what was coming next. 'Bottoms up,' she said.

And thirty seconds later, it was. I'm too much of a gentleman to reveal what me and the Destiny's Child beauty got up to in the back of that limo, but I will tell you this: All the hype about her dirtbox is completely justified.

When I'd done, she pulled her scuds up, took a crisp twenty pound note out of her designer purse, and kissed it, leaving a big lipstick print on it. 'This is for you, Burton,' she purred. 'That was the best anyone has ever done me.' As I took the note from her, I vowed to keep it forever, but I accidentally spent it later that night at the Abbey dog track. "

Road hump: Burton (above) pulled a string of sexy A-list punters to his Transit-based roadside garden ornament business (above right).

Once Knightley

By now, word had clearly got out in Tinseltown about Joycey's wooden garden ornaments, and A-list stars began scouring Swindon's highways and byways to search him out.

A bloke in a burger van had threatened to slash my tyres if I didn't move from his spot on the A420, so I was trying a new business location in a lay-by on the B4006 between East Wichel and Covingham. I was launching a brand new line – little wishing wells that you could put a plant pot in. I was confident that these would sell well, but a successful entrepreneur never puts all his eggs in one basket, so I had diversified my stock into feature film DVDs that I had bought off a man in the pub.

I had a good range at rock bottom prices, including some movies that were still showing at the cinema, so I was looking forward to getting plenty of business off passing motorists. But not in my wildest wet dreams would I have expected the first customer who turned up to check out my wares behind the wheel of a brand new Rolls-Royce. It was **KEIRA KNIGHTLEY**.

Well-wisher: Keira's wish was fulfilled by Joycey in the back of his Ford Transit.

She climbed from behind the wheel and slinked over towards me. 'How much are them wishing wells?' she asked, coquettishly. 'They're a new line, Miss Knightley,' I said. 'I'm knocking them out for ten pound a pop.'

pence

'Hmm. I'm not buying one unless I know they really work,' she said, tossing a ten pence into one of the wells and tightly closing her eyes. 'I wish a tall dark stranger would sort me out in the back of that van,' she giggled.

I'm a towering 5'8" in my socks, and at 57, I am still blessed with jet-black hair. What's more, Keira Knightley didn't know me from Adam, so I definitely ticked all the boxes. Moments later, the *Atonement* star was tearing at my shell-suit bottoms in the back of the Transit in a frenzy of passion.

What happened next as we slaked our lusts just inches from the traffic thundering along the busy M4 must remain between me and her. But I will say this; When the *Pirates of the Caribbean* actress finally clambered out of that van, I had given her a jolly rogering to remember.

biden

'My, them wishing wells don't half work,' she moaned, wiping herself down with a cloth. 'But I've only got a fifty pound note, I'm afraid.' I explained that it was early in the day, and I hadn't got a change float, so she said she'd go to the Esso garage in Chiseldon and get a Twix or something. 'Don't go,' she said. 'I'll be right back when I've got some tens.'

Unfortunately, a couple of minutes later, the pigs turned up and moved me on again because they said I was blocking a fire hydrant. They told me I was on my final warning; if they caught me again, they would definitely prosecute.

I never saw Keira Knightley again.

Royal blue

On the balance sheets and between the bedsheets, Joycey's business was flourishing, and he decided to take a gamble and launch a brand new, premium product in a brand new, premium retail location.

I'd parked the van up across a couple of disabled spaces at the Swindon Designer Outlet, just off the B4289. I didn't think anyone would mind, because it's never full during the week, and there's always a couple of blue badge gaps available. Or they could take one of the parent and child ones, so there really wasn't a problem.

I'd picked this fancy location because I was test-marketing a new up-market wooden garden ornament – a three-foot-high genuine Dutch windmill. Unlike the wheelbarrows, which were decorative only as the wheels were stapled in place, this windmill actually worked. The sails spun round on a three inch nail knocked in the front. Pile 'em high and sell 'em cheap is one approach to business, but big ticket items always earn you a bigger profit margin with every sale.

cheney

The windmill was a beautiful product, though I say so myself, and I was anticipating doing brisk business at the tempting introductory offer price of just thirty pound each. I had been expecting a high-end clientele, but the first customer who rocked up literally couldn't have been any high-ender. It was Her Royal Highness **MEGHAN MARKLE**!

'How much are you knocking them windmills out for?' the former *Suits* star turned princess drawled in her distinctive American accent. 'I'd love to stick one next the pond at Buckingham Palace. It would look top,' she gushed. I told her they were thirty pound, but that was just today only. Tomorrow, I would be asking their full price of fifty apiece or two for eighty-five.

gore

'That's a great price,' she said. 'But since I become a princess I don't carry no money on me.'

She looked at me, fluttering her eyelashes coquettishly. 'I don't suppose we could come to some sort of arrangement, could we…?' she said. 'One of them windmills in return for a right royal indulgence.' Well I didn't need asking twice, and I quickly ushered her towards the back of the Transit.

Going Dutch: Moneyless Meghan paid Burton for the windmill in kind.

I put some sacking on the floor before we got down to it, as I'm always picking up pallets and putting them in the back when I see them, and I didn't want my regal guest to get any splinters in her bumcheeks. Modesty – and indeed the laws of sedition and treason – prevent me from going into too much detail about what happened next.

Let me put it this way, by the time I'd finished doing Meghan Markle, my van needed two new leaf springs and a full set of shock absorbers. Mind you, to be honest it already needed them anyway, as it had failed its MOT three months earlier on the suspension.

executive

Meghan loaded the windmill into the boot of her Range Rover; sadly, it was to be the only thing that I sold that day. As she pulled off, I found myself being roughly grabbed from behind and slammed into the side of my van by retail park security guards. They pointed out in no uncertain terms that if I didn't – and I quote – "pack that fucking shit up and fuck off", they would break my legs.

Joycey is weighing up a number of offers from big name book companies who are all interested in publishing his barely credible life story. "I'm just holding out for one that will give me a fifty quid cash advance, so that I can pay off the first instalment of my fine," he told us.

She climbed from behind the wheel and slinked over towards me. 'How much are them wishing wells?' she asked, coquettishly

THE VIZ CROWN COURT

The criminal case you are about read is fictional, but the proceedings are authentic. Consider the evidence set before you carefully, because YOU are the jury, and your verdict will determine whether or not justice is done…

Will the defendant please rise..?

Raymond Cummerbund, you are charged that, on the 2nd of June this year, you did knowingly and with malice aforethought climb into the reptile enclosure of Fulchester Zoological Gardens, wherein you did attempt to engage in unlawful sexual intercourse with a crocodile…

How do you plead?

Not guilty.

Members of the jury, it is the prosecution's case that Mr Cummerbund is guilty of the sordid and debased crime with which he is charged...

...Indeed, we will bring forth numerous witnesses whose sworn testimonies will convince you beyond reasonable doubt that it was his intention to engage in bestial congress with the animal in question, to wit, a fifteen-foot saltwater crocodile of the genus *Crocodylus porosus*.

I give way to my learned friend, counsel for the defence.

Ladies and gentlemen of the jury. It is the defence's contention that Mr Cummerbund is an innocent man who has been the victim of a grave and egregious miscarriage of justice.

You will hear that my client does not dispute the fact that he was in the reptile enclosure on the day in question. Furthermore, he admits that his trousers were indeed round his ankles. Moreover, he readily concedes that, at the moment he was apprehended by police, he was gripping the animal around its waist in an unnatural fashion…

...However, he can, and indeed will, provide a perfectly innocent explanation for each and every one of these facts that will persuade you to acquit him of all charges and allow him to leave this court with his reputation unsullied and without a stain upon his character.

The defence will show that Mr Cummerbund saw that the crocodile in question was choking on a duck that it had been fed by zoo staff, and that my client jumped into its enclosure to perform the Heimlich manoeuvre, whereupon his trousers fell down, leading to a sorry misunderstanding.

The first witness for the prosecution, Mr Hampton Crane, has been chief reptile keeper at Fulchester Zoo for 24 years...

Mr Crane, could you describe to the court what you saw on the afternoon of June 2nd?

I saw a man with his his trousers round his ankles in the crocodile enclosure, buggering Hercules, our largest saltwater crocodile, up the arse.

Objection!

The witness is speculating, your honour. From his vantage point, he would have had no way of knowing whether or not the act of crocodile buggery was taking place.

Sustained. The witness box is no place for conjecture, hearsay and inference, Mr Crane. Kindly restrict your testimony to what you saw, not what you believed to be happening.

No further questions, m'lud...

...The prosecution calls its second witness, Mrs Edna Hopkiss.

Mrs Hopkiss, you were standing approximately five feet from the crocodile on that afternoon. Please tell the court, in your own words, what you saw.

There was a man, he was half naked...

...and he was having conjugal relations with the crocodile. His bottom was going up and down. I had my grandson with me and it was disgusting.

And do you see that man in court today, Mrs Hopkiss?

Yes, that's him there, stood in the dock. The filthy beast.

No further questions.

Mrs Hopkiss, do you wear glasses?

I do, but I don't see what that's got to do with anything.

...and when did you last have your eyes tested?

That's none of your business.

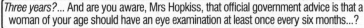

VERDICT FORM

On the charge of bumming a crocodile at Fulchester Zoo, I, a member of the Viz jury, hereby find the defendant, Raymond Percival Cummerbund...

☐ **GUILTY**

☐ **NOT GUILTY**

Cut out the form and return it to: *The Clerk of Fulchester Crown Court, PO Box 841, Whitley Bay NE26 9EQ,* to arrive no later than 1st November.

The verdict and sentence, if any, will be announced on page 209, just at the bottom, on the left. Enclose a stamped addressed envelope if you'd like a free Viz pen.

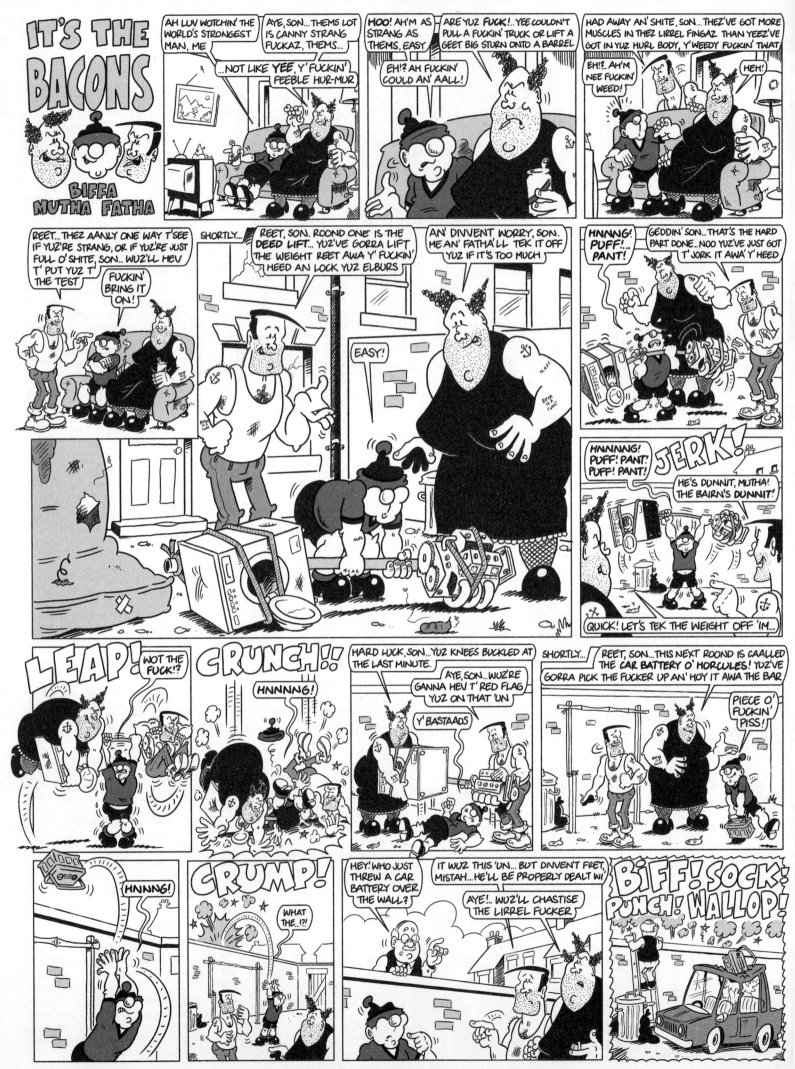

207

Letterbocks

Viz Comic, P.O. Box 841 Whitley Bay, NE26 9EQ ● letters@viz.co.uk

ST★R LETTER

THE world is really unfair at times. I have lived a good life and never hurt anyone, yet last week I got stung on the leg off a wasp. I bet people in prison never get stang. Why don't these spiteful insects just sting murderers and paedophiles and leave the rest of us alone?

Hector Golightly, Goole

I'M surprised Lee Harvey Oswald wasn't caught sooner than he was at that book depository. Surely the librarian would have gone straight over to investigate where the noise was coming from when he started shooting. All the ones I've ever come across go apeshit if they so much as hear a text coming through on your phone.

Jack Rubyson, Cromer

I WONDER if I could try my new mind-reading act on your readers. If they go and get a pen or pencil and draw something, I will reveal what it is at the end of the *Letterbocks* page.

Col Percy Fawcett, Durham

I THINK that dogging is a sordid and disgusting activity. It's a sorry state of affairs when you can't pull into a secluded lay-by for a quick wank without some dirty so-and-so peering at you through your car window.

Dan, Deal

WHY is it explorers never discover anything any more? If Christopher Columbus can discover the Americas with nothing more than a wooden boat and a compass, just think how easy it should be for modern explorers. What with helicopters, Google Earth and drones you would think they would be discovering places left right and centre. Frankly, I think its high time these so called 'pioneers' got a boot up the arse.

Robert Rawcliffe, Leyland

I DON'T know why everyone was moaning about the recent fishing dust-up with the French over scallops or some shit. I thought it was brilliant with boats smashing into each other and everything. We should get together with them, work out a few rules about how to score points, and do it every year.

Matt, London

ABOUT a fortnight ago, I did a fart in my bathroom, and it coincided with a lot of very jovial laughter in my neighbours' garden. I have since wondered if they were they laughing at me, or at something else entirely. Is it too late or too nosey to ask them? I would be grateful if any of your readers could advise me.

Mr B Jesus, Eastbourne

MY mum named me after a popular brand of trouser press that was in the hotel room where I was conceived. I wonder if any of your other readers have been named after brands of trouser press.

Corby Dullsworth, Luton

✱ *Well, readers, have you been named after a brand of trouser press, or indeed any type of equipment involved in the flattening of garments, such as an iron or mangle? Write in and let us know.*

WHAT a con these so-called 'internet scams' are. Only the other day I was contacted by a Nigerian prince who wanted to transfer all his inheritance into my bank account. Imagine my surprise when, instead of putting money into it, he withdrew £15,000. What's more that's the third time it's happened. I certainly shan't be doing that again.

Mike Hatchard, St Leonards on Sea

HOW come James Bond always says, "Bond...James Bond" whenever he checks into a hotel? It's not that common a name, although in larger hotels I suppose there is a chance that other Bonds may have made reservations.

Frampton Dubois, Hertford

T★P TIPS

GIG organisers. Save money on expensive dry ice machines by setting up the vaping area next to the stage.

Claire Maw, Huddersfield

COAT onions in No More Tears shampoo before chopping to ensure a tear-free experience.

Delaware Dave, Yeovil

TIE some very thin rope to your wheelie bin when you put it out. Then, when it's been emptied, simply pull it slowly back towards your house, making neighbours think you have a futuristic, self-moving bin. Fool them further by getting your wife to stand on the front lawn and point the TV remote at it.

Billy Grayson, Bundaberg

FOOL your neighbours into thinking you do falconry by occasionally standing on your front lawn wearing a welder's glove while spinning a bit of liver on some string.

Richard Low, Glasgow

SAVE money on heating your bathroom by simply wearing your dressing-gown backwards whilst having a shit.

Sven Tightqvist, Gothenberg

T★PS

toptips@viz.co.uk

YOU never hear of hijackers demanding that airline pilots take them to Cuba any more. Now that Castro is dead, I sincerely hope their tourist industry picks up once again.

Edna Crumbhorn, Derby

THAT TV advert where the woman is caught by her husband having it off in bed with a giant M&M is bollocks. I don't think any woman would want to have carnal relations with a large candy covered chocolate bean, unless it was shaped like a big shiny cock. And what's with the yellow one hiding in the wardrobe? Did he expect sloppy seconds or was he just having a voyeuristic wank?

Bob P, Kendal

IT was with some dismay that I realised that the girl having her arse kissed by that bloke is probably in her sixties by now, perhaps even seventies, and these days she would be hard-pressed finding someone who would want to kiss her arse. Unless you're into that sort of thing. Which I am.

Gary Ireland, Tauranga

HAS it crossed anyone's mind that the picture of the bloke kissing that bird's arse might in fact be a picture of the bloke *inspecting* her arse as opposed to going in for a peck? Looking at her face she seems pretty confident that everything is in order and it's going to get the thumbs up.

Mike Fordham, Chelmsford

I CAN'T believe how sensitive my wife has become lately. She always gets mad with me when I mention in company that she had liposuction at a clinic in Wolverhampton. Alright, I should have said Leicester. But, come on... Wolverhampton... Leicester... It's no big deal.

Tarquin Bucklesby, Nottingham

I'VE just come back from New York, and it's a load of rubbish - it's nothing like York. Where's the cobbled streets? Where's the Viking museum?

Ben, Whitstable

MY old man liked a pint or two, and I do too, but I look nothing like him. Let's see the so-called genetics experts explain that.

Ted Leicester, Stilton

I WAS reading that over 500 people have been into space. However, when the Apollo, Space Shuttle and Mir astronauts were on telly none of them were ever heard to swear. I'm pretty sure I would have turned the air blue if I had been launched into the sky on top of a firework filled with other people's farts for a week.

Col Percy Fawcett, Durham

AS a voter, I always feel very reassured when British politicians talk about 'ordinary people'. Let's hope they never lose that common touch.

E Talkabout, Pop Music

I DON'T know what all the fuss is about this scented bog roll. When I wipe my arse, the paper stinks of just one thing. Waste of bloody money. Rip off Britain!

Chester Dicklick, St Helens

The Viz Comic CROWN COURT

ON PAGE 205, the Viz Crown Court asked you asked you to come to a verdict on the guilt or innocence of Raymond Cummerbund, who was charged with engaging in unlawful sexual intercourse with a crocodile at Fulchester Zoological Gardens.

Viz readers take their civic responsibilities very seriously, and we had an enormous response. And you, the *Viz* jury found the defendant... **GUILTY** as charged.

Mr Cummerbund asked for 134 similar cases to be taken into consideration and was given to a 2-year suspended prison sentence.

WHOEVER stopped hiring Jimmy Nail to appear on television certainly knew what they were doing. Let's get them running the hospitals or schools or something.

Steve Fondue, Timperley

ACCORDING to some Americans, if it wasn't for their intervention in the Second World War, we'd all be speaking German. That might be true, at least we'd be drinking better lager and we'd have Oktoberfest, instead of Budweiser and trick or fucking treat.

Iain Devenney, Oxford

WHY is it that, whenever Amsterdam features on the telly, they show that same farty little bridge over the canal? Maybe if the residents laid off the jazz cabbage for ten minutes they could build themselves an impressive cathedral instead, or a hill to plonk a great big statue on.

Robert White, Sowerby Bridge

WHY is it that the people who have cosmetic surgery are already quite attractive? Surely ugly people would benefit from it more?

Tom Aspel, Dorking

THEY reckon that Pablo Escobar was raking in about $70 million per day at the height of his cocaine production business. That may be so, but despite his fleet of luxury cars, string of beautiful mistresses, personal zoo and extensive fleet of planes, you have to ask yourself… was he happy?

Danny Ocarina, Goole

IN these days of equality, is it not about time we had more women burgling houses? Come on ladies, get robbing, and don't forget to shit on the bed on the way out.

Carlton Finn, Leatherhead

LOADS of people are terrified of spiders, so it occurred to me that one way to make them a bit less scary would be to superglue little party hats onto their heads. Have any of your readers tried this, and if so, does it work?

Rhydderch Wilson, Swansea

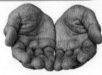

I ONCE blew off in the Alexandra Palace next to Brian May out of Queen. It caused a certain amount of agitation on his part, as I remember. Can any reader beat that?

Fat Al White, Wrenthorpe,

MITCHELL Brantub (*Letterbocks page 165*) might be pleasantly surprised to ride a penny farthing with 50p shaped wheels. That's because the 50p piece has the shape of an equilateral curved heptagon, or Reuleaux polygon, which is a shape of constant width, just like a circle. That's why you can use them in fruities.

John Shimwell, London

✱ *You are absolutely correct, John, but according to physicists, the centre of rotation would move about, so it would be a right fucker to pedal.*

WHY don't we see people leaving the dentist with a bandage round their face any more?

Jayne, Pissoff

WHAT'S all the fuss is about with these 'Escape rooms' everyone is doing? I did one recently and simply picked up a bin and smashed it through the window. I was out in under 30 seconds. Where's the challenge in that?

Lee Rivers, Cork

I LOVE putting the song *Jump* by Van Halen on really loud and then defiantly sitting down all the way through. No one tells me what to do.

Dean Moncaster, Leeds

I HAVE just cooked a nice gammon joint for tea. After removing it from the oven, the instructions advised me to let it rest for five minutes before serving. Surely it's me that should be entitled to a rest? All the ham did was sit in the oven for an hour. It was me who peeled the spuds and carrots.

Jane Hoole Garner, St. Ives

WHEN supertit Sting finally pops his clogs, will they write 'Sting' or 'Gordon' in flowers on his coffin? 'Gordon' would be more sombre and respectful, but 'Sting', being a letter shorter, would be cheaper at the florist. I hope he and Trudi discuss this matter well in advance.

Kelvin Celsius, Fratton

WITH reference to my mind reading act. You drew a big cock and balls with all hairs and that, didn't you?

Col Percy Fawcett, Durham

Win a 2021 VIZ Subscription in our Fantastic TOPS OF THE FORM

Tops-based Competition

with the late Ask the Family host and King of the Combover **ROBERT ROBINSON**

2020 will be remembered for one thing, and one thing only. Because that was the year we at *Viz Comic* gave away a year's subscriptiuon to one lucky reader. And that reader could be YOU.

For your chance to win this prize that money simply can buy (at www.viz.co.uk), just answer these three Top and Shirt-based brain-teasers, and send the answers in on the form. If you don't want to destroy your copy of *The Wizard's Sleeve*, a photograph or photocopy of the form will suffice. Send your answers, along with your name and address to:

Viz Comic Tops of the Form, P.O. Box 841, Whitley Bay, NE26 9EQ,

or email them to:
letters@viz.co.uk

If you are just doing the competition for fun, the answers are below.

Q1: Mr Smith has three tops. Mr Jenkins has two tops more than Mr Brown. Mr Brown has twice as many tops as Mr Smith and Mr Jenkins combined, whilst Mr Jones has fewer tops than anybody except Mr Jenkins. *How many tops do these gentlemen have between them?*

Q2: Here is a photograph of a top taken from an unusual angle. Can you tell what sort of top it is, *and whereabouts on that top this picture was taken?*

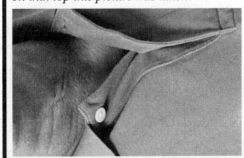

Q3: *Top to bottom:* Replacing one letter at a time, change the word **TOPS** to **ARSE** in the fewest number of moves.

TOPS
_____
_____
_____
_____
ARSE

VIZ Tops of the Form Competition

Q1: They have _____ shirts between them.

Q2: It is a _____ top, and it is the _____ bit.

Q3: ____ ____ ____ ____ ____

Name ....

Address ....

.... Post Code ....

Answers: Q1: They have 11 tops. Q2: It is a polo shirt, and it's the collar. Q3: It can't be done.

211

"...HAVE YOU EVER WATCHED [H]AUNTED?"

WHAT!?.. YES!..

...WELL, NO... BUT IT'S THE ONE WITH THE BIRD FROM BLUE PETER ON, ISN'T IT?.. NOT THAT JANET THINGY... THE ONE WHO GOT THE PUSH WHEN SHE GOT UP THE DUFF... THE OTHER ONE... WOTSERNAME...

YVETTE FIELDING

THAT'S THE ONE...

IT'S A LOAD OF OLD BOLLOCKS, TOM.

...MAYBE HE'S [S]TUCK IN TRAFFIC

AT ONE IN THE MORNING?

SORRY I'M LATE, TOM...

...HEY, I'LL TELL YOU WHAT, THIS PLACE MIGHT BE DEAD, BUT THE FUCKING BAR ON THE TOP FLOOR'S GOT SOME LIFE IN IT

PLENTY OF SPIRITS UP THERE IF WE CAN'T FIND ANY IN THIS PLACE

..LISTEN... CAN [YOU] HEAR THAT?...

WHAT?

[FU]CKING NOISE... LIKE [SOM]EBODY IS WALKING [ROUN]D IN TAP SHOES

...TIP!..TAP!..TIP!..TAP!.. ...LISTEN !..

OH, GOD... MY PALMS HAVE GONE SWEATY... AND THE HAIR ON MY NECK IS STANDING UP...

[N]O, IT WAS BRUCIE... I SAW HIM... ALL GREY AND SEE-THROUGH, [HE] WAS. HE CAME TAP DANCING THROUGH THAT WALL... PINCHED [ME] ON THE ARSE... DID HIS LITTLE POSE... AND THEN DRIFTED AWAY.

HE'S HAUNTING THE OLD GENERATION GAME STUDIOS... CHILLING, IT WAS... ABSOLUTELY CHILLING!

NEXT DAY...

LOOK AT THAT FOR A FUCKING HEADLINE, TOM. THE RATINGS FOR THE HALLOWE'EN MOST HAUNTED WERE THROUGH THE ROOF!

HMMM!?

BRUCIE GROPED YVETTE

[W]OULD YOU LIKE TO SEEK DAMAGES FROM THE OTHER SIDE..?

W.W. & S.

SLI-I-I-DE!

FUCK!

W.W. & S.

STORMY DANIELS says she was threatened by a "goon" working for Donald Trump in a Las Vegas parking lot. The sinister heavy warned the adult actress against talking in public about her torrid affair with the slapstick President before vanishing into the shadows. *But just who was he?* Chances are he was merely a hired thug on the payroll of the Trump organisation. But there is a more intriguing possibility: *What if he was actually a showbiz celebrity?* We've done some dirty digging to unearth four good-looking A-listers who are prime candidates. It's time to...

NAME THAT GOON

Tony Hadley, former ex-Spandau Ballet frontman

Hadley was a heart-throb back in his eighties heyday, so he certainly ticks the "good-looking" box. Perhaps, on the day in question, he had been on a stag weekend to the Nevada gamblers' paradise and suffered a bad run of luck on the Caesar's Palace fruities and tuppenny waterfalls. Although it would have been out of character, the skint New Romantic singer may well have agreed, against his better judgement, to put the frighteners on the vulnerable porn star in return for his airfare home.

Goon Rating: 7/10

Tom Jones, Welsh wet knickers magnet

It's not unusual to find Tom in Las Vegas. His shows there draw huge crowds, so it is easy to place him at the scene of the crime. But what would be his motive? Any money that Trump offered him to put the wind up Stormy would be mere chickenfeed to a man of his considerable means. No, the answer is much simpler; After spending half a century as one of the world's most famous men, Jones the Voice may have simply relished the opportunity to slip into the shadows as an anonymous goon for just five minutes.

Goon Rating: ★★★

Ben Dover, British erotic auteur

As a fellow adult performer, the star of such productions as *Outdoor Voyeur*, *Big and Bouncy* and *Fuck my Wife While I Watch*'s porn business contacts could have tipped him off about Daniels's whereabouts, allowing him to turn up unannounced to threaten her in the parking lot. And thanks to his well known acting skills, seen in such productions as *Soapy Vets*, *Boobtropolis* and *Pool MILFs 2*, Dover could easily have convinced the frightened scud artiste that he was indeed a genuine goon who, despite appearing in productions such as *Lesbian School Breakout*, *Best of Belgian Biscuits Vol. 12* and *Anal Hospital 24*, was definitely not to be fucked with.

Goon Rating: 80%

Declan Donnelly, the one on the right off of Ant & Dec

The *Saturday Night Takeaway* heart-throb certainly possesses the matinee-idol good looks that Stormy Daniels described to CBS's Anderson Cooper during her *Sixty Minutes* interview. But at a petite 5'1" tall, and tipping the scales at a featherweight 6 stone wringing wet, the former 50% of PJ and Duncan hardly makes a menacing goon. However, it's not out of the question that he could have been wearing platform shoes, and he's definitely been at a loose end recently while his double-act partner takes a well-earned break in the sauce clinic.

Goon Rating: Low to Medium

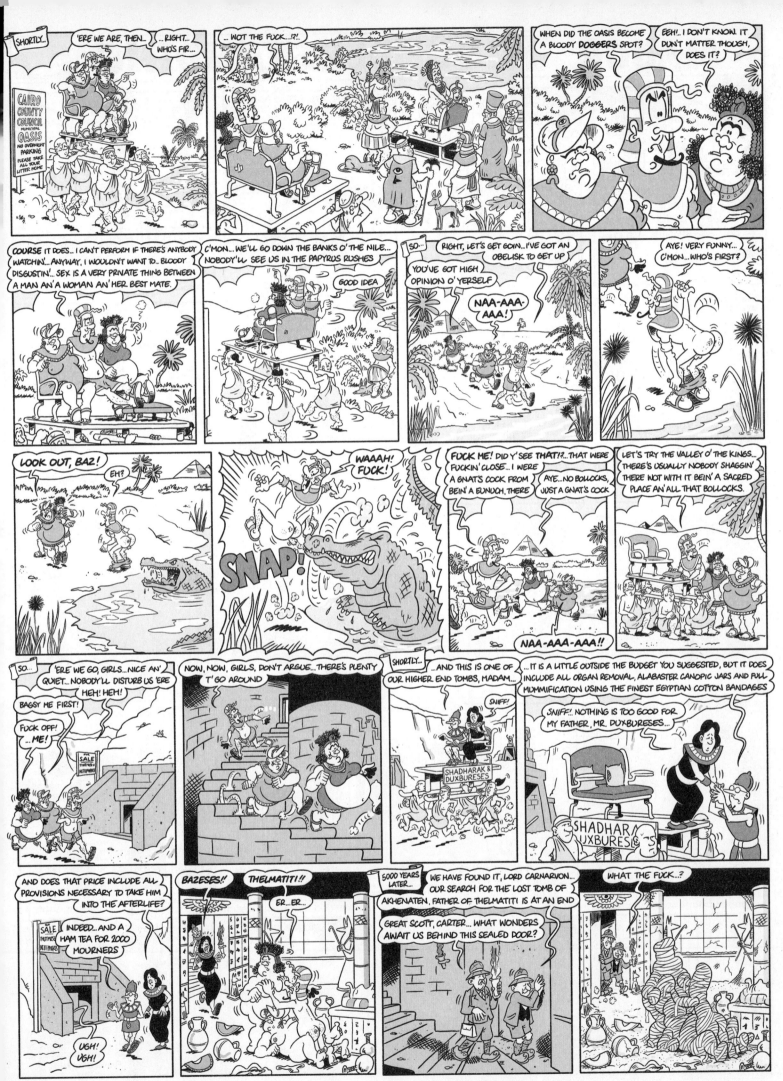

215

Think YOU could cut it as a top-flight atheist firebrand football official?
Find out below...

YOU ARE PROF. RICHARD DAWKINS THE REF

1 In the second half of a game, you award a free kick five yards outside the penalty area after an obvious handball for which you caution the offender. The defending team form a four-man wall ten yards away and you whistle to restart the game. However, as the opposing striker steps forward to take the kick, he turns to you and insists that an omniscient supernatural deity created the universe in seven days and that you, as an unbeliever are bound for the flames of hell. *What do you do?*

RAPSCALLION

2 A keeper brings down a striker in a one-on-one situation without making any attempt to get the ball. You blow your whistle and point straight to the penalty spot, only for the ball to continue rolling and dribble into the net. The striker celebrates, whilst the keeper rushes across to you and suggests that belief in Darwinian evolution is not wholly incompatible with religious faith. He's already on a yellow card. *How do you react?*

3 An attacker is brought down by a defender after what you deem a reckless challenge. He is injured and you signal for the physio to enter the field of play. You speak to the defender, but he protests innocence, saying that according to Thomas Aquinas's treatise on theological determinism, divine providence demands that everything is pre-ordained, and that by committing the foul he was merely carrying out God's plan, the workings of which we must not question. *What action do you take?*

A1. Take the striker aside and explain that if he believes in an all-knowing God, then he believes in a flying Spaghetti Monster, too. Do not take any action, but remind him that if he threatens you again with eternal damnation, you will caution him for ungentlemanly conduct. Then blow your whistle to indicate the free kick can be taken.

A2. The goal cannot stand as the ball crossed the line after the whistle was blown, and the penalty must be taken. The only decision now is whether or not to send the keeper off. Technically, he did not deny a goal-scoring opportunity, as the ball crossed the line, but his refusal to grasp the blatant contradiction between Darwin's findings and the case for intelligent design means he cannot remain on the pitch. Show him a straight red and order him off the field.

A3. Ensure that the injured player receives treatment and then ask him and the physio to leave the field. Explain to the defender that the only determinisms that affect our lives are biological, cultural and psychological determinism which, although strong, do not affect the free will we have when deciding whether or not to commit a foul. Then show him a yellow card for reckless play.

219

DANGER! IN YOUR KITCHEN!

WE ALL KNOW that the kitchen, with its sharp blades, boiling kettles and bubbling chip-pans, is the most dangerous room in the house. We try to minimise the risk of having an accident by taking simple precautions - for example, never leaving the cooker unattended, not allowing electrical flexes to trail, keeping knives and scissors safely locked away from children.

But the terrifying truth is that our kitchens harbour many more threats to our lives... *threats that we cannot foresee and can do nothing about.*

Here are some of the unforeseen dangers that are waiting to kill us each and every time we step into the kitchen, and against which we are powerless to protect ourselves.

METEORITE STRIKE: There are literally billions of meteors hurtling round our solar system at any one time. Each day, an estimated 100 tons of space rock smashes into the surface of the earth. Most pieces land harmlessly in the sea or fall onto uninhabited areas. But the terrifying truth is, there's no reason why a meteorite shouldn't hit YOUR kitchen. You might be standing by a window, innocently filling the kettle, making some toast or rinsing the teapot when a cricket-ball-sized lump of white-hot iron, travelling at 5 miles a second, smashes through the window and hits you square in the face. The good news is, you won't know a thing about it as you will be instantly liquefied by the ultrasonic shock wave from the impact. And don't think that simply moving your toaster and kettle away from the window will save you. This cosmic missile of annihilation has a kinetic energy of more than 1.5 Megajoules - enough to smash through your walls, roof or ceiling as if they're not there.

UNEXPLODED BOMBS: During the World War II, Hitler's Luftwaffe rained down over half a million bombs on the UK mainland. Although most detonated on impact, around 20% - up to 100,000 - never went off. These unexploded bombs still lie where they fell, and are unearthed regularly on building sites, in roadworks and in farmers' fields to this day. If your house was built before 1945, there's every chance that one of these deadly devices is lodged behind your cooker, in the back of a cupboard, or under the sink. The slightest movement, for example, pushing down the pop-up mechanism on your toaster, cracking an egg into a frying pan or dunking a biscuit in a cup of tea, could be enough to set up a vibration that will trigger its 70-year-old detonator back into action.

VOLCANO: The earth on which you live is a young planet. The thin veneer of human habitation exists atop a fragile crust floating on a vast, seething sea of molten rock. It is a sobering thought that just a few hundred metres below your home lie billions of tons of white hot magma under immense pressure. At any moment, that crust may crack like a crème brûlée, allowing a lethal spume of lava to burst up through your kitchen floor. There will be no warning. The tiles will bulge upwards alarmingly, followed mere nanoseconds later by the sickening stench of sulphur as the unstoppable pyroclastic tide of scorching liquid rock surges through the fissure, filling the room to the ceiling and capturing the excruciating torment of your final moments forever, Pompeii-like, in a kitchen-shaped block of basalt.

SNAKE ATTACK: One of the consequences of a modern global trading economy is that our white goods are now manufactured all over the world. It's quite likely that your toaster was made in Korea, your dishwasher was made in India, and your fridge was made in Japan. And that could be a big problem, because Japan is home to the Japanese Pit Viper (*Gloydius blomhoffii*), the Far East's most venomous snake. If one of these aggressive reptiles happened to slither unseen into the back of your fridge at the factory, it could well still be there, lying dormant and curled up around the workings. As the compressor warms up, so will the snake's blood, gradually bringing it out of its torpid state. Next time you go to open the fridge door, the viper will be waiting for you, coiled and waiting to strike, pumping enough neurotoxic venom to kill a carthorse into your veins. Writhing in agony as the blood clots in your arteries and capillaries, you will welcome the sweet oblivion of death when it finally comes after about a quarter of an hour of unimaginable suffering.

ELECTRIC SHOCK: We are all told to wash our hands before and after handling food, but is that good advice? Because, under certain very specific circumstances, the simple act of rinsing your hands under the tap could cost you your life. That's because the UK countryside is criss-crossed by a network of pylons supporting thousands of miles of high tension cables, each one carrying tens of thousands of volts. Many of these wires cross over reservoirs, and if one of them should snap and fall into the water, the current will flow through the water and into your house through the pipes. Going to wash your hands in these circumstances will be tantamount to signing your own death warrant. As the electrified water hits your skin, 10,000 volts will course through your body, rendering you paralysed as you are cooked alive from within. Your sizzling flesh will expand as it heats up until your skin splits like a grotesque sausage.

Next Week: *Dangers in Your Bedroom!*

Johnny Fartpants — The Boy With A Bum Like Thunder

THUB! THUB!

Hi readers! Mum and Dad want a fart-free festive season this year...

THUB! THUB!

...so they're bunging up my bottom with a big cork!

There you go, Johnny. That should keep your noxious emissions safely contained until Twelfth Night!

Ho-ho!

Christmas dinner...

...more sprouts, parsnips, and giblet gravy, Johnny?

Yes please, Mum!

Boxing Day...

Yum

Spoilt Bastard

Christmas Day... Here you go, Timmy... your Christmas dinner... roast turkey with all the trimmings

Where are the sprouts? You... you don't like sprouts...

You said all the trimmings, all of them, woman... Sprouts are an essential trimming!.. Yes, but... But...

What the blinking flip has that got to do with it?

You're doing it again, woman... you do it every year, you effing c. What?.. what am I doing?

You're trying to ruin my Christmas, that's what... and you're ruddy well succeed... Sob! Sob! Sob!

Look at me... I'm crying... ...I'm crying on Christmas Day...

Major Misunderstanding

Eeh, me friggin' heel's snapped — Ow! Me foot!

PERKIN'S DEPARTMENT STORE Est.
XMAS at PERKIN'S
SHIRL'S HEN DO

Brenda? You ok?

I think the ankle might be fractured. You'd better get her to A&E for an X-ray. Jesus! It hurts!

How am I gonna get her to hospital?

We keep a wheelchair in the back of the shop — you can borrow that. That'd be ideal.

Steady does it, Brenda. There you go.

PERKIN'S DEPARTMENT STORE
XMAS at PERKIN'S

Oh! Oh!

D.J. '18

Cockney Wanker

Orwight Christmas!

♫ Tam-ti-tam ♫ On the first day of Brexit my UKIP gave to me... a 'nana all nice an' bendee... ♫

'Ere! Shirl! Where's me fackin' Christmas Michael Winner?! The pinky an' perky ain't dan yet, wankah.

Do bleedin' wot?! Get it on the fackin' Cain an' Abel!

Yer've got t'cook it till the juices ran clear. Fackin' rabbish! That's jast brassels propaganda!

Juices ran clear my fackin' jacksie!

We ain't in the EU no mowah, gel. We don't 'ave to pay attention to their 'elf an' safety bollerks!

I'm takin' back control!

If Merke an' Tusk... the arse... dark an... ap t' them... aht o' the... we're fre...

I dunno... andadan in the... twenty...